PAUL LACROIX

was curator of the Imperial Library of the Paris Arsenal. Born in 1806, he was well known during his lifetime as the author of many popular historical works, including *France in the Middle Ages, France in the 18th Century,* and *Military and Religious Life in the Middle Ages,* besides the present volume. All these works, profusely illustrated, continued to be of interest to students of history for many years after the author's death in 1884. Their republication is new proof of their lasting appeal.

SCIENCE AND LITERATURE
IN THE MIDDLE AGES

SCIENCE
AND LITERATURE
in the
MIDDLE AGES
and the Renaissance

PAUL LACROIX

With over 400 wood engravings

FREDERICK UNGAR PUBLISHING CO.
NEW YORK

Republished 1964

First published 1878

Printed in the United States of America

Library of Congress Catalog Card No. 64-21614

PREFACE.

WITH this new and last volume, the subject of which is not less replete with interest than that of the three preceding volumes, we bring to a close our work upon the Middle Ages and the Renaissance.

In the beginning of the Middle Ages, at the commencement of the fifth century, the Barbarians made an inroad upon the old world; their renewed invasions crushed out, in the course of a few years, the Greek and Roman civilisation; and everywhere darkness succeeded to light. The religion of Jesus Christ was alone capable of resisting this barbarian invasion, and science and literature, together with the arts, disappeared from the face of the earth, taking refuge in the churches and the monasteries. It was there that they were preserved as a sacred deposit, and it was thence that they emerged when Christianity had renovated pagan society. But centuries and centuries elapsed before the sum of human knowledge was equal to what it had been at the fall of the Roman empire. A new society, moreover, was needed for the new efforts of human intelligence as it resumed its rights. Schools and universities were founded under the auspices of the clergy and of the religious corporations, and thus science and literature were enabled to emerge from their tomb. Europe, amidst the tumultuous conflicts of the policy which made and unmade kingdoms, witnessed a general revival of scholastic zeal; poets, orators, novelists, and writers increased in numbers and grew in favour; savants, philosophers, chemists and alchemists, mathematicians and astronomers, travellers and naturalists, were awakened, so to speak, by the life-giving breath of the Middle Ages; and great scientific discoveries and admirable works on every imaginable subject showed that the genius of modern society was not a whit inferior to that of antiquity. Printing was invented, and with that brilliant discovery, the Middle Ages, which had accomplished their work of social renovation, made way for the Renaissance, which scattered abroad in profusion the prolific and brilliant creations of Art, Science, and Literature.

Such is the grand and imposing picture which we have attempted to bring before our readers in a concise form, limiting ourselves to narrative and description, and not plunging into the imaginary regions of theory and historical discussion. The impartial and truth-loving historian confines himself to narrative, and though his personal opinions must, as a matter of course, show themselves in his narrative of facts, whether given in detail or abridged, he should not seek to force them upon his readers by systematic violence and by efforts of philosophical demonstration. The history of the Middle Ages has, more than any other period, given rise to these excesses of conflicting opinions. According to some, everything relating to the Middle Ages is bad and blameworthy; according to others, everything is admirable and good. We are not concerned to pronounce between these two extreme opinions; we have written our narrative in all sincerity and truth, and our readers can judge for themselves. Moreover, the greater part of our work was done for us. With respect to this volume, as to the preceding ones, we have simply analyzed several chapters of our first book, "The Middle Ages and the Renaissance," completing, and in some cases amending, the collective work of our former collaborateurs, and adding at the same time to this work, which is now deservedly appreciated, the chapters which were wanting, and the absence of which showed that it was imperfect.

It is none the less a high honour for us to have had the planning of this work, which is unfortunately left incomplete, and to have superintended the execution of a literary enterprise which obtained the most honourable encouragement, and almost unanimous praise. Our dear friend Ferdinand Seré, who died while engaged upon it, had struck the right vein with regard to the illustration of this magnificent book, in which were to be reproduced so many unpublished records of the art of drawing. But we had fallen upon evil times, and after expending much courage and perseverance, we had to stop before we had completed our programme, and terminate a work upon which we had spent so many years of labour. Thus "The Middle Ages and the Renaissance" had only five volumes instead of six.

I have written an absolutely new work, availing myself, however, of the original work, which remains as it was before. The four volumes of which the new work now consists are, at the same time, less extensive and more complete than the five volumes of the first one. Very few of the wood engravings which illustrate these four volumes, and none of the lithochromes, appeared in the first work.

With regard to the text, in compiling which I have made free use of the works of my former collaborateurs (so few of whom, alas! are alive to receive my thanks), I have not scrupled to avail myself of the excellent works which have appeared since the publication of the first "Middle Ages," and which have enabled me to recast altogether certain parts of this book. Thus, to speak only of the present volume, I have revised the chapters on *Philosophy* and *Universities*, after the valuable treatises on philosophy and history by M. Ch. Jourdain; the chapter on *Romances*, after the latest researches of M. Paulin Paris and the works of MM. Gaston Paris and Léon Gautier; and the chapter on *Popular Songs*, after the report of M. Ampère to the Committee of the Learned Societies. If I have succeeded in bringing into my work some of the fresh information which I have derived in abundance from my contemporaries, the credit lies with them. But it must not be forgotten that each of my chapters forms a sort of monograph, and that this monograph has often been made the subject of one, or even of several special treatises.

I could only make a succinct, and often incomplete, summary in compiling this book, which comprises so many different subjects; but I have at all events conformed as nearly as possible to the instructions of the late M. Firmin-Didot, who urged me to "leave to others the display of profound and minute erudition; content yourself with being an ingenious, intelligent, and, if possible, an agreeable interpreter; try to make yourself read and understood by everybody. The greatest successes are achieved less by savants than by vulgarisers."

PAUL LACROIX

(Bibliophile Jacob).

TABLE OF CONTENTS.

TABLE OF ILLUSTRATIONS.

ALEXAND. IIMOL

II. ENGRAVINGS.

SCIENCE AND LETTERS

IN

THE MIDDLE AGES,

AND AT THE

PERIOD OF THE RENAISSANCE.

UNIVERSITIES, SCHOOLS, STUDENTS.

Legend of the foundation of the Paris University by Charlemagne.—The Schools of the Notre-Dame Cloisters.—Origin of the name *University*.—The organization of the University.—The four Nations and the four Faculties.—The Rector and the other officers of the University.—The great and the little messengers. — Privileges of the University.—Its power and its decadence.—Its political rôle.—Creation of provincial Universities.—Great Schools of the Rue du Fouarre.—The Paris Colleges.—Turbulence of the Students.—Their Games.—Their Festivals.—The Lendit Fair.—Foreign Universities.

HE schools of Marseilles, Autun, Narbonne, Lyons, Bordeaux, and Toulouse, which, under the Roman dominion, had, thanks to the names of their famous professors and pupils, such as the poets Petronius and Ausonius, Trogus Pompeius the historian, the orators Salvian and Cesareus, &c., reflected so much credit upon Gaul, had, in the sixth century of the Christian era, ceased to be more than a mere souvenir. The reign of Dagobert (638) witnessed the extinction of the ancient genius of the land. The clergy, who remained the sole depositaries of human knowledge, had allowed themselves to be enveloped, in their turn, in the gloom of ignorance, when Charlemagne set to work to bring about a sort of intellectual regeneration throughout his vast empire. By his orders the Anglo-Saxon monk

Alcuin and some learned foreign clerks were summoned to the court.   It was under their supervision that he created within the walls of his own palace an academy, to which he made a point of belonging, and at the sittings of which he was sometimes present.   The mode of writing, which had become illegible, was remodelled ; the Latin tongue, which had been replaced by barbaric idioms, resumed its place ; the ancient manuscripts, which were lying in the monasteries, were revised and recopied with great care ; and thus the teaching of sciences and letters began to flourish anew in the ecclesiastical schools.

So it was that, long after the death of the great Emperor, the literary renaissance which was attributed to him, and which was perpetuated by the legends of the time, also acquired for him the title of patron and founder of the University : even to the present day the forehead of St. Charlemagne remains crowned with the literary aureole conferred upon him by the gratitude of our ancestors.

"In those days," says Nicholas Gilles, a chronicler of the fifteenth century, paraphrasing a passage from the Carlovingian chronicle of the Monk of St. Gall, "there arrived in France from Ireland two Scotch monks of great erudition, and very saintly men.   They preached and proclaimed in the cities and in the fields that they had knowledge to sell, and whoso wished to purchase it came to them.   This was told to the Emperor Charlemagne, who had them brought before him, and asked them if it was true that they had knowledge to sell, to which they replied that they had it by the grace of God, and that they had come to France to lend it and to teach it to all who wished to learn.   The Emperor asked them what remuneration they expected, and they replied that they asked for nothing more than a fitting place to teach in, and subsistence for their bodies.   When the Emperor heard this he was very joyful, and retained them with him until he had to set out for the war.   He then ordered that one of them, Clement, should remain in Paris, that children of all ranks, the most intelligent that could be found, should be sent to him, and provided him with proper schools to teach in, and ordered that their wants should be ministered to, and gave them great privileges, rights, and liberties ; and therefrom came the first institution of the body of the University of Paris, which was at Rome, whither it had been transferred from Athens."

Such are the facts which were generally taken as undeniable for more than eight centuries ; that is to say, until the learned Etienne Pasquier (1564), defending with ardour, but at the same time with impartiality, the ancient privileges of the University of Paris, had proved, in concert with Loisel the advocate and André Duchesne the historian, that these glorious traditions had no real foundation. It must be said, however, that such distinguished savants as Du Cange, Mabillon, and Crevier did their best to revive the legendary origin of the University; but, all questions of patriotism apart, it became clear that the academic or scholastic establishments of Charlemagne, like

Fig. 1.— Grand Initial, designed by pen (end of Fifteenth Century), representing Types of Students, in one of the Manuscript Registers of the German Nation.

University Archives.

many other creations of his universal genius, did not survive the indomitable will of their founder, and that the famous schools of Paris came into existence and developed themselves under the immediate influence of the Church.

The etymology of the word *university* must be sought in the Latin word *universitas*, which, in the Middle Ages, signified a reunion or category of persons. Thus, in the acts and ordinances published in the name of the schools of Paris, the form generally employed was, "Noverit universitas

vestra ; " and this formula, which applied to all the protocols, also figured at
the heading of all the diplomas issued by the masters and addressed to the
students.   It is easy to understand that the word *universitas*, gradually

Fig. 2.—Seal of the French Nation
(Fourteenth Century).

Fig. 4.—Seal of the English Nation
(Fourteenth Century).

Fig. 3.—Counter-Seal of the French Nation
(Fourteenth Century).

Fig. 5.—Counter-Seal of the English Nation
(Fourteenth Century).

From the Sigillographic Collection in the National Archives.

assuming a special or limited meaning, was finally taken to mean the
University or whole body of students, then the establishment itself to which
these students belonged, and, lastly, the large quarter of the town which was
almost exclusively reserved for them on the left bank of the Seine.

The annals of the University of Paris cannot, however, be traced further back than to the lectures of Peter Abelard, that great and popular teacher

Fig. 6.—Seal of the Normandy Nation (Fourteenth Century).

Fig. 8.—Seal of the Picardy Nation (Fourteenth Century).

Fig. 7.—Counter-Seal of the Normandy Nation (Fourteenth Century).

Fig. 9.—Counter-Seal of the Picardy Nation (Fourteenth Century).

From the Sigillographic Collection in the National Archives.

who has left so deep an impression behind him. When the young and unfortunate professor came to Paris for the first time (1057) to complete his studies, the school was still, so to speak, beneath the wing of the Church. It was in the cloisters of Notre-Dame that those gifted masters, William of Champeaux and Anselm of Laon, whose lessons he at first received, but both of whom he eventually surpassed, taught their pupils. Fifty years later there came the dawn of the University, for Henry II., King of England, proposed to submit the matters in dispute between himself and Thomas à Becket to the arbitrament of the schools of the *various nations* studying at Paris. This proof of esteem for the scholars of Paris says a great deal for

Fig. 10.—Seal of the Rheims University (1568).

Fig. 11.—Counter-Seal of the Rheims University (1568).

From the Sigillographic Collection in the National Archives.

the reputation which the cosmopolitan University must have enjoyed at that period, not only in France, but throughout Europe. In the year 1200 a charter from Philip Augustus, dated Béthesy, in which may be discovered almost the foundation of the privileges of the University, shows us this institution being carried on under a head whose immunity from the interference of the ordinary law is solemnly guaranteed, together with that of all its members. Lastly, in 1260, the University body stands out fully organized, and having attained its complete development.

It is necessary to give a summary sketch of this ingenious and complex organization, as it may be gathered from the researches of Vallet de Viriville and those of the learned M. Charles Jourdain, the last historian of the University of Paris.

From the very beginning a natural division established itself between the young men whom the fame of the great Parisian school attracted thither from all parts of Christendom. The students grouped themselves into nations,

Fig. 12.—Seal of the Aix University in Provence (Sixteenth Century).

Fig. 13.—Great Seal of the Bourges University (Fifteenth Century).

From the Sigillographic Collection in the National Archives.

and these nations having adopted, by analogy of language, interests, and sympathy, a more regular form, there were but four nations: that of France (Figs. 2 and 3), that of England (Figs. 4 and 5), that of Normandy (Figs. 6 and 7), and that of Picardy (Figs. 8 and 9). The French nation consisted of five tribes, which included the bishoprics or metropolitan provinces of Paris, Sens, Rheims, and Bourges (Figs. 10 to 13), and all the south of Europe, so that a Spaniard or an Italian, who came to study at Paris, was comprised in

the French nation. The English nation, which was subdivided into two
tribes, that of islanders and that of continentals, embraced all the northern
and eastern parts of Europe beyond the frontiers of France.   But when

Fig. 14.—A School of Mendicant Monks : a Birching.—Miniature of the Manuscript No. 21,252
in the Burgundy Library, Brussels (Fifteenth Century).

the two peoples separated from each other by the channel became violent
antagonists, and the name of England had got to be an object of general
execration for Frenchmen, the nation which for more than a century had

borne it became the German nation, and this is the only name made use of in the public documents after the return of Charles VII. to Paris in 1437 (Fig. 1). The Normandy nation had only one tribe, corresponding with the province after which it was called ; while the Picardy nation, on the other hand, had five, representing the five dioceses of Beauvais, Noyon, Amiens, Laon, and Térouanne, otherwise called des Morins.

The four nations together constituted at first the *University of Studies*, but afterwards a fresh division was established, according to the order of the studies of each nation, and the Faculties came into existence. From that time forward, the distinction of nations only existed in the Faculty of Arts, a denomination which comprised grammar, philosophy, and the humanities as they were taught in the schools. Looked at from another point of view, the liberal arts, so called, comprised the *trivium*, that is to say, grammar, rhetoric, and dialectics ; and the *quadrivium*, that is to say, arithmetic, geography, music, and astronomy.

When we consider the position held by the Church in society during the Middle Ages, it is not surprising that religious instruction should have been taken in hand at once, and have become the object of a special faculty, that of Theology. When, some time later, the mendicant orders were founded by St. Dominic and St. François, the ancient masters of theology and those of the Faculty of Arts refused at first to have anything to do with the new-comers; but they were compelled to do so by St. Louis and Pope Alexander IV., and the useful co-operation of the allies whom it had at first repelled soon turned to the profit and to the glory of the Faculty of Theology (Fig. 14).

In 1151 a clerk from Bologna, called Gratian, having united under the title of *Decree* the ancient and recent decisions of the ecclesiastical authorities, which comprised the whole canonical jurisprudence, Pope Eugène III. gave his approval to this compilation, and ordered it to be taught throughout Christendom. Such was the origin of the Faculty of the Decree, which was at first but a branch of the Faculty of Theology. At about the same period the Pandects of the Emperor Justinianus, discovered at Amalfi, in Calabria, added a very valuable source of documents to the study of law, which had hitherto possessed no other bases than the Theodosian Code, the barbarous laws and " capitularies " of the Kings of France. The labours of the Juris-consults everywhere received a new impetus, and especially in the University of Paris ; but notwithstanding it was not until much later that civil law came to rank beside canon law.   Several popes, considering profane or secular jurisprudence as useless, and even opposed to ecclesiastical law, issued bulls in which students were enjoined to learn only canon law.

It is towards the close of the twelfth century, also, that the study of medicine appears to have begun in the lay schools of Paris.   Up to that period the clerks, and especially the clergy, who alone possessed sufficient learning to pursue the study of medicine, had been the sole masters of the art; but in course of time ecclesiastical discipline hampered and even

Fig. 15.—Seal of the four Nations or Faculty of Arts (Sixteenth Century).
Paris National Library.   The Cabinet of Medals.

put a ban upon the study of it, as it had done upon that of civil law.   It was, therefore, only after great difficulties that a Faculty of Medicine was founded at the University.   It is true that medicine—a science of facts and observations—could not well make much progress amidst the prejudices of every kind, and under the blind authority of the categories, the formalities, and the empiric methods which so long clung to the University teaching. The Paris Faculty of Medicine could not, in these circumstances, hope to dethrone the famous schools of Salerno and Montpellier, which preserved the deposit of the medical knowledge of antiquity as it had been transmitted to the

Middle Ages by the Greeks and the Arabs. The three new faculties created at the University continued to be subordinate, notwithstanding their gradual development, to the Faculty of Arts (Fig. 15) ; the body of the four nations, of which this last-mentioned faculty consisted, assured it a clear preponderance, with the maintenance of certain essential prerogatives. Thus each nation elected a proctor, and each faculty a dean. The mode of election

Fig. 16.—Rector and Doctor of the University of Paris.—After a Miniature of the " Cité de Dieu " (Fifteenth Century). Manuscript of the Paris National Library.

for the proctors and their term of office varied, however, with different nations. The Faculty of Arts had four proctors (Fig. 15). The Faculty of Theology, besides its dean, who was the senior doctor, chose every other year a syndic, whose business it was to administer the private business of the company. The Decree Faculty had only a dean selected by seniority in the grade of doctor, and the Faculty of Medicine had a dean elected every year

from amongst the doctors in practice.   Deans and proctors, to the number
of seven, formed the higher tribunal of the University.   The Faculty of
Arts had, therefore, a clear majority of its own upon this tribunal ; it had,
moreover, assumed for itself the exclusive right of nominating the rector
or supreme head of the University, and he was bound to be a member of the
faculty (Fig. 16).   The Faculty of Arts also had the care of the archives,
the management of the Pré-aux-Clercs, and the nomination or presentation
of all the University officials not chosen by vote.

Originally the elected rector did not hold office for more than six weeks,

Fig. 17.—Master Jean de Vandeuil, Proctor of the Picardy Nation (Fifteenth Century).
Miniature of the Manuscript Register, No. 11 (1476—83).   University Archives.

but in the thirteenth century the period was extended to three months, and
towards the close of the fifteenth century the post came to be held in fact, if
not in right, for a twelvemonth.   The proctors of the nations (Fig. 17) were
at first invested with the right of choosing the rector, but so many scandals
were caused in this connection that the nations nominated four special
electors, who, before proceeding to a selection, swore to make a choice honourable and useful to the University.

The rector, whose office conferred upon him high prerogatives, exercised
a sovereign jurisdiction over all the schools, and recognised no authority as

superior to his own within the precincts of the University.   Often summoned to the King's Council, he took rank with the Bishop of Paris and
with the Parliament at all public ceremonials.   He gave to all the students,

Fig. 18.—Swiss Courier.—After a Statue preserved in the Town Hall at Bâle
(Fifteenth Century).

and also to the tutors, the *letters* or diplomas which conferred upon them
the privileges of their grade, and he received from them their oath of passive
obedience, "no matter to what dignity they might attain"—an oath the

merely formed part of their temporary functions. These titles were quite distinct and independent of the scholastic titles, grades, or degrees, which were only to be acquired by examination. Previously to the thirteenth century, it is certain that there were only two degrees in the University body : that of the students and that of the masters. Anybody who had the amount of knowledge or hardihood to face an audience could open a school, and it is to be remarked that daring often had its reward. Thus Abelard was often taunted with having dubbed himself of his own authority master of theology.

Immediately after the foundation of the University there were three degrees which students had to pass in turn. The first, that of *bachelor*, derived its name indirectly, according to several theologists, from the Latin word *baculum* (rod, and so, by extension, any weapon held in the hand), out of allusion to the different exercises which were the prelude to the military education of the young nobility. The first bachelors were the Bachelors of Arts. After having well studied his *trivium*, the candidate for the bacca-lauréat underwent an examination, and had to enter into arguments upon grammar, rhetoric, and dialectics. These arguments—*disputes* they were called—took place at Christmas and during Lent. The candidate, if he came well out of them, obtained the treble privilege, 1st. of wearing the round hat, a mark of his rank; 2nd. of being present at the masses of the nations; 3rd. of commencing in the arts, that is to say, of teaching in his turn, under the direction and superintendence of a master. The bachelor, who was at the same time both student and teacher, explained Aristotle's treatises on logic, natural philosophy, metaphysics, and moral philosophy; and when he believed that he had mastered all these subjects, which now seem so far behind us, he applied to the ecclesiastical authorities for a *license*. The right of conferring this second University degree was at first shared by the Bishop of Paris and the Abbot of St. Geneviève, as spiritual sovereigns of the scholastic territory; but afterwards it was accorded exclusively to the Chancellor of Notre-Dame, as delegate of the bishop.

The *licentiate*, as soon as he had been approved of by the Church, again came up before the masters of the Faculty of Arts, to obtain from them the third degree, consisting of the cap and other insignia of the order, which gave him the title of Master of Arts.

In the higher faculties, so called because the Faculty of Arts served, in a manner, as an introduction to the Faculties of Theology, Decree, and

Medicine, the procedure was much the same, excepting that the third grade or degree, which was only conferred after the candidate had sustained a long

Fig. 20.—Reception of a Doctor.—Fac-simile of a Wood Engraving taken from a German edition of Cicero's "De Officiis" (Fourteenth Century).—Paris National Library. Cabinet of Designs.

and difficult thesis in public, was more specially accompanied by the title of *doctor* (Fig. 20).

The University of Paris, like all the institutions destined to last and to succeed, was placed beneath the fostering protection of the Church and the Crown. Thus the generous assistance of the temporal power and the tutelary influence of the spiritual power never failed it. The Holy See loved and encouraged in the University the eloquent voice of France, which, since the reign of Clovis, converted by St. Clotilde, had placed at the service of the Catholic faith all the forces and influence of her national genius and character. The Kings of France were equally well disposed towards the University, which was, for the capital of their kingdom, a source of wealth and of honour, a reserve of eminent statesmen for their council, a nursery of clever and distinguished youths for their diplomacy. Thus sovereigns, spiritual and temporal, each in their own way, vied in showering favours upon this fruitful and powerful institution, which, nevertheless, showed itself, in certain grave circumstances, the reverse of grateful for the benefits heaped upon it by its august protectors.

The history of Paris teems with episodes, some curious, and only too many tragic, which denote the turbulent and seditious tendencies of the University students. These headstrong and undisciplined youths took advantage of the sort of inviolability which they owed to the blind and generous affection of their religious and lay patrons to gratify their love of disorder. The University itself set the students an example of disobedience when the smallest of its prerogatives was called in question. The University possessed three means of protesting against, or, as its historian, Egasse du Boulay, puts it, of remedying any infraction of its privileges. If the violation was committed by the secular power, it referred the matter at once to the King, as its jurisdiction emanated direct from the Crown. If the infraction was committed by the ecclesiastical authority, the University sent to Rome an embassy, consisting of its own doctors, who often found in the successor of St. Peter a former comrade, whose associations inclined him in favour of a University to which, as a graduate, he had formerly taken an oath of fidelity. If the Pope refused to comply with the request addressed to him by the University, the latter appealed to the universal Church and to the future council. Its last resource was what may be called a University excommunication. This meant a general stoppage of all studies and lectures. The masters and doctors in theology abstained from preaching in the churches. The intellectual, moral, and religious life of the capital was suspended. If the crisis lasted, the doctors, regents, and bachelors of the four faculties closed their schools, and threatened to emigrate in a body, taking with them a whole army of ushers and clients, who formed nearly a third of the population of Paris. No power existed in the thirteenth century capable of holding out long against this silent and inflexible protest.

Thus, in 1221, the University, having to complain of some undue exercise of authority by the Bishop of Paris, closed its schools for six months. In similar circumstances, four years later, the Papal Legate was assailed in his own house by a band of armed students, who wounded several of his retinue, and would have maltreated him if he had not avoided capture. At

Fig. 21.—St. Louis, King of France, going to Matins at the Cordeliers Church, Paris, " ung estudiant par mesprison lui tumba son orinal sur son chief." The King, instead of punishing the student, gave him the prebendary of St. Quentin, en Vermandois, "because he was in the habit of getting up at this hour to study."—Miniature of Manuscript of the Fifteenth Century. Burgundy Library, Brussels.

the close of the Carnival of 1228, Queen Blanche, who was Regent during the minority of her son, Louis IX., inflicted severe punishment upon the students who, under the influence of drink, had committed great disorder and had shed blood in the Faubourg of St. Marcel. The University, finding the remonstrances which it in consequence addressed to the King of no effect, dismissed the students and masters to their respective homes, left the capital for two years under an interdict, and only consented to resume the

normal course of teaching after having wrung from the Crown the repara-
tion which it had demanded at first (Fig. 21).

It must, however, be admitted that the University could only earn such
victories as these at the cost of its own privileges, and with much injury to
itself; for the masters, scattered here and there during the time that the
schools were closed, often co-operated in the foundation of rural universities
at the places where they had taken up a temporary residence, and settled
there permanently.   Moreover, these periods of disturbance and strife were
taken advantage of by other teaching bodies, who lost no time in opening
schools, and in creating chairs, and who often obtained through the spiritual
or temporal authority the favour of being admitted, either by a bull or an
ordinance, into the University itself.   It was in this way that in 1257 the
Dominicans, supported by Louis IX., who had been their pupil, and by the
popes, who had been their comrades, forced their way through the breach
into the University of Paris, and this in spite of the distrust and animosity
which their doctrines excited.   It was in the same way that the University
was compelled to open its ranks to, and confer the doctor's cap upon, Brother
Thomas Aquinas and Brother Bonaventura, who were the lights of the philosophic schools, but who remained far more attached, the one to the Order of
St. Dominic, the other to that of St. Francis, than to the Faculty of
Theology.   Moreover, the sort of moral and political omnipotence acquired
by the University in the Middle Ages was not the same at every epoch,
and it is easy to recognise in the course of its history different phases, in the
process of which its character and tendencies underwent various modifications.
In the first period the Paris schools were but the emanation of the Church,
which was gradually becoming secularised.   As the institution became more
and more stable, it got to be more in harmony with other establishments.   In
the year 1200 Philip Augustus issued a charter, uniting the University into
one body, and endowed the multitude of students gathered together from all
parts of the world with very valuable privileges.   From this laborious and
intellectual mass of students were recruited several popes and cardinals, a
great many archbishops or bishops, and a vast number of men of the
highest ability in other professions throughout the thirteenth century.   Up
to the middle of the fourteenth century the authority and importance of the
University continued to increase.   From 1297 to 1304 it was of material
aid to Philippe le Bel in his struggle with Pope Boniface VIII.   In 1316,

at the death of Louis X., and in 1328, at the death of Charles IV., its vote
went a long way towards securing the triumph of the Salic law, and preventing the government of France from falling into the hands of an English
prince. Councillor of the kings, instructor of the people, the University—
the permanent Council of the Gauls—pursued its high mission with great
credit, and this was the period when it reached the apogee of its splendour.
Then it was that all its members, masters and pupils alike, were recognised
as inviolable, exempt from all tolls, subsidies, imposts, and military service of
every kind. Then it was that, to complete the measure of its honours,
Charles V. conferred upon the University the proud title, which it never let
drop, of Eldest Daughter of the Kings.

But the period of its decadence was soon about to begin. Venality,
sophistry, and party spirit took possession of its leaders. In 1380 the gold
of the house of Burgundy was the stipend of several political creatures in
the ranks of the doctors in theology. In 1407 the Duke of Orleans,
brother of the King, was waylaid and murdered, and Master Jean Petit took
up the murderers' part in the pulpit, and justified political assassination.
Then came the English, to whose yoke part of the University submitted with
so much cowardice as to provoke, with a sort of complacent fanaticism,
the iniquitous sentence which condemned the heroic Joan of Arc to the
stake. Reprisals and punishment were not long in overtaking them. King
Charles VII. inflicted the first blow upon this ancient institution, which his
royal predecessors had protected, and it almost seems as if he punished the
University for not having sustained its ancient reputation for patriotism and
good sense. Not only did he recognise and confirm the existence of several
new universities in the provinces (Figs. 10—13), but, rejecting the demand
of the Paris University, which insisted that its only tribunal should be the
King's Council, ordered its disputes to be judged by the Parliament (1445).
Fifty-five years later, Louis XII., taking into consideration the wishes of
the States-General convoked during the reign of Charles VIII., curtailed
many of the privileges of the University; and, by his edict of August
31st, 1498, brought it within the jurisdiction of the common law. The
University attempted to resist, and, as in its palmy days, to resort to its
traditional practices. The rector ordered the schools to be closed, and no
sermons to be preached in the churches; but the King, absent from the
capital, received his *eldest daughter* with a bad grace. Upon his return,

escorted by his military household, all fully armed, he rode through the University quarter of the city without condescending to draw bridle to hear the harangue of the rector, who had come out to meet him, followed by all the officers and students. The University gave way, and this was her last attempt to maintain by force her feudal prerogatives.

The University ceased from this time to be the centre of intellectual domination. Printing was invented about this time, and diffused the *instruments* of study and knowledge in all directions. The Reformation proclaimed the liberty of self-examination, and the free schools established under the new religious doctrines throughout Europe obtained the preference. Paris ceased to be the exclusive source of science, but Rome remained the sole focus of divine light. The University lost its unity and its strength when it ceased to lean exclusively for support upon the Church and the Crown.

Having thus rapidly reviewed the vicissitudes which the University underwent up to the sixteenth century, it becomes necessary to notice the various scholastic establishments which, affiliated to it, or independent of it altogether, constituted the totality of the educational system in schools during the Middle Ages.

When Abelard came to Paris in 1107 he found two masters of great reputation, who gave their lessons in the Bishop's house, by the side of the cathedral. It was not far from this house, and at the very entrance to the cloisters of Notre-Dame, where Canon Fulbert and his pupil Héloïse lived, that Abelard first opened his school. A few years later, William of Champeaux resigned his archdeaconship, and withdrew to the priory of St. Victor, upon the left bank of the Seine, outside the walls of the city, in order to found a new school there. Abelard, expelled from the school which he occupied in the city, near the episcopal residence, took refuge upon Mount St. Geneviève, whither he was followed by his pupils. Notwithstanding, the cathedral schools continuing to increase, and being short of room within the enclosure of the city, were divided into two parts. The one, consisting of *artiens* (students of Arts), crossed the bridge, and took up their quarters close to the Church of St. Julian the Poor, which was a branch of the Metropolitan Cathedral (Fig. 22). The *theologians* retained their residence under the walls of Notre-Dame. It was in this way that the elements which a century later constituted the University began to collect. In a

short time the nations erected four large rooms or schools, close to the
Church of St. Julian the Poor, in the Rue Fouarre, or Feurre, so called

Fig. 22.—Bas-relief of the Principal Altar in the Church of St. Julian the Poor (Twelfth-Century
Work).—Two Scholars upon their Knees on each side of the Crucifix.

because the students had to sit upon straw (*fouarre*), grouped around the
chair occupied by the master.   Independently of these great schools, which

represented a sort of general school, any one who had obtained a license hired a room, and invited the public to take lessons from him. Thus the University quarter, which was afterwards called the "Latin quarter," became peopled with masters and schools. It soon became necessary to erect hotels or private dwellings to take in the students, who were at once eager to learn, and very scantily provided with money (Fig. 23). This was the origin of the Paris colleges, under which name were founded, in the early days of the University, various establishments, in which aspirants for religious orders studied at the expense of the monastic orders to which they

Fig. 23.—Interior of a School.—After a Design of the Sixteenth Century.—National Library.
Cabinet of Designs (Old Masters) on Wood.

belonged. Private charity soon created colleges of a similar kind for laymen, veritable houses of refuge, in which the students were provided, to use the apposite expression of one founder, with bread for the body and the mind. This double character of liberality and devotion is a prominent feature in the primitive constitution of these establishments, which were founded and endowed by pious persons with the view of assisting the education of the poor. Such were, in the thirteenth century, the Colleges of the Bons Enfants St. Honoré (1208), and of the Bons Enfants St. Victor (1248), the Colleges of St. Catherine du Valdes Ecoliers (1229), and of Prémontré

(1252), the Treasurer's College (1268), and, oldest of all, the College of the Eighteen, which dates from the first half of the twelfth century.

Nothing, however, can be imagined more pitiable and more deserving of sympathy than these colleges of the Middle Ages, in which, under the control of a *regent* or *principal*, a few masters, as poor as their scholars, devoted themselves to the education of a dozen or so of students, who shared with them their scanty pittance. With scarcely enough money to keep body and soul together, they were compelled to do some menial work, or else to appeal to public charity. In the fourteenth century, as we learn from the ditty called "Crieries de Paris," the scholars of the College of the Bons Enfants, in the Rue St. Honoré, wandered about the streets, and, holding out their hands to the passers-by, exclaimed—

> " Les Bons Enfants orrez (hear) crier :
> Du pain !...."

Some few colleges were better off than this woe-stricken house, for, being endowed with fixed revenues by their founders, encouraged and enriched by the clergy and the great, they prospered and continued in existence until the Revolution.

The one which long remained the most famous of all, the Sorbonne, owed its name and its origin to the liberality of the learned Robert Sorbon, who, after having undergone privations of every kind in his youth, became the chaplain and confessor of Louis IX. By letters patent in 1250 the saintly King, himself contributing to this foundation, granted for the use of the future college a house and stables adjoining, situated in the Rue Coupe-Gueule, in front of the ruins of the palace of the Thermæ, or of the Cæsars. This college was specially destined for a certain number of needy youths, who, after having taken their arts degree, gave themselves up to the study of sacred lore. It is needless to remind our readers that the Sorbonne, rebuilt, enlarged, and richly endowed by Cardinal Richelieu, who bequeathed to it a part of his property, became at last the seat of the Faculty of Theology.

Created upon the model of Robert Sorbon's foundation, a great many colleges, instituted by men of mark either in the Church or in society, were erected as if by magic—no less than sixty were built between 1137 and 1360 —in all parts of the University quarter, which extended in the shape of an amphitheatre from the summit of Mount Geneviève down to the Seine, and which also spread along the then deserted banks of the stream, from the bridge of La Tournelle to what is now the bridge of the Saints-Pères.

Two of these colleges call for special notice. The first is the College of Navarre, which was founded in 1304 by Queen Jeanne de Navarre, wife of Philippe le Bel. This college, constructed to receive seventy students, of whom thirty were students of arts, twenty of theology, and twenty of grammar, soon became a model for establishments of a similar kind, and the high reputation which it had acquired endured for four centuries. The University deposited its valuable archives in the chapel of the college, which was dedicated to St. Louis, the ancestor of the royal founders. The sons of the highest families, and even princes of the reigning house, received in this learned retreat the elements of a classical education, and moreover, by the terms of the charter, the King was the first bursar of the Navarre College, which may be considered as one of the most aristocratic institutions of that time, and also the one in which the rules and regulations were the least strict.

The Collége de Montaigu, established at a later date in the Rue des Sept-Voies, upon Mount St. Geneviève, was scarcely less famous than that of Navarre, but its history is a very different one. Though it was originally founded by the wealthy Parisian family of Montaigu, upon such liberal terms that an income of ten livres (equivalent to twelve or fifteen pounds sterling in the present day) was secured for the maintenance of each student, it was so badly managed by the regents that the total revenue of the college fell to eleven sols in gold, equivalent to about £40 at the present time. At this period (1483) the college passed into the hands of Jean Standonck, one of the most original characters amongst the ancient schoolmasters. Son of a Mechlin tailor, arriving in Paris with an ardent desire to obtain a liberal education, and received out of charity by the Abbey of St. Geneviève, whose hospitality he repaid by doing odds and ends of work, Jean Standonck, being endowed with an uncommon degree of energy and perseverance, rose from the condition of a servant to that of pupil, and eventually became a master. Selected by his fellows to manage the affairs of the Montaigu College, he succeeded in restoring order and economy in the house, in founding twelve fresh bursarships, and meeting all expenses, without incurring any new debt. But he only effected all these improvements by imposing upon his students a very austere régime, and compelling them to lead a life as full of privations as his own had been. Arduous study, frequent fasts, a meagre pittance, and a rigid discipline, such became the proverbial condition of the Montaigu students—a condition wittily expressed in their Latin motto: *Mons acutus, ingenium acutum, dentes acuti* (a sharp-pointed mountain, a sharp-pointed mind, and sharp-pointed teeth). Attired in a cape of coarse cloth, closed in front, and surmounted by a hood fastening at the back, they were called the *pauvres capettes* of Montaigu, and they were to be seen daily fetching their share, conformably with their statutes, of the bread which the Carthusians of the Rue d'Enfer distributed to the poor. Erasmus and Rabelais, both of whom learnt by personal experience, at a few years' interval, the hardships of the Montaigu régime, have immortalised, each after his own fashion, their melancholy college recollections; the first in one of his ingenious colloquies, by pouring his maledictions on the inhuman treatment, the unhealthy lodging, the unwholesome and insufficient food which had seriously injured his health while a student there; the second by putting in the mouth of his mock heroes many a stinging epigram about the *collége de pouillerie*.

Independently of the University and of the colleges, there also existed in France, as in all Christendom during the Middle Ages, several kinds of schools, some elementary, open to both sexes, and generally termed *little schools*, or *French schools*, as all that was taught in them was reading and writing, with a few rudiments of the vulgar tongue and sacred music; the others, reserved for boys, and called the *great schools*, or the *Latin schools* (Fig. 24). Both of these schools, generally attached to the churches, were in most cases under the control of a single superintendent responsible to the bishop of the diocese. This superintendent, called either rector or head-master of schools, received from each scholar a fixed annual fee, payable in two instalments, and a supplementary sum, also divided into two parts, one of which was set apart for the repair of the building, and placed in the hands of the provost, while the other was used for the purchase of birches, which were kept in hand by the head-porter or *bircher* (Fig. 25). These schools only received free scholars whom their parents or relatives undertook to board. They had at their disposal, most of them under the patronage of some private founder, if not under the auspices of the parochial chapter, a certain number of purses or *gratuities*, which were given to the needy students in return for some small services which they were required to render.

Thus, for instance, in the schools at Troyes, the *primitives*, so called because of the early morning work they had to do, were exempted from the payment of any fees, in return for which they had to clean and sweep out the school-rooms twice a week.

We learn from an inventory of the silver plate of Marie d'Anjou, wife of Charles VII., for the years 1454-55—an inventory in which are mentioned the school books used by Charles, Duke of Berry, their second son—what were

Fig. 24.—The Schoolmaster, from the *Danse macabre*, Guyot Marchant edition (1490).

the works used for the elementary classes previously to the invention of printing. These books, which had already been used for the education of the Dauphin, afterwards Louis XI., are: 1st, an A, B, C; 2nd, a psalter, called the *Seven Psalms*, which children had to get by heart; 3rd, a *Donat*, or treatise of the eight parts of the discourse by Ælius Donatus, a grammarian of the fourth century; 4th, an *Accidens*, another grammar treating of the cases and conjugations of verbs; 5th, a *Cato*, a collection of moral distichs in Latin, with a French translation, attributed to Valerius Cato, a poet and grammarian mentioned very favourably by Suetonius; 6th, a *Doctrinal*, or Latin grammar, taken from the great work of Priscianus, a grammarian of the fourth century, and made into Leonine verse (the last syllable of each line rhyming with the middle syllable) as a help to the memory, by Alexander de Ville-Dieu, who in 1209 was a distinguished teacher in the Paris schools.

These works, although intended for primary instruction, were also meant to give the pupils some elementary knowledge of the Latin tongue, which, in almost general use during the Middle Ages, was at once the language of the Church, of letters, and of sciences, and was the common idiom

Fig. 25.—The Schoolmaster, after a Drawing by Soquand (1528).

amongst all Christian nations. This will explain how it was that Latin was not only taught, but spoken, to the exclusion of the vulgar tongue, in the Universities, the colleges, and the principal schools. It was not until later, when the modern spirit had propagated amongst the people a multitude of new ideas and sentiments difficult to translate literally into Latin, that the struggle began between the language of the ancients and the living tongues —a long and eventful struggle, which, after heroic efforts in favour of the beautiful language immortalised by the masterpieces of the ancient classic writers, ended in Latin being finally relegated to the list of dead languages. It is interesting to note what efforts were made by the University of Paris, by the imposition of fines and punishments, in the fifteenth, and even up to the beginning of the seventeenth century, to repel the invasion of French, which the scholars naturally brought with them when they arrived from home.   It is true that a regulation, passed in 1434, allowed the use of two kinds of Latin : the congruous Latin, which every student who had reached his *doctrinal,* or Latin syntax, used exclusively ; and the incongruous Latin, which students were permitted to speak amongst each other in the elementary classes.   French, even in private conversation and out of school hours, was generally prohibited.

But the Latin tongue, limited, so to speak, to the domain of the University, recovered all its credit and renown when, at the epoch of the Renaissance, the literary masterpieces of Rome were once more sought after, studied, and commented on with ardent emulation by the learned, circulated in a number of new and revised editions, and welcomed with enthusiasm by all literary Europe.   Then it was that men of mark and genius, such as Erasmus, Melancthon, and Mathurin Cordier, composed colloquies and dialogues, which made the language of the Augustan age more familiar to the youth of the age of François I. and Charles V.   But these efforts, though successful for the time, were not long triumphant, and it is a singular and significant fact that of the books of study published at this period the only one which has survived was written in French, viz. the *Civilité puérile et honnête,* which first appeared at Poitiers in 1559, with the title, far more appropriate to the character of the book, of " A mirror in which the young may learn good morality and the decencies of life."

But if the books of study used in the ancient schools are now out of date and long since forgotten, such is not the case with the different kinds of recreation in which boys and young men used to indulge as a relaxation from a course of study often abstract and always severe.   The *Gargantua* of Rabelais, and the familiar dialogues of Mathurin Cordier, enable us to frame a list of games which are still played, though in some cases under slightly different names ; as, for instance, the ball, prisoner's-base, leap-frog, quoits, *clicquette* (pieces of wood, or shords, which were beaten one against another to make them ring), ninepins, bat and trap, spinning-tops and whipping-tops, the *fossette,* or pitch-farthing (which was formerly played with nuts), odd or even, cards, draughts, tennis, heads or tails, tip-cat, &c.

These were the peaceable games of children and scholars, but they were too tame for the turbulent tastes of the older students, whose bad reputation is still proverbial. From all time, grave magistrates, illustrious writers, famous citizens, and even saintly personages have prefaced their career of

Fig. 26.—The sergeants of the provost of Paris apologizing, in 1440, for having infringed the privileges of the clergy and the University. This stone was built into the outer wall of the Monastery of the Grands-Augustins, and remained there until the Revolution. It is now at the School of Fine Arts.

labour, study, and virtue by a more or less prolonged sowing of wild oats. At all times, moreover, Paris offered only too many temptations to vice and dissipation. It is easy, therefore, to understand what must have been the condition, in the twelfth and thirteenth centuries, when the police as an institution, were hardly known, and when public morality still felt the effects of long years of decadence, of a population of students penned up in a territory which they looked upon as a freehold, consisting, as they did, of youths on the verge of manhood and of full-grown men, belonging to various nationalities, and left to their own passions. When it is further remembered that a degree of arts could not be obtained before the age of one-and-twenty, and one of theology till the age of thirty-five (after eight years' study in the latter case), no wonder that this turbulent quarter was a nuisance, and even a danger for the honest and peaceful inhabitants of Paris.

The whole city was more than once disturbed, and public safety endangered, by the aggressive and disorderly habits of the students. Not a day passed without quarrels and fights, arising out of the most futile causes. The insulting epithets which the students applied to each other show, moreover, the antipathies which prevailed amongst them, and the coarseness which was common to them all. The English had the reputation of being cowards and drunkards ; the French were proud and effeminate ; the Germans dirty, gluttonous, and ill-tempered ; the Normans boastful and deceitful ; the Burgundians brutal and stupid ; the Flemish bloodthirsty, vagabond, and house-burners ; and so forth for the rest.

With all this, the person of a *clerk* (a title appertaining to every student who had obtained his license) was, according to the canons of the Church, inviolable ; to lay hands upon a student was to commit a crime which entailed excommunication, and which the Pope alone could absolve (Fig. 26). This will explain the audacity and arrogance of the students, and it is no wonder that the civil authorities were, for all the most minute precautions, continually at a loss how to repress the excesses of these riotous youths, who, going about day and night in armed bands, indulged in every kind of disorder, and did not stop at any crime.

The establishment of the colleges led to a decided change for the better. Previously to this happy innovation the students took advantage of the most trifling religious or literary occurrence to increase the number of festivals, which were celebrated with no lack of dancing, masquerades, banquets, &c. All these scholastic rejoicings were afterwards reduced to two *refreshments* (days intended for a carousal), one at the beginning, the other at the end of the public examinations, a period at which the candidates elected a captain from amongst themselves, and to a fête in honour of the patron saint of each nation. This was exclusive of the great festivals celebrated in honour of such and such a *patron* of the University corporation.

The University, after having at first been placed beneath the guardianship of the Holy Virgin, patroness of the Church and of the city of Paris, and whose image is to be traced at every epoch upon the seals and other dis-

Fig. 27.—The legend of St. Nicholas, after the Bourges stained glass of Fathers Cahier and Martin (Thirteenth Century). The lower part refers to the popular story of the three students whom an innkeeper and his wife assassinated and put into a salt-tub, and whom the saint brought to life again. At the top the same saint is seen bringing by night a sum of money sufficient for the dowry of three poor maidens whom their father was unable to provide for.

tinctive emblems of the schools, had adopted as patrons and protectors several saints to whom special homage was rendered, viz. St. Thomas à Becket of Canterbury, St. Cosmo, St. Adrian, and St. Andrew. Afterwards the only saints fêted were St. Nicholas and St. Catherine (Fig. 27), the one patron of the clerks, the other of young people generally, but especially of girls. The nations also had their special patrons. When the wars with the English lessened the popularity of St. Thomas of Canterbury, the nation of

France invoked by preference St. William of Bourges, an ancient pupil of
the University.   One tribe of the Picardy nation honoured St. Firmin, the
first Bishop of Amiens, while the other tribe fêted St. Piat, Bishop of
Tournay.   The patron saint of the Normandy nation was St. Romain, Archbishop of Rouen.   The nation of England, after having stamped upon its
seal the image of Edmund the Martyr, Bishop of Norwich, and of St.
Catherine and St. Martin, made a point, when it became the nation of
Germany, of celebrating the festival of St. Charlemagne, who was looked
upon as the founder of the clergy throughout Christendom.

The patron festivals were, therefore, very numerous in the University of
Paris, and the students were always ready to interrupt their studies to take
part in the solemnities which were generally held in the famous Pré-aux-
Clercs, their veritable domain, beginning at the Faubourg St. Germain des
Prés, and extending down to the Seine, all along what are now the Rue St.
Dominique and the Rue de l'Université.

Of all the festivals at which the students took part in a body, the most
popular was the Lendit fair, which they looked upon as instituted expressly
for their amusement, though it dates back beyond the foundation of the
University itself.

The Paris Cathedral, having received from Constantinople in 1109 some
authentic fragments of the cross, the Bishop, in compliance with the wishes
of the population who could not find room in the Cathedral, where the
relics had been deposited, carried them in great pomp, accompanied by his
clergy, to the plain of St. Denis, where there was room enough for the vast
concourse of worshippers who assembled to contemplate and adore these
relics.   It is a well-ascertained fact that the schools of the cloister of Notre-
Dame took part in the procession.   The same ceremony and procession were
renewed at stated periods; and, in the course of time, a market or fair was
established upon the very spot consecrated by the religious ceremony.   Every
year, on the 12th of June, the day after the feast of St. Barnabas, the Lendit
(or rather the *Indict*, that is to say, the day appointed) fair was opened.
It was also called the feast of the parchment (see the volume, " Arts in the
Middle Ages," chapter *Parchment, Paper*).   Early in the morning of that
day, the students, attired in their best, assembled on horseback at the top
of Mount St. Geneviève, to accompany the rector of the University, who,
arrayed in his scarlet cloak, and wearing his doctor's cap, proceeded on a

Fig. 28.—Rector of the Prague University and Scholars of the different Nations who studied in the same University. From an ancient Picture still possessed by the Prague University.

mule or hackney, and accompanied by the deans, proctors, and myrmidons, to the plain of St. Denis, where the market for the sale of parchment was already opened.   The rector, upon reaching the fair, caused to be put aside as much parchment as would be required by the University for the coming year, and received from the sellers a donation equivalent to £100 in the present day.   After this the students alighted from their horses, and, instead of forming part of the procession back to Paris, amused themselves at the fair.   This invariably led to riot and disorder, and not a year passed without blood being spilt.   Thus, from the fifteenth to the sixteenth century, the decrees of Parliament against the carrying of arms or sticks, decrees which were continually being renewed and always neglected, testify to the gravity of the evil and to the obstacles in the way of putting a stop to it.   At last, in 1566, the fair was transferred from the plain to the town of St. Denis, and at about the same period paper began to supersede parchment even in public documents.   The rector, therefore, ceased getting a supply of it at the Lendit fair, and the students had no further pretext to attend this fair, which soon fell into disuse.   By the beginning of the seventeenth century the only vestige left of it was the general holliday which the rector granted to the students of the University upon the first Monday after the feast of St. Barnabas.

The clerks and students of Paris were also the principal actors in, if not the inventors of, certain ridiculous and burlesque ceremonies which, commenced in the Church, and, after having been tolerated by it, under the name of the Feasts of the Fusans, of the Ass, and of the Innocents, were only suppressed by the action of the Church itself (see in this volume the chapter on *Popular Superstitions*).   These singular and absurd buffooneries, which were so popular amongst the students, were, in course of time, succeeded by more sober recreations, such as theatrical representations within the colleges, open-air games, periodical excursions to the country, as, for instance, those to Our Lady of the Vines and Our Lady of the Fields, or the *May* excursion, which terminated in the planting of a tree in full bloom before the rector's gate. But, as Vallet de Viriville remarks, it took many years to efface the old traditions of violence and insubordination, for the French chroniclers of the sixteenth century represent the students of their time as amusing themselves in a manner that generally exceeded the limits of propriety.   To pace the streets at night, without regard for the tranquillity of the citizens or for the

Fig. 29.—Seal of the University of Oxford.

Fig. 30.—Seal of the University of Cambridge.

Fig. 31.—Seal of Balliol College
(founded 1269), Oxford.

Fig. 32.—Seal of the University of Prague.

modesty of their wives and daughters, to belabour the watchmen and throw the sergeants into the Seine, were deeds of valour recorded in the souvenirs of the University, and long talked of by the pupils of the Navarre and Montaigu Colleges.

The student of the Middle Ages was, as a peculiar type, essentially Parisian at first, though he soon became naturalised in all the towns where a University was founded after the twelfth century. He was, perhaps, the

Fig. 33.—External View of Leyden University, founded in 1575 by William of Nassau. From a contemporary Drawing in the work entitled, "Illustrium Hollandiæ, etc., ordinum alma Academia Leydensis" (Lugd. Batav., 1614, in quarto).

greatest gossip and pedant in Italy, where the University of Bologna, founded in 1158, soon led to the creation of Universities at Naples (1224), Padua (1228), Rome (1245), and Pisa (1333). Students of this stamp naturally became still more arrogant and quarrelsome in the Germanic Universities which were founded in succession at Prague (1348), Cologne (1385), Heidelberg (1386), and Leipsic (1409). The English students at Oxford (1200) and Cambridge (1257) were less noisy ; the Spanish students in the Universities of Valencia (1209), Salamanca (1250), and Valladolid (1246) were more

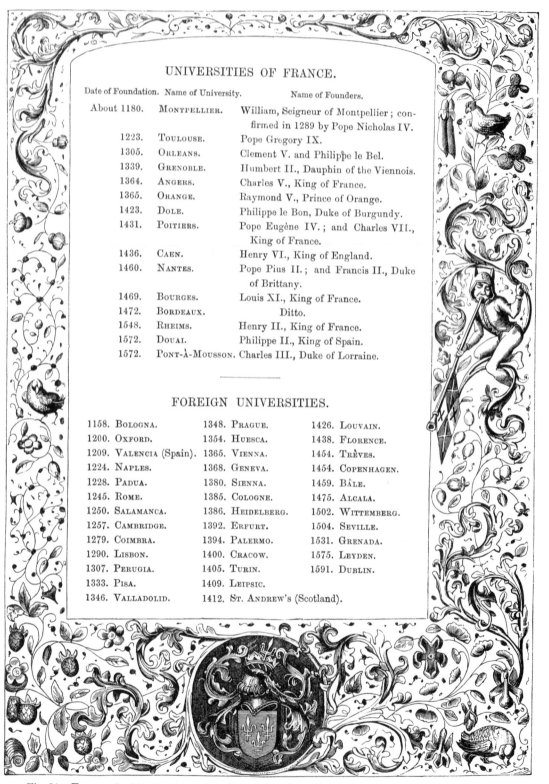

UNIVERSITIES OF FRANCE.

Date of Foundation.	Name of University.	Name of Founders.
About 1180.	MONTPELLIER.	William, Seigneur of Montpellier; confirmed in 1289 by Pope Nicholas IV.
1223.	TOULOUSE.	Pope Gregory IX.
1305.	ORLEANS.	Clement V. and Philippe le Bel.
1339.	GRENOBLE.	Humbert II., Dauphin of the Viennois.
1364.	ANGERS.	Charles V., King of France.
1365.	ORANGE.	Raymond V., Prince of Orange.
1423.	DOLE.	Philippe le Bon, Duke of Burgundy.
1431.	POITIERS.	Pope Eugène IV.; and Charles VII., King of France.
1436.	CAEN.	Henry VI., King of England.
1460.	NANTES.	Pope Pius II.; and Francis II., Duke of Brittany.
1469.	BOURGES.	Louis XI., King of France.
1472.	BORDEAUX.	Ditto.
1548.	RHEIMS.	Henry II., King of France.
1572.	DOUAI.	Philippe II., King of Spain.
1572.	PONT-À-MOUSSON.	Charles III., Duke of Lorraine.

FOREIGN UNIVERSITIES.

1158. BOLOGNA.	1348. PRAGUE.	1426. LOUVAIN.
1200. OXFORD.	1354. HUESCA.	1438. FLORENCE.
1209. VALENCIA (Spain).	1365. VIENNA.	1454. TRÈVES.
1224. NAPLES.	1368. GENEVA.	1454. COPENHAGEN.
1228. PADUA.	1380. SIENNA.	1459. BÂLE.
1245. ROME.	1385. COLOGNE.	1475. ALCALA.
1250. SALAMANCA.	1386. HEIDELBERG.	1502. WITTEMBERG.
1257. CAMBRIDGE.	1392. ERFURT.	1504. SEVILLE.
1279. COIMBRA.	1394. PALERMO.	1531. GRENADA.
1290. LISBON.	1400. CRACOW.	1575. LEYDEN.
1307. PERUGIA.	1405. TURIN.	1591. DUBLIN.
1333. PISA.	1409. LEIPSIC.	
1346. VALLADOLID.	1412. ST. ANDREW'S (Scotland).	

Fig. 34.—Framework of the first page of the MS. of the "Douze dames de Rhétorique" (Sixteenth Century).
Paris National Library.

pompous and austere; the Portuguese students at Coimbra (1279) and Lisbon (1290) were more proud and vain; the Swiss students at Geneva (1368) and Bâle (1459) appear to have been rather torpid and full of formality, while the Dutch students at Louvain (1426) and Leyden (1575) were remarkable for their close application to work. But the Paris student hardly changed in any respect; he remained the same gay and mirthful companion that Rabelais has depicted in the Panurge of his "Pantagruel."

PHILOSOPHIC SCIENCES.

Annihilation of the Pagan Philosophy.—New Christian Philosophy.—Martianus Capella.—Boethius and Cassiodorus.—Isidore of Seville.—Bede, Alcuin, and Raban Maurus.—John Scotus Erigena.—Origin of Scholasticism.—Gerbert.—Realism and Nominalism.—Béranger of Tours.—Roscelin and St. Anselm.—William of Champeaux and Abelard.—Gilbert de la Porrée and St. Bernard.—Amaury de Bène.—Albertus Magnus and St. Thomas Aquinas.—The Franciscans and the Dominicans.—William of Ockham.—Decadence of Scholasticism.—Platonists and Aristotelians.—The Philosophy of the Renaissance.—The Lutheran Schools.—P. Ramus.—Montaigne.

HE love of knowledge, says Aristotle, is natural to all men. It is the passion to which the wise men of antiquity were slaves, and which still inflames the learned in our own day. It is the source of all science and of all philosophy. From an etymological point of view, what is philosophy? It is the love of knowledge. The Middle Ages, notwithstanding the ardour of religious faith at that period, were not without philosophy; for during that period, memorable for the fervour of belief, the human heart was not insensible to the noble passion which is innate in it of knowing and understanding all things. Men sought with more or less success to discover the truth, and hence resulted the various aspects which the philosophy of the Middle Ages offers to those who study it.

In the first centuries of the Christian era, when the traditions of the schools of antiquity seem lost, the cultivation of science was abandoned by all save a few, and even with them the whole of their philosophy consisted in a few ill-defined aphorisms. They were succeeded by a few bold thinkers, who, anxious to obtain the credit of being thought masters, put forth the

most daring statements, some wholesome and others dangerous, which took
root a little later; and the thirteenth century shows us the thinkers of the
Middle Ages grappling vigorously with barbarism, and gradually attaining a
philosophy which reconciled the verities of the faith and rational conceptions.   But this philosophy was, in turn, attacked by daring innovators,

Fig. 35.—Boetnius takes counsel of Dame Philosophy.—Miniature of the "Consolation of
Boethius," Translation of Jean de Meung, Manuscript of the Fifteenth Century.—Library
of M. Ambroise Firmin-Didot.

and, well founded as it was, could not resist their onslaught.   Men's minds
became very agitated, new systems came into existence, and the Christian
faith grew weaker; and so we find ourselves no longer in the century of
St. Louis, but in that of François I. and Leo X.

Such are the principal phases through which philosophy passed during the long period which began with the last tumults of the barbarian invasion, and ended with the Renaissance in the sixteenth century. Its history is for the most part difficult to study, and always very dry; yet it has been made the subject in our day of many works, the best of which, despite its numerous defects, is that of M. Hauréau, from which we shall borrow largely, availing ourselves also of the valuable researches of M. Charles Jourdain, the

Fig. 36.—The Wheel of Fortune.—Miniature from the "Consolation of Boethius," Translation of Jean de Meung, Manuscript of the Fifteenth Century.—Library of M. Ambroise Firmin-Didot.

editor of Abelard's works, and the historian of the philosophy of St. Thomas Aquinas.

Amongst the Christian writers who preserved a few remnants of ancient learning amidst the ruins of the Roman empire must be mentioned, first of all, Martianus Capella, philosopher and poet of the fifth century, the author of the "Satyricon," a sort of encyclopædia in prose and in verse, which was long adopted in the schools of the Middle Ages as the poetic summary of the teaching which it attributes to the seven liberal arts—grammar, dialectics, rhetoric, geometry, arithmetic, astronomy, and music. This great work, which is more remarkable for wit and imagination than for learning and good taste, may be looked upon as the final flicker of ancient thought—as the first glimmer of the dawn of modern thought.

Almost contemporaneous with Martianus Capella comes the patrician Boethius, minister of Theodoric, put to death by order of his master, the learned interpreter of Aristotle's treatises on Logic, and author of a work in prose and in verse, which he entitled, "Of the Consolation of Philosophy" (Figs. 35 and 36), and which was one of the most popular books of the Middle Ages. A contemporary and friend of Boethius at the court of Theodoric was Cassiodorus, also famous for his learning and for his fondness for ancient works, copies of which he had made, and which he, more than any one else, was instrumental in preserving for the benefit of future generations. Cassiodorus was the author of a treatise on the Mind, another on the Seven Liberal Arts, a great work on Divine Institutions, and letters which form a very valuable contribution to the history of his time.

A century after Boethius and Cassiodorus, the part which they had played in Italy fell in Spain to Isidore of Seville, who, discouraged at first by the difficulties of study, obtained by force of perseverance the foremost place amongst the writers of his time for the extent and variety of his works. In addition to Commentaries on Holy Writ, and a History of the Visigoth Kings, he has left a great work, "De Originibus, or the Etymologies," in the twenty volumes composing which he sums up the elements of theology, jurisprudence, natural history, agriculture, mechanics, and the liberal arts.

In another part of Europe, Ireland, converted to Christianity by St. Patrick, became rapidly covered with monasteries, as densely populated as many towns, and which still retained some remnants of literary culture. In England, at the monastery of Jarrow (Durham), was educated the venerable Bede; there he lived, taught, and died (735), just as he was completing the commentary of a Psalm, leaving behind him various works, amongst which are several treatises useful as an introduction to the study of science.

It was in an English monastery, too, at York, that Alcuin, the most energetic and learned of the assistants employed by Charlemagne to improve the condition of his schools, was brought up. The books which he has left behind him are instinct with the noblest enthusiasm for philosophy, which he does not separate from the liberal arts, but the importance of which he foresees, and which he looks upon as the best preparation for the study of divinity.

The work of Alcuin was continued by his disciple, Raban Maurus, who died Archbishop of Mainz in 856. He contributed to the first progress of the vulgar tongue by the composition of a Latin-Teuton glossary for all the books of the Old and New Testament. The voluminous collection of his works comprises, together with commentaries upon the Sacred Scriptures, a treatise upon the " Instruction of Clerks," another upon the " Calculation of Time," and, above all, an encyclopædia in twenty books, which he entitled, " On the Universe," and in which he treats successively of God, of the Divine Persons, of the angels, of men, and of the other creatures.

A man possessing more original but less solid and reliable qualities than Raban was the Irish John, surnamed Scotus or Erigena, who figured in the reign of Charles the Bold (Fig. 37) amongst the masters of the Palace School founded in Paris by Charlemagne. Scotus, whose talent was subtle and hardy, and who was well versed in the Greek language, got lost in the mazes of a philosophy which compromised the verities of the faith by confounding them with the pantheistic hallucinations of the school of Alexandria. His principal work is a treatise upon the " Division of Natures," in which he teaches that the creation is eternal ; that God derived the world from himself, and formed it of his own substance ; that the Creator and the creature must not, therefore, be regarded as objects distinct from one another ; that the creature exists in God ; and that God, by an ineffable marvel, is created in the creature, &c. No wonder that these strange doctrines were anathematized by the Church, and that in the early part of the Middle Ages they had few adepts. The name of John Scotus had but a momentary celebrity, and was soon forgotten.

There is no need to dwell upon several other masters, such as Heiric and Remi of Auxerre, whom posterity has almost forgotten, much as they were thought of by their contemporaries. But a few words are essential about that remarkable man, Gerbert, born in Auvergne in the first half of the tenth century, educated at Aurillac by the monks of the Abbey of St. Géraud, mixed up in the course of his life in the events which agitated France, Germany, and Italy, councillor of the Emperors of Germany, in turn schoolman, diplomatist, Archbishop of Rheims and Ravenna, Pope in the year

Fig. 37.—Count Vivien, Titular Abbot of St. Martin of Tours, dedicating to Charles the Bold
    a Bible written in his Abbey. Charles is seated on his throne, surrounded by his nobles and
    guards. The Abbot comes before him, escorted by ten priests, r'ght and left.—Miniature from
    "Charles the Bold's Bible," Manuscript of the Fifteenth Century.—National Library, Paris.

1000, and, amidst the cares of public life, finding time to cultivate the
sciences, a gifted dialectician, well versed in mathematics and physics, and
inventor of an hydraulic organ and clock.   The learning and good fortune

of Gerbert made such an impression upon the popular mind that he was reputed to have sold himself to the devil.

Towards the middle of the twelfth century there were some symptoms of the change which was coming over men's minds, and which was destined to profit both sacred study and secular science.

A discussion took place as to the dogma of the Eucharist. It was commenced by the Archdeacon Béranger, a native of Tours, who denied that in the sacrament the bread and wine were transformed into the body and blood of Christ. The doctrine of Béranger was reproved by the whole Church; several councils condemned it, amongst the fiercest of its adversaries being Lanfranc of Paris, Archbishop of Canterbury.

Béranger had represented reason as having confidence in herself, and being more disposed to follow, in the interpretation of the Christian mysteries, her own lights than mere tradition. Faith—docile, humble, and submissive, but faith making an effort to arrive at an understanding of Divine truth—was represented by the pious and illustrious St. Anselm, the successor of Lanfranc at Canterbury. Amongst other works, St. Anselm has bequeathed to us the "Monologium" and the "Prologium," in which, without resorting to the scholastic formulæ, and without going back to Holy Writ for any important proofs, he demonstrates the existence and the attributes of God by the very idea of God, and the logical sequence of that idea. This is the argument which, five hundred years afterwards, runs through the philosophy of Descartes. The works of St. Anselm earned for him the title of the second St. Augustine.

But at the same period there arose a controversy, wholly philosophical in appearance, but which had a close affinity with theology, as to the nature of general and universal ideas—that is to say, of the ideas which can be applied to several things; as, for instance, the idea of humanity applies to all men. Are general ideas merely convenient formulæ for abridging mental effort and assisting the memory? or is there, apart from special ideas, a distinct essence, an unchangeable model of their common characteristics, and the expression of which in the intelligence is an idea or notion of the same kind— that is to say, general? The question was raised from the very earliest times, and Plato had decided it in the sense of the reality of ideas: it was handed down to the Middle Ages by the books of Aristotle, or rather by those of Porphyrius, his interpreter; and, after having long been dormant in the schools, solved now in one sense, now in another, it acquired, towards the close of the eleventh century, an extraordinary importance, when a canon of Compiègne, Roscelin, maintained that all reality is in the individual ; that general ideas, or the *universals*, as they were then called, have no real object ; that they are purely verbal abstractions, mere words, *nomina;* whence the term *nominalism* applied to this doctrine. His opponents, who attributed to the *universals* a certain amount of reality, were called *realists*. Roscelin, applying his theory to the dogma of the Trinity, argued that the three Divine Persons, having only in common the resemblance or identity of power and will, constitute three distinct beings, and, so to speak, three Gods.

St. Anselm protested, in the name of the Church, against this interpretation of the dogma, of which it was the negation. Condemned in 1092 by the Council of Soissons, Roscelin retracted ; but the discussion which he had raised was destined to last a long time. The school was divided into two camps : upon the one side the nominalists who, in presence of the anathema launched against Roscelin, scarcely dared to avow their opinions ; upon the other the realists, amongst whom may be mentioned, besides St. Anselm, Odo of Cambrai, Hildebert of Lavardin, and William of Champeaux. The last mentioned, who died Bishop of Châlons-sur-Marne in 1120, expounded the doctrine of realism in the schools of Paris, at the cloister of Notre-Dame, and at the Abbey of St. Victor. The original part of his teaching was the theory of the universal. He maintained that as the universal is the primitive substance properly so called, individuals are merely *modalities* or fashions of being, who manifest themselves, soon to disappear, upon the surface of the unique and indivisible subject. Pressing the consequences of his system a little further, he would have been brought to deny human personality and liberty—an error from which he was saved by the sincerity of his religious faith. William of Champeaux none the less recognised reason as the arbiter of natural philosophy, and his disciple, Bernard of Chartres, declared that human thought is an emanation of the Divine thought.

Pierre Abelard had at first followed the lessons of William of Champeaux, but he afterwards declared against him and the realist doctors in a public course of philosophy which he commenced on his own account, without any patronage—*sine magistro,* as his rivals tauntingly said. From the very first his success was so great that thousands of enthusiastic hearers assembled to listen to his arguments and embrace his doctrine. He outdid his predecessors in subtlety, boldness of thought, and especially in eloquence; he carried all his hearers with him; and his system, which was but another form of nominalism, was generally accepted in the schools, and received the name of *Conceptionalism.* It consists in the argument that the universals are neither realities, as asserted by the realists, nor mere words, as the nominalists would have it, but conceptions of the intelligence, which, having observed the resemblance that several individuals have to one another, resumes these resemblances in a notion which it extends to all these individuals. There exist only in nature individuals; the only reality of general qualities themselves is in the individuals which possess them; but, in presence of individual objects, there is the thought which perceives their relations to one another, which extracts from them what they have in common with each other, and which thus engenders the notion of kind and species; in a word, the universals.

If Abelard had confined himself to propounding this theory, he would have, in all probability, escaped the censure of the Church and some of the troubles of his after-life. But, like Roscelin, he claimed to apply his philosophic doctrine to the interpretation of the mystery of the Trinity. Like Roscelin, he failed, was condemned by two councils, and ended his days, repentant and submissive, at the Abbey of Cluny.

While Abelard was going astray in the paths of a perilous theology, other masters who believed themselves to be wiser than he was, carried away in their turn, struck upon the same shoal. One of them, Gilbert de la Porrée, was at first well received by the Church, for, notwithstanding the boldness of his doctrine, he was raised to the bishopric of Poitiers. He had been an ardent adversary of the opinions of the nominalists, but without declaring himself openly for the realists. His realism consisted in supposing that if " the generation of things began from the moment that the breath of the Creator produced motion, the primordial forms have not, however, been altered in their nature by the new act which produced the second forms; thus the primitive and real substances of the air, of fire, of water, of the earth, of humanity, of corporeity, &c., have been, are, and ever will be in themselves permanent, immovable, separate from the subaltern substances or born forms, which communicate the essence to the sentient phenomena " (Fig. 38). According to Gilbert, it is form which gives being. The principle of the common essence—that is to say, of the species or kind—will

Fig. 38.—The Ecclesiastical Hierarchy, with the political authority by which it is supported. The Religious Orders and the Afflicted appear in the fore-ground, and, according to an allegory also represented at Florence, the black and white dog at the feet of the Pope is meant to represent the Dominicans protecting the lambs from heresy in the form of a wolf.—Fragment of the great Fresco, the "Church Militant and the Church Triumphant," painted by Simone Memmi, Sienna Cathedral (Fourteenth Century).

not be a negation, like the *non-difference*, but an affirmation, like the *conformity*. But gradually far-seeing minds, alarmed by the novelty of these theories, grew apprehensive as to the consequences which they might have upon the faith. Gilbert de la Porrée had not hesitated to declare that the essence being, in the order of generation, above the substance, the *Divinity* must be something superior to the individual of the Divine system, who, in

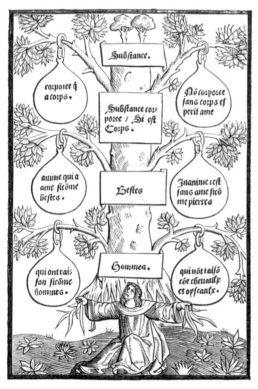

Fig. 39.—The Tree of Beings and of Substances.—Fac-simile of a Wood Engraving of the "Cuer de Philosophie," translated from Latin into French, at the request of Philippe le Bel, King of France. Printed at Paris for Jehan de la Garde, bookseller, in 1514.

human language, is called God. This declaration caused great scandal; the author of it was accused of blasphemy against the Divine Persons, and was cited to appear before an ecclesiastical tribunal at Rheims (1148), and answer the accusation which was sustained by St. Bernard. He not only expressed his regret at having unwittingly propagated perilous doctrines, but he retracted them and abjured his errors. St. Bernard insisted that these doctrines should be solemnly condemned, declaring that they were culpable, inasmuch as they might have troubled innocent consciences (Fig. 39).

In spite of the perils which the abuse of reasoning might entail upon the faith, Peter, surnamed the Lombard, who was Bishop of Paris in 1159, furnished abundant material for his controversy in his book " Les Sentences,"

Fig. 40.—Plenary Court of Dame Justice.—An Allegory referring to Book V. of Aristotle's " Ethics." Upon the pendants are inscribed " Fortitudo," " Private Justice," " Legal Justice," " Mansuetudo," " Eutrepelie," " Distributive Justice," " Commutative Justice."— Miniature of a Manuscript of the Fourteenth Century.—Burgundy Library, Brussels.

a vast collection of extracts from the writings of the fathers on the principal points of metaphysics and Christian morality. The author obtained the name of *Maître des Sentences,* and his work became the basis of theological teaching, and no other work, perhaps, except the Bible, has had so many interpreters. John of Salisbury, whom Louis le Jeune raised, in 1176, to the bishopric of

Chartres, had attended in his youth all the principal masters of his time, and had not attached himself to any of their schools. A man of refined mind, a gifted writer, a great admirer of antiquity, he had no inclination for the frigid subtleties of the logicians of his day, and though he was animated by a sincerely religious faith, he inclined towards scepticism in philosophy.

The abuses of dialectics encountered a fierce opposition from two monks of the Abbey of St. Victor, Hugh, and Richard, his disciple, both of whom were familiar with the profane sciences, and, to a certain extent, friends of philosophy, but both the declared adversaries of arid speculations, and partisans of that method which raises us to God less by the light of the mind than by that of the heart, less by reason than by faith and love. They were, in the twelfth century, the representatives of Catholic mysticism.

At that time, however, Christian Europe had not got beyond the logical works of Aristotle ; but at the close of the twelfth century the " Physics," the "Metaphysics," and the "Ethics" of that great philosopher travelled westward. They found their way into the Catholic Universities in Latin translations, some from the Greek text, others from the Arabic version which had long been employed in the Mahometan schools. To these translations must be added the commentaries from the pens of Arab writers. The unlooked-for appearance of these monuments of the philosophical genius of Greece and of the East made a profound impression upon men's minds. Some men lost their heads, such as Amaury de Bène, David of Dinant, and their disciples, a great number of whom perished at the stake, victims of their errors and of the alarm they had caused in the ranks of Christian society. Others, more circumspect, more attached to tradition, endeavoured to turn to the profit of religion these treatises and commentaries, hitherto unknown, which had enriched the literature of the West. They sought to discover in them truths which the Church was accustomed to teach, and which they set to work to advocate (Fig. 40). The "Physics" and "Metaphysics," first of all proscribed, gradually became, for the most pious of the doctors, subjects of assiduous study and the source from which they drew a part of their doctrines. Alexander of Hales, surnamed the *Irrefutable Doctor*, who died in 1245, was one of the most able interpreters of the philosophy of Aristotle. After him, William of Auvergne, who had studied the philosophers of the Neo-Platonist school of Alexandria and the Arab philosophers, employed his theological erudition in combating the erroneous consequences which the modern partisans of these

Fig. 41.—The Hour of Death.—Allegoric Miniature placed at the beginning of the Service for the Dead in a "Liber Horarum."—Manuscript of the Fifteenth Century.—The Library of M. Ambroise Firmin-Didot.

The sinner, at the point of death, with his sins staring him in the face, turns away from them to listen, but too late, to the advice of his good angel; his conscience, black with his faults, reminds him of them all, and remorse like a serpent is devouring his heart. He remains suspended between hell, a monster vomiting flames and awaiting his prey, and God, who with his right hand threatens him with his justice, and with his left expresses his desire to show mercy.

philosophers had drawn from their doctrine. He was raised to the see of Paris, which he occupied until his death (1249); and his episcopacy, which did honour to the Church, also rendered good service to the cause of sound philosophy.

Another doctor of that time, Jean de la Rochelle, who acknowledged Avicenna as his master, wrote a "Treatise on the Soul," which ranks as one of the principal monuments of philosophy in the thirteenth century.

The appearance of a man not less remarkable for his genius than for his learning, and who renewed and extended the course of teaching by introducing into it the experimental study of nature, was Albertus Magnus, whose reputation spread through France, Germany, and Italy. Born at Lauingen, in Swabia, in 1193, and belonging to an old family in that country, he commenced his studies at Padua; and from thence he proceeded to the schools of Bologna and Paris, in order to perfect himself in all the sciences by attending the lectures of the best masters. At the age of twenty-nine he joined the Order of St. Dominic, and was immediately commissioned by his superiors to go and teach philosophy in the Dominican house at Cologne. He returned to Paris in 1228, and was received Doctor. There he opened, at the Monastery of the Preaching Brothers in the Rue St. Jacques, a public course of lectures, which inaugurated the success of the Dominican school. "From all parts," says M. Hauréau, "people flocked to his lectures, and the students would not listen to anybody but this insignificant-looking man, worn to a skeleton by study, but for whom, as it seemed, neither heaven nor earth had any secrets; whose learning was, compared with that of others, like the light of the sun to the flickering fires of a burnt-out lamp; and whose eloquence ravished all who heard him, communicating to them the divine passion for knowledge." Appointed Provincial of the Dominicans in Germany, Albert was compelled to abandon his teaching in order to visit the monasteries of his order, travelling on foot, and subsisting on alms. He had the good fortune to discover in the libraries of these monasteries several ancient works which he had thought lost: he had them copied out under his own eyes, and thus saved many precious relics of Latin antiquity. He was summoned to Rome by Pope Alexander IV., who conferred upon him the freedom of the sacred palace, and soon afterwards raised him to the episcopacy. But Albert, after holding the bishopric of Ratisbon for three years, resigned his charge in order to resume his favourite studies, and returned to the monastery of the Dominicans at Cologne, where he opened a fresh course of teaching. His contemporaries surnamed him the *Universal Doctor;* and when he died in 1280, aged eighty-seven, he left behind him countless works upon every branch of human learning—amongst others, some voluminous commentaries on all the books of Aristotle.

Albertus Magnus has erroneously been classed amongst the realists; he belonged rather to the nominalists, having declared in favour of the doctrine of Abelard upon the principal questions which excited the controversy of the schools. Thus, far from considering the kinds and species as substances, he looked upon them as essential modes, as manners of being inherent in the

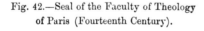

Fig. 42.—Seal of the Faculty of Theology of Paris (Fourteenth Century).

Fig. 43.—Counter-Seal of the University of Paris (Fourteenth Century).

substance of individuals. He defined, after the fashion of the nominalists, the things which are the object of empirical research; that is to say, the beings which together make up the universe. Albertus Magnus was never persecuted, or even looked upon with suspicion, because of his doctrines; he had the good sense to stop short at the limits beyond which lay heresy. His doubts and indecision began at the point where it was dangerous to follow up the argument, and to resolve problems which the Church will not allow to be approached except by the foot of faith.

These problems the great St. Thomas Aquinas, the pupil and contemporary of Albertus Magnus, brought, so to speak, within the limits of orthodoxy, and, starting from well-understood principles, deduced from them their ultimate consequences by the superiority of his dialectical method. This method enabled him to range his opinions and judgments in logical order, and at the same time saved him from taking a single step in the direction of heresy. His "Somme de Théologie" and his "Somme contre les Gentils" rank with the most remarkable productions of human genius. The precision and surety with which the author of these two works maintained his balance amidst the mazes of the questions involved are something marvellous. St. Thomas Aquinas was born at Naples in 1227, upon the territory of Aquino, from which he derived his name, and he was only thirteen years of age when he completed his studies at the school of Naples. The Preaching Brothers of that city induced him to join their order, notwithstanding the efforts of his family, which was both noble and influential, to make him adopt a judicial or diplomatic career. After taking the vows, he was sent first to Paris, and afterwards to Cologne, where he attended the lectures of Albertus Magnus. Thomas was of a pensive and dreamy disposition, talking little, and avoiding argument and dispute. His fellow-pupils nicknamed him the "Dumb ox of Sicily." His master had one day occasion to question him upon several intricate matters in the presence of a numerous audience, and Thomas Aquinas answered him with remarkable boldness and accuracy. Albert, turning with delight towards the audience, which had listened in silence to the able answers of the young Neapolitan, said, "You call Thomas a dumb ox, but the day will come when the lowings of his doctrine will be heard all over the world." Thomas, eager to learn and study, returned to Paris, and again became a student in the house of the Dominican Friars in the Rue St. Jacques; but at the expiration of three years he was recalled to Cologne by his esteemed master, with whom he studied for another four years sciences of all kinds, sacred science in particular. In 1248, when Albertus became the Provincial of his order in Germany, Thomas returned to Paris, to the house in the Rue St. Jacques where he had already learnt so many useful lessons, and it was there that he completed his theological studies by a commentary on Pierre Lombard's "Sentences." After being received Doctor, he began his lessons, in which he developed with marvellous lucidity the various parts of his "Sum of Theology," which became the basis of his great reputation. He continued his teaching to large audiences for many years, and he wrote without intermission a vast number of theological treatises, forming altogether

eighteen folio volumes. The University of Paris had adopted him as one of
her sons, and was proud of being able to own him as such. But Charles of
Anjou, King of Naples, was anxious to place him at the head of that University, and induced Pope Clement IV. (Fig. 44) to recall him to Italy. Thomas
Aquinas reluctantly obeyed, for he was in declining health, and afflicted with
premature infirmities. The frequent journeys which he had been obliged to
take in the interests of the Church added to his fatigues, and while on his

Fig. 44.—Portrait of Clement IV.—Fresco Painting, on gold ground, in Mosaic, in the
Basilica of St. Paul-without-the-Walls at Rome (Thirteenth Century).

way to the Council of Lyons, in 1274, he was compelled to break the journey
near Terracina, at a Cistercian monastery, where he died, after a few days'
illness, at the age of forty-eight.

Thomas Aquinas, whom the Church afterwards placed amongst her saints,
left the highest reputation behind him in the Paris schools. He was called
the *Second St. Augustine*, the *Angel of the Schools*, the *Angelic Doctor*, the
Doctor of Doctors. In fact, his was the only theology taught in most of the
Catholic schools subsequently to the thirteenth century.

Fig. 45 —St. Augustine, Bishop of Hippo, wearing the dress of his order under his episcopal
cape, surrounded by monks to whom he is giving the books of prayer. At his feet is Aristotle,
holding in his right hand a pendant upon which is written, "Dicimus mundum esse æternum,
non habere principium, neque finem." Aristotle declares the eternity of matter, a doctrine
refuted by St. Augustine.—From a Picture in the Campana Museum.—Italian School of the
Fifteenth Century.

However, the scholastic spirit had not quenched the ardour for research, and St. Thomas, notwithstanding his immense authority, had more than one opponent. The dispute took place, it is true, upon the ground of philosophy, between the Orders of St. Dominic and St. Francis. Albertus Magnus, by declaring himself the enemy of the realists, had excited the hostility of the Franciscans, who adhered to the opinion of their first doctor, Alexander of Hales. St. Thomas, out of respect for his master, Albert, had joined the camp of the nominalists, but he was often at variance with them, and could not follow Albert the Great in all his conclusions of doctrine. Thus, notwithstanding his deep study of the natural sciences, he had less inclination for physics than for metaphysics, and his favourite subjects of discussion were those relating to the spiritual substance, its faculties, its functions, and its acts. When it was a question of explaining the nature of ideas, he inclined towards realism. A disciple of St. Augustine, and, through him, of Plato, he held that ideas are distinct forms, which exist in permanency in the Divine intellect; they are, according to him, substantial entities forming part of a world which is the pattern of the external and the intellectual world (Fig. 45).

The philosophical doctrine of St. Thomas Aquinas was not attacked in earnest until after his death, though the questions were mooted while he was alive. Henry of Ghent and Roger Bacon had warmly espoused the cause of the Franciscans and the doctrine of Alexander of Hales, which was pure realism. St. Bonaventure (Fig. 46), who died at about the same time as St. Thomas Aquinas, had waged war more against rationalism than nominalism. He belonged to the Order of St. Francis, and he had certain mystic tendencies, urging his hearers to avoid the schools and despise science. The detractors of philosophy ranged themselves to the banner of John of Wales, who was also a Franciscan; and this was not the only defection in their ranks, for Richard of Middleton professed nominalism at the University of Paris, but he met a stout adversary in William of Lamarre, who advocated the Franciscan doctrine against the Dominicans. And so the struggle went on. The best supporter of the doctrine of St. Thomas was his pupil and fellow-countryman, Egidio Colonna, who acquired in this war of the schools the curious nickname of *Doctor fundamentarius,* his partisans having ascribed to him the honour of having laid the foundation of nominalist science.

The Franciscans got the best of the dispute, under the leadership of one
of the most celebrated masters of his time, the formidable opponent of the

Fig. 46.—St. Bonaventure.—From a Fresco Painting by John of Florence, in the Chapel of
Nicholas V. at the Vatican (Fifteenth Century).

school of St. Thomas. This was the doughty Duns Scotus, who was surnamed
the *Subtle Doctor*, and whom the Franciscans called the Column, the Torch,

the ever-shining Star of Science. He was born in 1274, in the British Isles—in England according to some, in Ireland according to others; but the probability is, as his name implies, that he was Scotch. He donned the garb of St. Francis before going to study at Merton College, Oxford, and his talents at first lay in the direction of mathematics. But he soon filled the chair of philosophy in the college where he had completed his classes, and thousands of pupils assembled to hear him (Fig. 47). He studied theology, and obtained his doctor's degree at Paris, and the superior of the Franciscans sent him to Cologne, where he taught both theology and philosophy. He died in 1308, at the early age of thirty-four, leaving behind him an enormous mass of philosophical treatises, which were not collated till the seventeenth century, when they were published in twenty-five folio volumes.

Albertus Magnus had sought in natural philosophy the fundamental basis of knowledge, and St. Thomas thought that it was to be found in theology, while Duns Scotus endeavoured to trace it back to logic. According to him, syllogism is the sole rule of certainty. But, as M. Hauréau remarks, starting from this principle, the journey is full of perils. Duns Scotus, in fact, was very near falling into them, and only escaped by taking refuge behind the quibbles of sophistry. He was, nevertheless, a firm believer and full of piety, and it was from his ardour in dialectics that he was led to uphold the most extreme views of the realists. In his researches into the distinct nature of every compound, he endeavoured to extract from it the various qualities which he found inherent in or adherent to the same subject. In this way he looked upon matter separated from all form, form separated from all matter, or merely matter separated from certain forms, and at the same time united to certain others. Each of these notions, each of these distinct conceptions, he made to correspond with a nature, an existence of its own. It was to obscure and intangible lucubrations such as these that scholasticism devoted voluminous treatises, which led to passionate discussion, and which were the main subject of conversation amongst the students while they were pacing up and down the Pré-aux-Clercs (Fig. 47).

The champions of St. Thomas and Duns Scotus waged war against each other for several centuries in the vague domain of obscure abstractions. Alexander of Hales was superseded by Duns Scotus, as represented by his disciples and followers, viz. François de Mayronis (surnamed the *Enlightened Doctor*), Antonio Andrea, John Bassolius, and Pietro d'Aquila (Fig. 48). The

Fig. 47.—View of St. Germain des Prés and of the Pré-aux-Clercs during the reign of Charles V.—1, the Abbey of St. Germain des Prés ; 2, the Louvre ; 3, the Petit Bourbon ; 4, the Seine ; 5, Montmartre.—Fac-simile in Miniature of the Engraving "History of St. Germain des Prés," by Dom Bouillart, in folio (1724).

Dominicans did not give up the contest, and St. Thomas had many fervent and eloquent successors. "In order to avoid being accused of betraying their cause," says M. Hauréau, "all Franciscans were obliged to declare against St. Thomas, and all Dominicans against Duns Scotus. The few exceptions were denounced as schismatics. Thus, for instance, Pierre d'Auriol, surnamed in the University of Paris the *Eloquent Doctor*, was, although a Franciscan, one of the nominalists. A dialectician of the first rank, he attacked without mercy psychological realism in St. Thomas, and did not spare the natural species, the image-ideas of his school. This fierce controversy, which indirectly attacked the doctrine of Duns Scotus, caused great excitement in the ranks of the realists, most of whom belonged to the Order of Franciscans. Upon the other hand, the secession of Durand de St. Pourcain, called the *Very Resolute Doctor*, who, while professing philosophy, forgot that he was a Dominican and upheld the doctrines of Duns Scotus, was a gain to the Franciscans. M. Hauréau says, "From this epoch, the fact of belonging to one particular order in religion ceased to imply implicit obedience to any one philosophical sect; the ties of discipline were loosened, and though the two schools still existed, each individual took up the position which seemed best in his own eyes."

It was from England, once more, that came the next celebrity of scholasticism. William of Ockham, born in the town from which he took his name, was a pupil of Duns Scotus, and proved worthy of his great master, After having passed his youth with the Dominican Friars at Guildford, he repaired to Paris, where he found more scope for expounding his doctrine of nominalism. At first he had upheld the realist doctrines of his master, but the force of logic drove him into the opposite camp. His system is best described in the words of M. Hauréau, who says that William of Ockham, by an analysis of the faculty of knowledge, saw that it was seconded by the intuitive, which we call perception, and by the abstractive, which we call abstraction. With these two energies correspond the simple ideas which the view of tangible objects affords us, and the compound ideas which the intelligence forms by comparison, by abstraction. William of Ockham further demonstrated that the realists, having misapprehended human intelligence in its manner of being and its manner of action, had fallen into a profound error in their definition of Divine Intelligence. God is the name of the mystery; everybody can see and judge his works; nobody can appreciate the nature of God. Realism, therefore, has committed a grave and dangerous error in attempting to explain the nature of Divine ideas. God imagined the world before creating it: St. Augustine has stated this; but is it necessary to go any further? Why people the thought of God with *elements,* and *intelligibles,* and *spiritual atoms?* To credit God himself with all these imaginary things, does not this imply the placing of limits and bounds upon his omnipotent will, and submitting Him, by analogy, to the same conditions

Fig. 48.—Italian Doctors (Fifteenth Century).—Miniature of " The Life of St. Catherine of Sienna."—Manuscript in the Paris National Library.

as his creatures? Is it becoming to reduce the nature of God to a conception derived from experience, formed by human reason, representing a sum of qualities abstract from things, but not defining the pure essence of God, inasmuch as that mysterious essence escapes by its very nature all the investigations of intuitive energy? Such was the principal thesis of William of Ockham, who was the most thorough-going interpreter of nominalism during the Middle Ages.

This great doctor was not attacked by the Sorbonne, though he had many formidable adversaries, but his attitude towards the Papacy, with reference to the dispute between Philippe le Bel and Boniface VIII., marked him out for the resentment and vengeance of the Court of Rome. He had sided with the French king, and was well seconded by Michael de Césène, General of the Franciscans, when he continued his aggressive attacks against John XXII. and the Papal power. The Pope resented the attack, not so much in his individual capacity as in that of Vicar of Christ, and he summoned William of Ockham and Michael de Césène to Avignon, where the Holy See had fixed its residence during the establishment of an antipope at Rome. The two Franciscans, having obeyed the order, were cast into prison, and their trial bid fair to result in summary punishment; but they managed to escape to Aigues-Mortes, where they were received on board a vessel belonging to Louis of Bavaria. Welcomed by him, they ended their days in obscurity within his dominions.

The doctrine of William of Ockham survived him in the schools, and the doctors who endeavoured to oppose it had few followers. Walter Burleigh himself, notwithstanding his courageous endeavours to revive the cause of realism, could not secure any attention. The nominalists were everywhere the most numerous and the most zealous. Their masters were esteemed doctors, doughty dialecticians, evangelic and zealous party leaders; such as Robert Holcot, Thomas of Strasburg, Jean Buridan, and Pierre d'Ailly. Most of them were professors, and their teaching acquired them influence and renown.

Above all these discordant doctrines there rose the venerable voice of Jean Charlier de Gerson, Chancellor of the University of Paris, who, protesting against the abuses of dialectics, said, " Let us put an end to frivolous disputes; let us make use of Reason solely in order to arrive at the truth, which it cannot do without the aid of Faith. It is the rule of Faith that we need follow, and if some refractory or stubborn minds still cling to the quibbles of philosophy, let us deplore their being led astray, and humbly seek in the bosom of the Church, far from the schools, peace, light, and life." This touching appeal, by one who well deserved the title of *Evangelical and Very Christian Doctor*, for a return to mystic theology (Fig. 49) did not find an echo in many minds; it did not prevent the young from being led away in the heat of dialectics, and siding with the philosophers of logic.

But all these systems, springing from logic pursued to its final limits, were destined to fall of themselves, involving in their ruin that of nearly all

Fig. 49.—Miniature of the "City of God," by St. Augustine, translated by Raoul de Presles.—Manuscript
of the Fifteenth Century. St. Geneviève Library.—The upper enclosure represents the saints who have
been already received into heaven ; the seven lower enclosures represent those who are preparing themselves, by the exercise of Christian virtues, for the heavenly kingdom, or who are excluding themselves
from it by committing one or other of the seven capital sins.

their champions. The triumph of nominalism completed the discomfiture of scholasticism, which was no longer so popular in the Universities, and which was gradually being confined to the cloisters. It may be added that the struggle between the rival schools was much abated by the discovery of printing; for, owing to this invention, which was called divine, the works of ancient philosophy, which had been used as texts for the oral teaching of the professors, became multiplied amongst the friends of science. These printed books, making their way everywhere, were calculated to take the place of the lessons which students had previously come to learn at the Universities famous for the ability of their masters of dialectics. As M. Hauréau very justly observes, "Before the invention of printing, students learnt the lessons of science from one master, and nearly always became his partisans : to quit one school for another required no common degree of courage. But afterwards students were enabled, before making their choice, to weigh the merits of ten masters at a time." These masters were the books issued from the presses in every country of Europe (Fig. 51).

The philosophy of the Renaissance was just coming into existence when the fugitive Greeks, after the capture of Constantinople by the Turks, imported into Italy manuscripts containing the works of Plato and of philosophers of the Alexandrian school. These works, which it was believed had been lost, and of which only a vague recollection had been preserved by tradition, were welcomed in the middle of the fifteenth century with even more respect and enthusiasm than the books of Aristotle had been in the twelfth century. The comparison of ancient philosophy with the scholasticism of the more modern schools was not to the advantage of the latter, which seemed too narrow, too obscure, and too servile. The writings of Plato gave a better idea of the opinions of Heraclitus and Pythagoras, and opened new vistas to many minds which were eager to shake off all bonds, and to emerge from the paths in which theology had been guiding them for the last four or five centuries (Fig. 50).

This period of philosophical renovation began by a sharp discussion between two Grecian philosophers of Constantinople, Gemistes Plethon and Theodoros de Gaza : the first a fanatical partisan of the Alexandrian school of Plotinus, the second a faithful votary of Aristotle. The old scholasticism was dead; the chairs which it formerly had at Florence and the great cities of Italy were tenanted by the new doctors, who expounded the principles of

Plato and Aristotle. The names talked of in the schools were those of
Ermolao Barbaro, Angelo Politien, and Lorenzo Valla. A student of Louvain,
Rudolph Agricola, came to take lessons from these illustrious masters, and
returned to Flanders to propagate their doctrines. In Spain, as in France,
these doctrines, taken from the ancient philosophers of Greece and of Egypt,
were hailed with unanimous enthusiasm. The University of Paris was
powerless to arrest this stream of novelties which the Italian Renaissance

Fig. 50.—Bachelors of the Faculty of Theology, and Professors of the Faculties of
Theology, Jurisprudence, and Medicine at the University of Pont-à-Mousson.—From
the Funeral of Henry II., Duke of Lorraine, by Claude de la Ruelle.—National
Library, Paris. Cabinet of Engravings.

poured upon the West. There was an end to schools and to discipline;
license, anarchy, and confusion reigned supreme.

Upon the one hand, Nicholas de Cusa declared with Pythagoras that
knowledge is hidden in the mysterious notion of numbers, and he went so
far as to represent the Divine Essence as an harmonious centre in which all
differences are blended. Upon the other hand, Marsilius Ficinus, who died in
1499, founded a Platonist academy, and, under colour of explaining the Holy

Gospels, he worshipped exclusively his divine Plato. Then, again, we have the infant prodigy, Jean Pic de la Mirandola, who, after having studied all the sciences known at that time, and after having, at the age of three-and-twenty, argued the thesis "De omni re scibili," endeavoured to reconcile the philosophy of Aristotle and Plato by the aid of wild cabalistic and astrological evocations. This was the origin of a new school of cabalists, magicians, and astrologers. They were, no doubt, consummate men of learning, those Germans and Italians (Fig. 52), who sought to bring to the light of day the material and immaterial arcana of nature. Thus, Jean Reuchlin associated in his writings cabalism and scholasticism. George of Venice held that in the mysteries of generation and of life substance is the unique and absolute being, the only God. Theophrastus Paracelsus, who is no other than Philip Bombastes of Hohenheim, mixing metaphysics with physics like two medical substances, affirmed that God, of whom he made the principle of universal life, has united the body and the soul by an animal fluid. There was a wide interval between these vain musings and the safe doctrine of St. Thomas Aquinas, or the dialectical abstractions of Duns Scotus.

Aristotle still had followers who alleged that they remained faithful to his doctrine, but the general tendency of the time carried them over the precipice. Peter Pomponacius of Mantua (born in 1462, died in 1526) announced that he took his stand upon peripateticism, but he raised a very dangerous question by inquiring whether or not Aristotle admitted the principle of the immortality of the soul. He concluded in the negative, adding that reason and faith must supplement the silence of the master in this respect. This reverse was not taken any account of by his adversaries, who reproached him, the one side with outraging Aristotle, and denounced him as a heretic; the other side with having made a treacherous use of the doctrines of peripateticism to advance an abominable heresy. Pomponacius had, notwithstanding, many devoted followers, who went more or less astray in the occult sciences or in scholasticism, amongst them being Augustine Niphus of Calabria, and Julius Cæsar Scaliger of Padua.

As to scholasticism, the aberration of its opponents obtained for it several ardent champions. Such were Thomas de Vio, surnamed Cajetan, born in 1469, who became cardinal, after having professed the philosophy of St. Thomas; his pupil, Leonicus Thomæus of Venice, who devoted all his energies to the restoration of pure logic, which was neither more nor less than the doctrine of Aristotle; James Zabarella of Padua, who was fully versed in all the great philosophers of the thirteenth century, and who sought to make them harmonize with Aristotle.

These in their turn were succeeded by the old Arab commentators of the books of Aristotle, Averroes in particular; Achillini of Bologna, and Zabarella merely reproduced the opinions of the last named. But the most illustrious of the new Averroists was Jerome Cardan of Pavia, that great genius who, by the elevation to which he raised all the sciences, became the

Fig. 51.—Dame Philosophy.—Miniature of the " Treasure," by Brunetto Latini. Manuscript of the Fifteenth Century.—The Arsenal Library.

wonder of his century. M. Hauréau says of him, " This man, whose mind, enthusiastic, restless, and incapable of repose, welcomed all doctrines of every kind, was the slave of every system in turn; first worshipping, then insulting all the gods, even the god of conscience; he was not an individual, he was a whole generation of philosophers." He had more play of mind than of judgment, and his inconsiderate ardour, regulated neither by good sense nor by a sincere faith, led him into the most monstrous anomalies. Like Averroes and all the pantheists, he upheld the double principle of the unity of substance and the unity of motion. He was accused of being an atheist, but he dissembled his real opinions so well that he was pensioned by the Pope, and died at Rome (1576), drawing horoscopes and selling elixirs.

This same school naturally produced several lunatics and victims of hallucination, some inclining to pantheism, and others to scepticism, the latter having studied medicine and the former scholasticism before they were smitten with a desire to know and to define the essence of God and the essence of the soul. Andrew Cesalpin of Arezzo, who had been physician to Pope Clement VIII., was, upon good grounds, suspected of pantheism, and even of atheism, for having maintained with Averroes that God was not so much the cause as the substance of all things. Notwithstanding the errors contained in his works, he escaped all persecution, and died a Christian death at Rome in 1603. But the unhappy Jordano Bruno, a Dominican monk, was less fortunate than Andrew Cesalpin. Possessed of talents more prolific than judicious, endowed with a brilliant imagination, and carrying his confidence to the point of presumption, Bruno, who had already been denounced for the boldness of his systems, was about to be proceeded against by the ecclesiastical authorities when he fled into Naples. He wandered from city to city during twenty years, and printed at London, Paris, and Frankfort several philosophical treatises, in which he attacked both the Catholic dogma and the doctrine of Aristotle. His boldness proved fatal to him, and, having the imprudence to return to Italy, the Inquisition caused him to be arrested, tried, and condemned to the stake as a relapsed heretic. He was burnt at Rome in 1600.

While the doctrine of Aristotle was supreme in North Italy, the schools of the kingdom of Naples accorded the preference to Plato and to the Alexandrian philosophers; but whether under the auspices of Plato or Aristotle, it was none the less pantheism which reigned everywhere alike. Thus Telesio was pantheist in his chair at Cosenza; Patrizzi, who occupied the chair at Ferrara, was not only a pantheist, but came to profess this pagan doctrine in the very University of Rome. The great names of Plato and Aristotle served as a cloak for the tendencies of their interpreters. The Inquisition did not consider itself called upon to defend the Church against science, for the apostles of the Aristotelist and Platonist philosophy had no part in the schemes of the heretical innovators.

It was necessary, however, to select a philosophy for the Lutheran schools.

That of Plato was rejected; and Melancthon obtained the adoption of that of Aristotle, and himself prepared, for the teaching of philosophy and in conformity with Aristotelian principles, several elementary works which were received with merited favour. Erasmus (Fig. 53), who remained a Catholic with Lutheran tendencies, also followed the example of Melancthon, and undertook the translation of several treatises of Aristotle, revising them for the use of the Bâle school. But the philosophy of Aristotle took another direction and attained another aim when carried into the Netherlands. The Flemish Justus Lipsius, born near Brussels in 1547, followed in the wake of

Fig. 52.—The Natural Sciences in the presence of Philosophy.—Fac-simile of a Wood Engraving attributed to Holbein in the German Translation of the "Consolation of Philosophy," by Boethius, Augsburg Edition, 1537, in folio.

the Stoics, applied their moral philosophy to the theories of peripateticism, and did not separate theology from philosophy. Gaspard Scioppius and Thomas Gataker were his principal disciples.

France also had her share in these philosophical innovations. She had been the first home of scholasticism, but the civil and religious wars of the sixteenth century had caused an almost total suspension of study. But Pierre Ramus, more commonly called La Ramée, born in Picardy in 1515, set to work to revive the teaching of philosophy, condemning Aristotle, and

recommending his pupils to read Plato.   He endeavoured to make logic
generally comprehensible by freeing it of sophistical verbiage, and he very
ingeniously made use of this new logic to inculcate in the minds of his pupils
the maxims of the Reformation, for he was a Calvinist with fanatical
tendencies.   He was cited before the parliament, not for his religious
opinions, but for his blasphemies against peripateticism, and though his trial

Fig. 53.—Portrait of Erasmus, after a Wood Engraving of the Sixteenth Century.
National Library, Paris.   Cabinet of Designs.

was not of an inquisitorial character, he was condemned, deprived of his
professor's chair at the Royal College, and compelled to leave the country.
His implacable enemies, Antonio de Govea, Jacques Charpentier, and others
saw in him less the Huguenot than the detractor of Aristotle.   Ramus, who
had become the chief of the small school of Ramists, went to lecture in the

towns on the banks of the Rhine. After three years' exile he returned to France, and was included in the massacre of St. Bartholomew. His personal enemy, Jacques Charpentier, of Clermont (in the Oise), professor of mathematics at the Royal College, was accused of having had him massacred by his pupils during that terrible night.

Plato, notwithstanding the efforts of Ramus, had not many followers in the University of Paris, where scholasticism endeavoured to regain its sway. Aristotle continued to be the favourite of the school, and his philosophical

Fig. 54.—Battle of Beggars and Peasants over a Barrel of Wine in the Chapter headed, "Comment les vices se combattirent les uns aux autres pour les vivres."—Miniature of the "Roi Modus."—Manuscript of the Fifteenth Century.—Burgundy Library, Brussels.

predominance was fostered by the decrees of the Parliament and the royal ordinances. But the true French spirit was less in the direction of the study of logic, even reformed and renewed, than in moral philosophy, especially when it had a tendency to be sceptical and sarcastic (Fig. 54). Montaigne, at the close of the fifteenth century, was, so to speak, the founder of this philosophy, which neither denies nor affirms anything, which calls everything in question, and makes light of all subjects. He was born at the

Château de Montaigne, in the Périgord, upon the 28th of February, 1533. Though he attended all the classes at the College of Bordeaux, he may be said to have been self-taught, and to have become a philosopher in his own way through his intercourse with the poets, historians, and philosophers of antiquity. He delighted in the works of Seneca and Plutarch, but he would not "bite his nails over Aristotle, the monarch of modern doctrine." In after-years, when he wrote his immortal "Essays," he unhesitatingly declared against the dialectics of the schools—against every kind of doctrinal teaching. "It is pitiable," he writes, "that in our century philosophy should be, even for men of intelligence, a vain and fantastic name, which is without use or value in opinion or in fact. I believe that sophistry, by choking up the approaches to it, is the cause. It is a great mistake to depict it as inaccessible to children, of a forbidding countenance, full of frowns, and fearful to look at. Nothing can be more cheerful, sprightly, I was almost saying frolicsome." Michael de Montaigne inaugurated in France the philosophy of the *libertines*—that is to say, of the free-thinkers—different in some respects from that which François Rabelais professed, fifty years before, in his Pantagruelic works, and which John Calvin denounced as a pagan doctrine, accusing the *libertines* of atheism and impiety. "Scepticism," writes M. Hauréau, "had the last word in this propaganda in favour of the sprightly and almost frolicsome philosophy; and the young, only too easily led away by such remarks, gladly left, under the guidance of this new teacher, the arduous paths of study to revel in the intercourse of poets, and to turn the melancholy eyebrows of the logicians into derision."

Fig. 55.—Seal of the Faculty of Theology, Prague.

Fig. 56.—Seal of the Faculty of Law, Prague.

MATHEMATICAL SCIENCES.

Ancient Systems of the Planetary World.—Ptolemy and Aristarchus of Samos.—Boethius, Pappus, and Gerbert.—Schools of Bagdad.—Mathematical School in Spain, Italy, England, and France.—Astronomical Researches of the Arabs.—Roger Bacon and Master Pierre.—Albertus Magnus and St. Thomas Aquinas.—Progress of Mathematics.—Popes and Kings protectors of the Exact Sciences.—The King of Hungary, Matthias Corvinus.—Principal Works composed in the Fifteenth Century.—Pic Mirandola.—Peter Ramus.—Tycho Brahe and Copernicus.

S a proof of the forward state of the exact sciences in the Middle Ages, it would be sufficient to instance a Roman basilica or a Gothic cathedral. What immensity and depth of mathematical calculations; what knowledge of geometry, statics, and optics; what experience and skill in execution must have been possessed by the architects and builders in hewing, carving, and fitting the stones, in raising them to great heights, in constructing enormous towers and gigantic belfries, in forming the many arches, some heavy and massive, others light and airy, in combining and neutralising the thrust of these arches which interlace and hide each other up to the very summit of the edifice—all as if the most complicated science had humbly made herself the servant of art, placing no obstacle in the way of its free development!

From the commencement of the Middle Ages and henceforward, mathematics were not so much the object of special and public teaching as of individual and solitary study, either in the shade of the cloisters or amidst associations of artisans who zealously preserved the traditions of their predecessors.

In the University centres, as in the Arab and Jewish schools which had so much importance, practical science was generally made subordinate to speculative science. Thus the theory of the calculus, the formulæ of algebra, the projections of lines through space, the problems of triangulation, were by preference applied to astronomical observations, so that the transcendental mathematics were always inseparable from astronomy.

It was as follows that Claudius Ptolemæus, a Greek or Egyptian astronomer, constituted the mundane system in a "Cosmography" written in Greek, which became one of the bases of mathematical and astronomical science in the Middle Ages :—"The world is divided into two vast regions; the one ethereal, the other elementary. The ethereal region begins with the first mover, which accomplishes its journey from east to west in twenty-four hours; ten skies participate in this motion, and their totality comprises the double crystalline heaven, the firmament, and the seven planets." According to Ptolemæus, the double crystalline heaven was placed between the first mover and the firmament. The elementary region, comprising the four elements of fire, air, water, and earth, reigned beneath the cavity of the sky, and was subject to the influence of the moon. The terrestrial globe, composed of earth and water, existed motionless in the centre of the world, and was surrounded by the element of air, in which was mingled that of fire.

This system was not, however, exclusively adopted by all the philosophers. Some of them accorded their preference to the system of Aristarchus of Samos, who did not place the earth in the centre of the world, and who attributed to it a rotary motion around the sun, which was suspended motionless amidst the planets and the planetary circles. According to Aristarchus of Samos, Mercury, the planet which is nearest the sun, completed his motion around it in three months, whilst Venus took seven months and a half to execute hers. The earth, apart from its motion round the sun in the space of a year, effected a second motion, revolving upon its own axis, in the space of twenty-four hours, thus causing the succession of day and night. The monthly motion of the moon around the earth was accomplished in about twenty-seven days. The fourth planet, Mars, took two years to accomplish his revolution round the sun; Jupiter, much farther distant, took twelve years, and Saturn thirty.

The system of Ptolemy eventually triumphed over that of Aristarchus, and at the close of the fifth century the great Boethius (Fig. 57), the favourite minister of Theodoric the Great, who loved and patronised literature and science, made a Latin translation of the "Cosmography," to which he appended various mathemathical works, some translated from the Greek, others of his own composition, none of which have come down to us. We still possess two books on Geometry by Boethius, but we have lost his Latin translations of the treatise of Nicomachus upon Arithmetic, of the "Geometry" of Euclid, of a treatise upon the Squaring of the Circle, as also several original treatises in which he commented with great erudition on the cosmogonic doctrines of Pythagoras and Ptolemy. King Theodoric, who afterwards had him put to a

Fig. 57.—The Planetary Systems.—Fac-simile of a Wood Engraving attributed to Holbein in the German Translation of the "Consolation of Philosophy," by Boethius, Augsburg Edition, 1537, in folio.

cruel death (525), at that time wrote to him in the following complimentary terms :—"By means of your Latin translations, Rome has received from you all the sciences and arts which the Greeks had brought to such a high pitch of perfection. Those who know both Latin and Greek will prefer your translations to the original. The four portions of mathematics have been to you a sort of door, as it were, giving admittance to the science of mechanics, and this science you have extracted from the very entrails of nature."

The school of Alexandria was the centre of mathematical studies, and Boethius undertook to acquaint the Roman world with the principal works of the Greek mathematicians. Pappus, one of the most celebrated, who, at the close of the fourth century, formed his *mathematical collections*, was not translated into Latin until the Renaissance. The influence of Boethius upon the progress of the exact sciences in Europe was not destined to survive him, and for more than two centuries mathematics were applied only to architecture, hydraulics, and celestial cosmography, with regard to which the most absurd notions were entertained.

However, science was still worthily represented in the schools of Alexandria and Constantinople. Two geometers belonging to them, Anthemius of Tralles and Eutocius of Ascalon, flourished in the reign of Justinian (527— 565). The former, busying himself more especially with the problems of mechanics, contributed to the erection of the basilica of St. Sophia at Constantinople, and obtained great renown as an architect and sculptor; the latter, by his commentaries on the mathematical writings of Archimedes and Apollonius of Perga, made them of practical and general utility.

But it was in the East, and in the very extreme East, that the pursuit of mathematics, applied to the study of astronomy, had acquired the greatest impetus. In China the Mandarin Yhiang noted the eclipses, drew up a catalogue of the stars, marked the degrees of longitude, and formed a new calendar. In India the first astronomical tables were established by aid of the Send-hind, the sacred book of the Brahmins. The Caliph Al-Mansour ordered these tables to be translated into Arabic. Following his example, the Caliph Haroun Alraschid constituted himself protector of the mathematical sciences, which fitted in so well with the genius and tendencies of his people: he had the books of Euclid, Diophantus, Ptolemy, Pliny, and the best mathematicians, astronomers, and cosmographers of Greek and Latin antiquity, translated into Arabic and Syriac. Under the Caliphs the school of Bagdad attracted an immense number of students, who came to learn the exact sciences. Geometry and astronomy were taught concurrently with medicine. It is true that, owing to the prejudices from which even the most eminent in science were subject, all the powers of calculation were employed in the measurement of the sidereal conjunctions, and in stating precisely the action of the moon upon the human body and upon the fecundation of germs.

From Asia Minor, Greece, and Egypt, the exact sciences passed to the Arab schools of Spain at Cordova, Seville, and Granada, where they were cultivated with much success. Many Jewish rabbis, physicians, and astronomers addicted to the art of divination, to astrology, and even to magic, contributed in a large degree to the scientific and intellectual movement in the Iberian peninsula; but they were obliged to conceal their Hebrew origin under Arab pseudonyms.

Charlemagne, when he instituted his palatine academy, did not omit the exact sciences, which found a place upon the same footing as the speculative sciences, literature, and the arts. Astronomers and geometricians naturally ranked with natural philosophers, musicians, and poets. The Irish man of

Fig. 58.—Mathematician Monks; one teaching the Globe, the other copying a Manuscript.—After a Miniature of the Romance of the "Image of the World."—Manuscript of the Thirteenth Century.—National Library, Paris.

letters, Dungal, was selected by the great Emperor to superintend the investigations necessitated by the reform of the calendar, and to collate the annals of celestial phenomena, and he was assisted by Alcuin, Amalaire, and Raban Maur.

At the death of Charlemagne, the exact sciences, which had flourished for a brief space at his court, seemed to shrink into the seclusion of the monasteries (Fig. 58). Dungal set his pupils the example of retirement, as he became a monk at the Abbey of St. Denis, where he died in 829. The Order of St. Benedict had almost made a monopoly of the exact sciences, which were held in high honour at the Abbeys of Mount Cassini, in Italy; of St. Martin, at Tours (France); of St. Arnulph, at Metz; of St. Gall, in Switzerland; of Prum, in Bavaria; of Canterbury, in England, &c. It was there that were formed the able architects and ecclesiastical engineers who erected so many magnificent edifices throughout Europe, and most of whom, dedicating their lives to a work of faith and pious devotion, have, through humility, condemned their names to oblivion.

Gerbert, born at Aurillac about 930, and admitted while very young into a monastery of that town, was one of those monks who devoted their time to the sciences; but he distinguished himself from amongst his contemporaries as much by the extensiveness of his learning as by the practical direction which he gave to his labours by the applications that he contrived to extract from them. Linguist, geometrician, astronomer, and mechanist, he went to complete his mathematical studies at the schools of Cordova and Toledo, and thence repaired to Germany, where the Emperor Otho III. conceived a great liking for him. He held the see of Ravenna, after having been Archbishop of Rheims, and was elected Pope under the title of Sylvester II. Gerbert was, beyond question, the first mathematician of his day. He it was who popularised the use of numerals and the system of numbering which we still employ—a system very different from that of which the Romans made use, but falsely attributed to the Arabs, as traces of it are to be found in the works of Boethius. It was not, however, to the introduction of Arab figures into Europe, but to the use which he made of his universal learning, that Gerbert owed his fame. During his stay at the imperial court he fabricated with his own hands, amongst other curious works, a clock worked by water, and the movement of which was regulated by the polar star. His inventions caused him to be looked upon as a sorcerer, and of his numerous scientific works all that remain extant are several treatises on Geometry and Cosmography.

His pupil and friend, Adelbold, a native of Liége, after studying the sciences there under the learned Hériger, acquired an early celebrity as the brilliant rival of Fulbert of Chartres, and of Abbon, Abbot of Fleury. The Emperor Henry II. attached him to his household as chancellor or secretary, and was loath to lose his services by raising him to the see of Utrecht.

Adelbold, like Gerbert, was accused of magic, and though he did not make a clock, he constructed several splendid churches with truly marvellous rapidity, and it was no doubt owing to the jealousy of the masons that this accusation was made against him. The only scientific work which Adelbold left was a treatise on the Globe, dedicated to Pope Sylvester II.

The salutary influence of Gerbert and Adelbold made itself felt in the Catholic world at the approach of the year 1000 A.D., which, owing to the

Fig. 59.—Perseus and Andromeda.—After a Miniature of the Fourteenth Century, "Liber de Locis Stellarum Fixarum."—Spanish Manuscript.—In the Arsenal Library, Paris.

superstitious ignorance of the people, was looked forward to with dread as destined to usher in the reign of Antichrist. These two illustrious savants protested against the threat of the millennium, and announced in advance the eclipses and comets which were considered to be sinister presages of the end of the world. Instead of recognising their learning and admiring their genius, people believed that they were holding criminal intercourse with the spirits of evil.

The exact sciences continued to be taught and to make progress amongst the Greeks, the Eastern peoples, and the Arabs in Spain. Astronomy was still the favourite science in the Mussulman schools, and the wise men of Islam were always drawing up astronomical tables. Al-Battany spent fifty years of his life upon his Sabean Table; Aben Byhan (died in 941), Mohammed al-Saghany (died in 989), Absoufy and Aboul-Waffa (at the end of the tenth century), and the most celebrated of all these philosophers, Aly ben Abdel-Rhaman, spent their whole existence in drawing up different astronomical tables, calculating according to the laws of the motion of the stars, for astronomy was at that time a science rather of calculation than of observation. The Spanish schools (Figs. 59 and 60) were not behindhand with the academy of Bagdad and the school of Alexandria, although the scientific celebrities in them were not so numerous in the eleventh as they had been in the tenth century. The most famous of these Arab savants were Spanish Jews: such as Soliman ben Gavirol (died in 1070), who was not less distinguished as a poet and moralist than he was as a mathematician, and Abraham ben Chija, who at about the same period drew up a Celestial Cosmography which was held in high repute for more than six centuries. The rabbis who were most famous for their mathematical and astronomical works, written in Arabic, such as Ibn-Zarcali, Abraham Arzachel, Aben-Ezra, all more or less mingled with the theorems and calculations which they took from the exact sciences fanciful deductions from the Talmud.

Astronomy in those days was very often no more than astrology; that is to say, the art of drawing horoscopes and making predictions by a study of the position of the stars and of the mutual relations of the planets. The Eastern peoples, Persians, Arabs, Jews, were much addicted to these practices. They endeavoured to ascertain the future by means of the celestial conjunctions, and believed that they could read in the heavens not only the fate of empires, but the destiny of all human beings. This so-called philosophical doctrine was inaugurated in the ninth century by the Arab astrologer Albumazar, in his book on the Great Conjunctions. He asserted that the appearance of the prophets and of religions had coincided with the conjunctions of the planets. Thus, according to him, the conjunction of Jupiter with Mercury produced the Christian law; but, in a given time, the conjunction of the Moon with Jupiter would bring about the total downfall of all religious beliefs. A doctrine such as this, as insane as it was impious, naturally excited the reprobation of the Church. Judicial astrology was forbidden in all Christian countries, and condemned by the Holy See. The Catholic professors very properly denounced this chimerical science, as opening a path to fatalism of the most reckless and culpable kind.

While astrology was prohibited as an occult science, and the Church was anathematizing it, astronomy took her place as one of the seven liberal arts which were taught, for more than a thousand years, at the school of Alexandria. When the University of Paris was being formed upon the

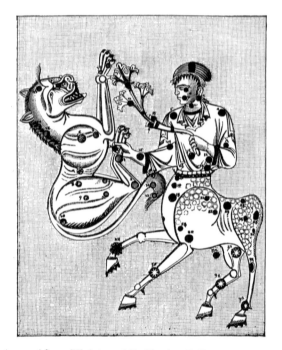

Fig. 60.—The Centaur.—After a Miniature of the Fourteenth Century, " Liber de Locis Stellarum Fixarum."—Spanish Manuscript.—Arsenal Library, Paris.

model of that celebrated school, astronomy, as a matter of course, was included in the *quadrivium*, which formed the second order of study, and which further consisted of arithmetic, geometry, and music. But the *quadrivium*, representing higher education, was followed by a very limited number of students, most of them not getting further than the *trivium*, which comprised only the primary sciences or the humanities, grammar, rhetoric, and dialectics.

The same was the case in all the schools of Europe; but those of Italy and England accorded more time to mathematical sciences towards the close of the twelfth century. At Pisa, a learned mathematician, Leonardo Fibonacci, better known as Leo of Pisa, brought back from his journey to the East the algebraic notation which Gerbert had invented, or rather propagated in Europe, two centuries previously; and Fibonacci has often been credited with the introduction of Arab figures and the use of the abbreviative method in lengthy calculations. Amongst the professors at Oxford about this period there was another mathematician not less remarkable, who, though he had not travelled like Fibonacci, had the talent to discover all the formulæ of the exact sciences. This was Robert, surnamed Grossetête, who was the master and friend of Adam of Marisco and of the celebrated Roger Bacon.

Roger Bacon, in all his allusions to Robert Grossetête, speaks of him in the most respectful terms. He describes him as one of the most enlightened, the best informed, and most eminent men of his day; as fully conversant with all languages, even Greek and Hebrew, which were then but little known; as very dissatisfied with the Latin translations of Aristotle which were at that time used in the Universities, and endeavouring, with the assistance of his friends and pupils, to provide better ones; as allying the love of science to that of letters; as being as much versed in mathematics and astronomy as was possible in his day; as the interpreter of Aristotle's logic; and as the author of a treatise upon the Celestial Globe. It may be mentioned, also, that, in addition to these uncommon qualities of philosopher and savant, Robert Grossetête possessed sincere piety and deep theological learning. Raised to the episcopal see of Lincoln (he died in 1253), he left behind him letters, still extant, which contain unequivocal proof of the sincerity of his devotion to the Papacy, of which he was falsely represented as an open enemy.

Adam de Marisco belonged, like Robert Grosstête, to the Church. He passed the greater part of his days in England, in a Franciscan monastery, but the life of the cloister did not deaden in him the love of science. Roger Bacon almost always speaks of him, as of the Bishop of Lincoln, as one of the lights of his age—as a master in grammar, mathematics, and astronomy.

But it was, above all, the name, the learning, and the genius of Roger Bacon (born in 1214) which predominated in the scientific history of the thirteenth century. The school itself, often as he combated its views, gave him the title of *Admirable Doctor*, and he proved himself worthy of it by the general curiosity which animated him, by the ardour which he displayed for

Fig. 61.—A Lesson in Astronomy (Thirteenth Century).—Miniature from the Breviary of St. Louis.—In the Arsenal Library, Paris.

the advancement of science, and, above all, by the grandeur and originality of the views expressed by him in his works. He represents more accurately than any one else in the thirteenth century the movement which was already urging so many minds to the study of nature, and to the experimental method without which the mysteries of nature remain unfathomable. Whilst St. Thomas Aquinas was devoting to Christian theology all the resources of his dialectics and all the glow of his piety, Roger Bacon applied himself to natural philosophy and mathematics, paying special attention to the study of languages, which he looked upon as closely connected with the progress of the natural sciences (Fig. 61).

But a too exclusive devotion to these his favourite studies eventually led Roger Bacon astray, and he came to look with contempt upon all methods except his own. Upon repairing to Paris after his residence at Oxford, he unhesitatingly attacked the system of teaching in the Universities, accusing the masters and professors either of ignorance or bad faith; and, though himself belonging to the Order of St. Francis, he declared war upon the Franciscans and Dominicans in France, whom he did not consider equal to the learned friends he had left behind him in England, such as Robert of Lincoln, William of Sherwood, John of London, and, above all, the person whom he spoke of as *Master Nicholas.* "Experience is worth more than Aristotle," he said; "all the metaphysics of the school are not to be compared with a little grammar and mathematics; Alexander of Hales and Albert are presumptuous schoolmen who exercise a fatal influence; let us beware of becoming subject to it, and let us complete for ourselves our education, which is scarcely as yet begun."

From this time he applied himself to the study of four ancient languages, higher mathematics, astronomy, optics, and Platonist philosophy. He was assisted in his studies by a man of incomparable genius, a French savant belonging to Picardy, whom he always speaks of as *Magister* Petrus or *Magister* Peregrinus, and who would be absolutely unknown if his illustrious pupil had not handed his name down, in his "Opus Tertium" and his "Opus Minus," to the admiration of posterity. Magister Petrus led a solitary life, avoiding the society of his fellow-men, whom he looked upon as mad, or as sophists incapable of enduring the light of truth; he endeavoured to penetrate the secrets of nature; he observed the stars, and sought out the causes of the celestial phenomena; he imposed upon science the task of multiplying the metamorphoses of matter; he invented arms and instruments of war; he gave a practical and useful application to alchemy; he paid attention at the same time to agronomy, surveying, and architecture, and he sought to extract from the devices of sorcerers and magicians whatever experimental science could discover therein. In a word, Magister Petrus deserved the surname which his pupil gave him of *Magister Experimentorum.*

Such a guide was invaluable to Roger Bacon in the wonderful inventions attributed to him, for in most of his researches and experiments he was doubtless assisted by the advice of Magister Petrus. His works, more particularly his " Opus Majus," show to what a height he elevated science, substituting the experimental for the scientific method. It is easy to understand how the invention of gunpowder, telescopes, magnifying glasses, &c., came to be attributed to him. He merely put into execution, as it would appear, the scientific discoveries of his master, who had observed the phenomenon of refraction and the properties of the loadstone, and who constructed a movable sphere which reproduced all the motions of the stars. Roger Bacon also devoted his attention to philosophy, and as early as the year 1269 he proposed the reform of the calendar (Figs. 62—67).

But the attitude which he had assumed, and the severity of his criticisms upon the most illustrious of his contemporaries, made him many bitter enemies.

His principal adversaries—or rather, perhaps, his rivals—were, like himself, monks of the Franciscan Order. He was denounced to his superiors as being guilty of heresy in his teaching of science, and he was confined in a prison where he could not have any communication with his pupils. The latter, most of whom belonged to the same religious order, and all of whom were famous astronomers or mathematicians, such as Thomas Bungey, Jean de Paris, John Bacon or Baconthorp, nicknamed the Prince of Averroists, did not venture to espouse his cause for fear of being involved in his disgrace. He had, however, a friend in Clement IV., to whom he had dedicated his " Opus Majus," and was, by his order, set at liberty. But, at the death of that pontiff, he was again imprisoned and treated with still greater severity, for he was refused the use of writing materials. He managed, however, to revise and perfect his " Opus Majus," which contains the substance of his doctrine, and he wrote two epitomes of it, far more advanced than the original, with the titles of " Opus Minus " and " Opus Tertium." Both of these books, though they long remained unpublished, were not destroyed, notwithstanding the persecution to which their author was subjected during his lifetime, but it is not many years since they first saw the light. This man of genius, who

Fig. 62.—The Burgher in Winter.

Fig. 63.—The Sower.

Fig. 64.—Lovers in Springtide.

Fig. 65.—The Sheep Shearer.

Fig. 66.—A Ride in Summer.

Fig. 67.—The Reaper.

Miniatures from the Calendar of a "Book of Hours."—Manuscript of the beginning of the Sixteenth Century.

had received the title of *Admirable Doctor*, died about 1294, almost forgotten by the men of that generation, without having been able to realise that regeneration of the scientific school which he had made the object of his life. It should be added, however, that he had become a dupe to the Arabism of Albumazar and the Aristotelism of Averroes, and that he acquiesced in all the wild conceptions of astrology and alchemy.

The Oxford school, to which the illustrious Roger Bacon belonged, appears to have been the cradle of English scepticism, which, after a long and sullen opposition to the teaching of the Catholic dogma, finally terminated in the most uncompromising heresy. The contemporaries of Bacon were all more or less of sceptics. John Basingstoke, who became Archdeacon of London and of Leicester, where he died in 1252, entered upon scholasticism with much mistrust and doubt. He made a journey into Greece, to give the agitation excited by his works upon the Bible time to cool down, and there devoted himself to the study of the exact sciences, and brought back to England the figures and ciphers which the Greeks used to signify numerals. Another pupil of the Oxford school, John of Holywood, called *Sacrobosco*, had already a reputation as astronomer or cosmographist when he came to study at the University of Paris, where he afterwards taught mathematics with great success. He composed a treatise on the Celestial Globe (" De Sphæra Mundi "), which was an imitation and abridgment of Ptolemy's book, and which continued to be a classic work in all the schools of Europe for more than three centuries. He also left a work considered to be of great value upon the Reckoning of Time (" De Anni Ratione "), a treatise upon Astrolabe, and another on Algorithms. Like most mathematicians of his day, he also sought to predict the future and to draw horoscopes.

The school of Canterbury, less impulsive than that of Oxford, pursued very steadily the study of the exact sciences under the superintendence of eminent prelates, amongst whom may be mentioned Thomas Bradwardin, Archbishop of Canterbury, surnamed the *Profound Doctor*, and Richard Walinford, Abbot of St. Albans, who were the first mathematicians of the fourteenth century. Denmark, at the same period, was rejoicing in the discoveries of a learned astronomer, De Duco, author of a new Ecclesiastical Computation and of a valuable treatise upon the Calendar.

All the greatest astronomical discoveries were effected in the East, in Persia, Arabia, and even in the provinces of Lebanon. Nassir-Eddin, a

Persian, invented some ingenious instruments for mathematical calculations, and he collected, under the title of "Ilkhanian Tables," a number of daily observations upon the state of the sky and the course of the stars. The Armenian Ezenkansti not only observed the celestial phenomena, but he described them in verse, and celebrated them in his poetry. Astronomy comprised studious and zealous followers even in Morocco, where Aly Aboul-Kalan wrote his book on "Beginnings and Endings," supplementing the compared results of telescopic observations with the most minute calculations.

But, from the close of the thirteenth century, the savants of Italy had

Fig. 68.—Astronomer accused of Sorcery, holding a Disc with Magic Figures.—Capital Letter in a "Book of Jurisprudence."—Manuscript of the Thirteenth Century. In the Library of M. Ambroise Firmin-Didot.

devoted themselves by preference to mathematics, though the study of the exact sciences was too often suspected of heresy. Campano, who had translated Euclid, had some difficulty in defending himself from the suspicions and denunciations of the theologians, while Pietro d'Abano, who professed medicine and astronomy at the University of Padua, had the misfortune to lean towards the errors of Averroism, and to fall a victim to astrology. Accused of sorcery, and condemned to the stake, he escaped that punishment by suicide (1316), or else died suddenly—it is not known which— before the sentence was executed. The principal mathematicians belonged to the school of Florence. Dugomari, called Paul the Geometer, and Abbaco contributed simultaneously to the progress of the exact sciences, but none of their pupils were capable of taking their place.

Mathematics were but little cultivated in France, though in the fourteenth century may be mentioned Jean de Lignières, whom a chronicler calls "the restorer of the science of the stars," and Jean des Murs, canon of the Cathedral of Paris, who compiled some valuable works on Arithmetic. Bonnet de Lates, a physician in Provence, conceived the idea of an astronomical ring for measuring the height of the sun and the stars (Fig. 68). This mathematician failed, however, to guard himself from the errors of contemporary science, and his weighty study of astronomy did not save him from making predictions based upon the conjunctions of the planets and so forth.

During the Italian Renaissance mathematics were not neglected, and they were taught with success during the fifteenth century at Rome, Naples, Padua, Bologna, Pisa, and more especially at Florence. They were at that time almost entirely extricated from the dangerous illusions of astrology, and no longer involved noble minds in the fatal paths of doubt and heresy. They were professed, moreover, by some of the principal doctors of the Church, and were in a certain degree honoured by the direct protection of the Holy See, when Æneas Sylvius Piccolomini, one of the first mathematicians of his century, was elected Pope, with the title of Pius II. (1458—1464). Pope Pius II. was a man of general learning, but his favourite study was that of cosmography. At the same time, Cardinal Nicholas de Cusa, his rival in learning, found time, while fulfilling his diplomatic functions at the Court of Rome, to write works on Mathematics, Geometry, and Astronomy, in which he maintained the system of the earth's rotation around the sun, and admitted in principle the plurality of worlds, two centuries before Galileo.

The example of Pius II. induced his successors, Paul II. and Sixtus IV., to favour the exact sciences. It was Sixtus IV. who summoned to Rome the celebrated Königsberg astronomer, Johann Müller, called *Regiomontanus*, who had been recommended to him by Cardinal Bessarion. Regiomontanus, the most celebrated pupil of G. Purbach, had already obtained a great reputation in Italy, whither he accompanied Cardinal Bessarion in 1463. The course of astronomy which he commenced at Padua in that year attracted an enormous audience. He afterwards became astronomer-royal to Matthias Corvinus, King of Hungary. But, unfortunately for him, he was unable to resist the entreaties of Pope Sixtus IV., who induced him to come to Rome.

Fig. 69.—Ptolemy's System, explained by Johann Müller, called Regiomontanus.—Fac-simile of a Wood Engraving of the "Epitome . . . Johannes de Monte Regio" (Basileæ, ap. H. Petri, 1543, in folio).

It is generally believed that the envy and revenge of his scientific rivals had something to do with his premature death in 1476. Although he died at under forty years of age, he had written a number of astronomical and mathematical works, which had a great success both during his lifetime and after his death (Fig. 69). His researches upon the calendar and upon triangulation were the basis of the remarkable labours of the Wurtemberg astronomer, Stöffler (1452—1531), who can claim the honour of compiling the great Roman Calendar ("Kalendarium Romanum magnum").

The teaching of mathematics was very brilliant at Naples during the reign of Alfonso of Aragon, the Magnanimous (1415—1458). People came thither from all parts to hear the Tuscan professor, Buonencontro, who, in his double capacity of poet and orator, gave an unusual charm to the exposition of the celestial phenomena, and who had the good fortune to allude openly to astrology, and even to magic, without provoking the remonstrances or the repression of the ecclesiastical authorities. These were the preludes of the Reformation, which made its presence felt in science by proclaiming the right of free examination before applying it to the dogmas of religion. It must also be said that the Greek savants, who had emigrated into Europe, and especially into Italy, after the occupation of Constantinople by the Turks, brought with them more fondness and aptitude for the occult than for the exact sciences. Several of these Greek savants had been received by Matthias Corvinus, King of Hungary, who, in his admiration for the sciences, gave the palm to astrology and alchemy; and the observatory attached to his palace at Buda was used less for observing the position of the stars, and studying the laws of their motions, than for seeking thereby to forecast the future. His library was composed of the most rare and magnificent manuscripts, but a great part of them referred to alchemy and the philosopher's stone. While harbouring these Greeks from Constantinople, who claimed to be alchemists and astrologers, Matthias Corvinus also placed great confidence in a true Italian savant, Fioravanti Alberti, who had little dealing with astrology, and who applied almost exclusively to works of architecture and design his profound knowledge of mathematics, and especially of geometry.

At this epoch astrology was everywhere beginning to supplant astronomy. There was not a sovereign or prince in Europe but had in his service an astrologer, more or less able and crafty, who in many cases sailed under the colours of a physician. King Louis XI. never arrived at any important decision without having consulted his Neapolitan astrologer, Angelo Cattho de Sopino, whom he created Archbishop of Vienne in Dauphiny, as a reward for the accuracy of his sidereal predictions. The Emperor Maximilian was always accompanied by his physician, Grunpek, whose prescriptions were dictated by the stars, and who paid more heed to the politics than to the health of his august master.

The exact sciences still found a home, however, in Italy at Florence, where Buonencontro and the Alberti had formed a numerous school, and the application of mathematics to arts and industry was the result of a

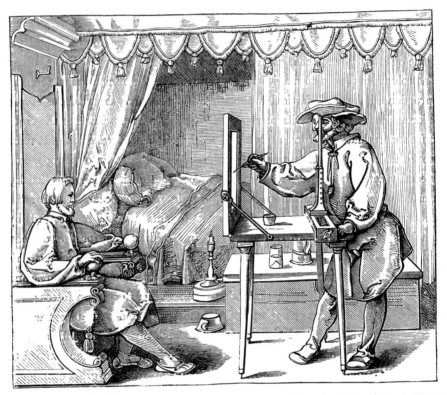

Fig. 70.—Instruments of Mathematical Precision for executing Portraits.—Fac-simile of a Wood Engraving by Albert Dürer, "Institutionum Geometricarum Libri Quatuor" (Parisiis, ex officina Christiani Wecheli, 1535, in folio).—In the Library of M. Ambroise Firmin-Didot, Paris.

serious and solid course of teaching. At the end of the fifteenth century the astronomer Pozzo Toscanelli traced for Christopher Columbus, who derived material assistance from his teaching, the route which he must take across the ocean in order to reach the western coasts of the Indies; the mathematician Paccioli was animated by Christian faith when he wrote his great cosmographical and philosophical work entitled, "De Divina Proportione;" and the great Michael Angelo, surrounded by a group of younger artists, who looked upon him as the regenerator of modern art, sought in the science of mathematics the most wonderful secrets of architecture and sculpture. Like Michael Angelo and Leonardo da Vinci, there was not a single great artist of that day who was not, in addition, a consummate mathematician (Figs. 70 and 71).

The mathematicians, it is true, did not all develop into artists, notwith-

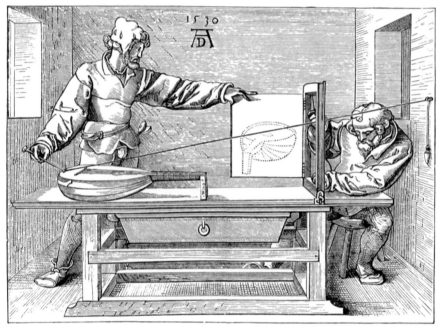

Fig. 71.—Instrument of Mathematical Precision for designing Objects in Perspective.—Fac-simile of a Wood Engraving from Albert Dürer's Work, "Institutionum Geometricarum Libri Quatuor" (Parisiis, ex officina Christiani Wecheli, 1535, in folio).—In the Library of M. Ambroise Firmin-Didot, Paris.

standing the general tendency which led them to cultivate the arts. At Ferrara Alumno remained cosmographist, and devoted part of his life to composing voluminous works upon celestial mechanics ("De Fabrica Mundi"); at Perugia the Dantes, who were not of the same family as the writer of the "Divine Comedy," devoted their time to purely mathematical works; and one of them, Egnazio Dante, who collated in his repertory of the "Scienze Mathematice in Tavole" (the Mathematical Sciences in Tables) all the problems resolved by his predecessors, constructed an immense table, upon which were marked with great precision the equinoxes and the solstices.

In Spain, as in Portugal, where the adventurous spirit of the nation favoured long sea voyages and expeditions to the East and West Indies, the exact sciences contributed to the progress of navigation, especially in regard to hydrography and astronomy. A Portuguese Jew, Abraham ben Samuel Zacuth, published at Lisbon a perpetual almanac, which was afterwards

Fig. 72.—German Astronomer and Cosmographist.—Fac-simile of a Wood Engraving of the Sixteenth Century, by J. Amman.

completed and perfected by Alfonso of Cordova, a Seville physician, who also published some excellent astronomical tables.

England and Germany (Fig. 72) were not behindhand in this forward movement of science; but the savants of these two countries belonged more or less to the sceptical school which brought about the Reformation, and found means in all their works, however excellent from a scientific point of view, a pretext or an opportunity for attacking the Catholic religion. It might have been supposed that mathematics were offensive weapons placed in the hands of blind sectaries of heresy. At the same time it would be unjust to under-estimate the importance of the labours of Batecumbe, an Englishman, who composed so many works on astronomy; of Peyrbach, an Austrian, who conceived an ingenious theory of the planets; or of Gaspard Peucer, a Saxon, who described the motion of the stars, and represented for the first time the true configuration of the earth.

But it may be said that all the science of the Middle Ages is summed up in the memorable book of Pic Mirandola, "De omni re scibili," which

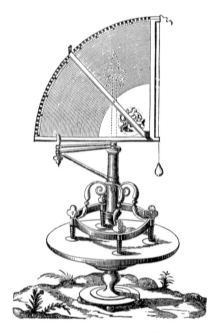

Fig. 73.—Arc with Double Compartment for measuring the Shortest Distances of the Stars.

Fig. 74.—Small Quadrant, or Quarter of a Circle, in Copper Gilt.

Fac-simile of Copper Engravings in the Work, "Tychonis Brahe Astronomiæ Instauratæ Mechanica" (Noribergæ, apud Levinum Hulsium, 1602, in folio).

contains nine hundred propositions embracing the totality of human knowledge at this epoch. Pic Mirandola was but nine-and-twenty years of age when he undertook to sustain in public these nine hundred propositions against any one who would accept the immense responsibility of this scientific and oratorical tournament, in which, as may be supposed, the mathematical and astronomical sciences held a large place. No one came forward to pick up the glove, but Pic Mirandola's book, submitted to pontifical censure, was condemned as heretical with regard to a number of points, in dealing with which the writer had openly declared himself the partisan of Averroism, a bastard kind of scholasticism which linked the principles of Plato and Aristotle to the vagaries of Albumazar.   He was not persecuted, as Roger Bacon and Pietro d'Abano had been, but he voluntarily submitted himself to exile, and found a peaceful asylum in France, under the protection of the University of Paris, in which he had previously studied the higher sciences, and even cabalism.

Averroism, with its attendant mysteries of astrology and magic, continued to reign in the schools of Italy and of Germany, making its baneful influence felt in the exact as well as in the speculative sciences.   Its principal centre was the University of Padua.   The illustrious Jerome Cardan of Pavia (died in 1576) had begun his career of professor by teaching mathematics at Milan, and it was then that he invented a new mode of resolving algebraic equations.   But his passion for astrology and the occult sciences soon dragged him into a vicious circle of wild crazes and visions.   So it was with Cornelius Agrippa of Nettesheim (born at Cologne in 1486), with Theophrastus Bombastes, surnamed Paracelsus (born at Einsiedlen, in Switzerland, about 1493), who would have been two great philosophers, two great physicians, and two great mathematicians, if they had not preferred to be astrologers and cabalists; but, as it was, they lived in poverty, and died in misery, one at the Grenoble Hospital (1535), the other at the Hospital of Salzburg (1541).   Another dreamer, who, lika Agrippa and Paracelsus, was a man of universal attainments, and who, like them, visited all the Universities and courts of Europe, Lucilio Vanini, born in the kingdom of Naples, lived as wretched and precarious a life as they did, and came to a still more miserable end.   As M. Cousin has remarked, Vanini had no other God than Nature, and his morality was that of Epicurus.   He was burnt alive, as an atheist, at Toulouse, upon the 9th of February, 1619.

France was, however, more hospitable for the astrologers and sorcerers, though the celebrated Pierre La Ramée, surnamed Ramus, Principal of the College of Presles, at Paris, where he himself taught philosophy and mathematics in 1545, opened an eloquent campaign against the extravagances of astrology (Fig. 79).   But Ramus was one of the apostles of the Reformation, and his philosophic reasoning was no match for the allied forces of madmen and impostors who dishonoured true science.   Cosmo Ruggieri, whom

Catherine de' Medicis brought to France as astrologer-royal, was not capable of doing more than compiling prophetical almanacs, and yet his credit at court extended over four reigns. As to Pierre de Nostredame, surnamed Nostradamus, who set up for astronomer and physician, though he had never studied either medicine or astronomy, he merely observed the stars for the purpose of making predictions therefrom, and his mathematical calculations were confined to the composition of horoscopes. He was in great favour

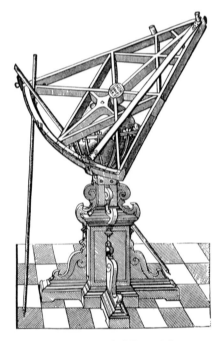 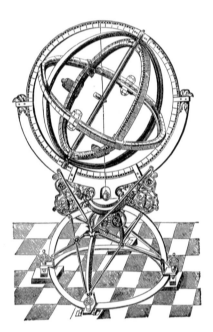

Fig. 75.—Astronomical Sextant for measuring Distances.

76.—Equatorial Rings or Circles.

Fac-simile of Copper Engravings in the Book, "Tychonis Brahe Astronomiæ Instauratæ Mechanica" (Noribergæ, apud Levinum Hulsium, 1602, in folio).

with Charles IX. and the Queen-mother, who loaded him with presents, but he had the prudence to withdraw from the court and live in retirement at Salon, in Provence, where he died in 1566, leaving behind him a great reputation and a large fortune. He did not leave any astronomical work, but merely some collections of pharmaceutical receipts and unintelligible prophecies in rhymed verse, and written in a mystic and barbarous tongue.

To discover the true science of astronomy in the sixteenth century, it was necessary to go, not to France, but to Poland, where Nicholas Copernicus, born at Thorn, in 1473, had returned home, after professing mathematics at Rome, without awaking the susceptibilities of the Roman clergy, who would not admit of the utterance of any scientific idea contrary to the facts set forth in Holy Writ.   But, once settled at Frauenburg, where he was appointed to a canonry, he threw off the reserve imposed upon him by the fear of ecclesiastical censure, and unhesitatingly declared that he accepted, with certain rectifications, the system formerly taught by the philosophers of

Fig. 77.—Marque of Jehan St. Denis, Bookseller at Paris, Rue Neufve Nostre-Dame, at the Sign of St. Nicholas: "Petit Compost en françoys" (printed in 1530, small octavo). "The present book, for the use of simple persons who do not understand Latin, contains a small and easy process for understanding the course of the sun and moon, festivals, and time according to the order of the 'Latin Compost.'"

ancient Greece, according to which the planets revolved, from east to west, around the sun, while the earth described two distinct motions, one of rotation upon its own axis, the other of circumvolution around the sun.   Copernicus, however, waited for some time before publishing this system, which was violently attacked by the defenders of biblical lore, and he took the precaution of dedicating to Pope Paul III. his book, "De Revolutionibus Orbium Cælestibus," in which he had expounded the whole of his system.   He did not live to see this book published, for it appeared on the very day of his death in 1543; and he thus escaped the posthumous condemnation passed upon the work, which was placed in the Index by the Court of Rome in 1616, notwithstanding its having been dedicated to a pope.

Fig. 78.—Portrait of Tycho Brahe, engraved by Gheyn, at the end of the Sixteenth Century. In the Library of M. Ambroise Firmin-Didot, Paris.

Copernicus confined himself to astronomy; his successor and imitator, the celebrated Tycho Brahe (Fig. 78), who did not, perhaps, excel him, but who was in some respects his equal in his learned treatises on Astronomy, fell a victim in many instances to the errors of astrology, and even of cabalism. He had laboured in all the observatories of Germany and Sweden, when the King of Denmark constructed for him upon the island of Haven, near Copenhagen, a magnificent observatory, in which, for seventeen years, he followed the motions of the planets and the stars, in order to connect them with the system which he had conceived to replace those of Ptolemy and Copernicus (Figs. 73—76). According to his system the earth was motionless in the centre of the world, and the sun and moon revolved around it, while the other five planets gravitated around the sun. But Tycho Brahe, acceding to the pressing invitation of the Emperor Rudolph II., who was anxious to get him to his court, turned astrologer, in order to obtain the pension which was paid him, and lost himself in the vagaries of cabalism. He died at Prague in 1601, leaving behind him a European reputation, which his works, very inferior to those of Copernicus, scarcely justified.

And yet Copernicus and Tycho Brahe were the creators of true astronomy, and it may be said in their praise that, at a time when astrologers, necromancers, and diviners were alone in favour, like Cosmo Ruggieri at the French court, and John Dee at the court of Queen Elizabeth, the observations and systems of the Polish astronomer and the Danish astronomer inaugurated a new era in the scientific world, and opened the route which was afterwards followed, and with so much renown, by Galileo, Keppler, Huygens, and Newton. As has been remarked by the learned Dr. Hoefer, "Copernicus begat Keppler, and Keppler begat Newton. What a genealogical tree!"

Fig. 79.—Portrait of Bernard Abbatia, Astronomer to the King.—Fac-simile of a Wood Engraving of the "Prognostication sur le mariage de Henry, roy de Navarre, et de Marguerite de France" (Paris, Guillaume de Nyverd, 1572, small octavo).—The Latin motto, "Nulla dies sine linea," signifies "There's no life without an ending," or "There is no day which is not regulated by the stars."

NATURAL SCIENCES.

HE great work of Pliny the Elder, which contains in its one hundred and thirty-seven books the sum and substance of all the knowledge of antiquity with regard to arts and sciences, is unquestionably replete with erudition, but it is also typical of the extreme confusion which then prevailed in the domain of natural and physical sciences. The tendency to sophistry and paradox, the subtleties of dialectics, had changed the direction of scientific studies, and abruptly closed the broad vistas which the admirable labours of Aristotle opened to the human mind, in teaching it to study directly and materially Nature, which all the ancient religions had made divine, under the manifold form of the gods and goddesses of paganism (Fig. 80). The observation of facts and the search of causes seemed to have become useless; the marvellous and the strange were preferred before simple and logical truth; and prevalent opinions were accepted without putting them to the test of criticism or the control of experience. With regard to the theory of the elements and the three reigns, as to the history of minerals, plants, and animals, the most absurd and extravagant fables, allied to the wildest conceptions of popular credulity, had become current. Pliny, however, whose statements were often adduced in support of them, was not merely an observant compiler of facts; he had watched and studied for himself, and he died a victim to science, in attempting to contemplate too closely the great eruption of Vesuvius, which destroyed the cities of Pompeii and Herculaneum (B.C. 79).

When the Roman decadence set in, the natural sciences, which had remained motionless for four centuries, were at the same point as they had been left by Claudius Ælianus, who, in his "History of Animals," collected without any cohesion the vague or erroneous notions which he had gathered from various Greek and Latin authors whose works are no longer extant. These sciences, almost abandoned, had been relegated, together with specu-lative philosophy, amongst the misty conceptions of the sophists, and were merely interpreted by a few rhetoricians, such as Nemesianus, Calpurnius, and Ausonius, who translated in their descriptive poems the ideas of pagan antiquity as to the phenomena and products of nature. Pliny is always cited in works which treat incidentally of any facts appertaining to the physical world. Moreover, in these times, from the fourth to the eighth century, so unfavourable to science, writers, whether physicians, historians, or philosophers, merely treated of material things from a utilitarian point of view; they spoke of minerals, plants, and animals without reference to their organiza-tion, their shape, or their physiognomy; they examined and appreciated them solely from the point of view as to the best use that could be made of them in industry or social life; and the only scientific classification they gave them was to place them in the Hexameron, or theory of the six days of the creation, according to the Genesis of Moses (Fig. 81).

Charlemagne himself, notwithstanding his great genius, does not seem to have taken any interest in the study of natural history, and we know that it was not included in the course of study at the Palace School. The Emperor was doubtless familiar with all wild animals, from a hunting point of view; with the domesticated animals, from the point of view of rural economy, and with plants in connection with agriculture, for he paid great attention to the care of his lands and gardens. Thus, in his Capitularies, he lays special stress upon the good kinds of fruits, vegetables, and grain for the use of the table, and scarcely gave a place for the exotic vegetables, &c., sent to him from Spain and Greece. It was at this epoch that a monk in the monastery of St. Gall, Walafrid Straba, described with no little accuracy,

in a Latin poem entitled " Hortulus," the vegetables which he had cultivated with his own hands. Another poet, almost his contemporary, and
believed to be a Frenchman, Macer Floridus, also composed a similar poem
upon the culture and virtue of herbs, amongst which certain solaneæ had
already been remarked as most effective for curing various diseases. This
culture of medicinal herbs took place in most of the monasteries, and was the

Fig. 80.—Esus, the great God of Nature among the Gauls, worshipped in the Forests.—Celtic
Monument discovered at Paris, under the Choir of Notre-Dame, in 1771, and preserved in the
Cluny Museum.

origin of those botanical gardens which afterwards contributed so much to
the progress of medicine. (See below, chapter on *Medical Sciences*.)

Though from the eighth to the tenth century the natural sciences were
altogether neglected in the West, it was not the same with Eastern peoples,
who sought not so much to embrace the vast totality of physical knowledge
as to perfect themselves in the study of materia medica, for all the sciences

led up to medicine. During the prosperous reign of Al-Mansour, in the eighth century, a large school was founded at Bagdad, which became a refuge for the sciences when exiled from Athens and Alexandria. There were translated into Syriac the works of Aristotle and Galen, the two lights of Greece and of Rome, whom the Arabs in turn translated for the use of their schools at Granada and Cordova. The legendary caliph, Haroun Alraschid, followed the example of Al-Mansour, his predecessor, and showed still more generosity towards the savants. His son, Al-Mamoun, obedient to these traditions, carried the love of science so far as to declare war upon the Emperor of Constantinople, in order to compel him to send into Asia Minor not only several Greek savants, but also some ancient manuscripts relating to arts and sciences.

The Arabs had before this cultivated several branches of natural history, and made some valuable botanical discoveries, thereby enlarging the domain of materia medica. Thus, in place of the violent purgatives, such as hellebore, which were previously resorted to, the Arab doctors recommended the moderate use of cassia, senna, and tamarinds : a quantity of plants useful for medicinal purposes were brought from India, Persia, and Syria by Rhazes. At the same time Serapion the younger commentated Dioscorides, and added to that work a description of the newly discovered plants ; and Avicenna scoured Bactriana and Sogdiana in search of medicines, and especially of vegetable preparations. Mesué wrote his treatise on Medicine (" De Re Medica "), which, several times translated into Latin, was used as a manual in all the schools up to the Renaissance. But, apart from the materia medica, disorder and confusion prevailed in the works composed by the Arabs, who were not acquainted with Aristotle's " History of Animals," or the " History of Plants " by Theophrastus, and whose translations of, and commentaries upon, Pliny and Dioscorides are a mass of nonsense, and for the most part unintelligible.

Constantine of Africa first introduced into Europe certain Arab works upon the materia medica, but in his own works, though they give proof of a certain experience in practical medicine, it is easy to see that he was not well informed in matters of detail, and this because there was a want of method in his study of nature. Thus, in dividing medicines into four distinct classes, he ranged them upon a sort of scale according to their degree of relative activity. At about the same period the natural sciences were represented with no little éclat in the East by several Arab botanists, such as Ebn-Taitor, a native of Malaga, who travelled into Asia to study plants previously to becoming minister of the Caliph at Cairo; and Abdallatif, author of a very accurate description of the plants and animals of Egypt, who, in the dissection of a mummy, corrected several important errors which Galen had made in matters of osteology. This knowledge of human anatomy is all the more remarkable because the law of Mahomet absolutely forbids dissection of dead bodies. Thus a great part of such science as there then was in the

Fig. 81.—God creating the World by Compass.—Miniature from Brunetto Latini's "Trésor." Manuscript of the Fifteenth Century.—In the Arsenal Library, Paris.

world came directly from the Arabs, and especially from the caliphate of Cordova. It was there that Gerbert, who became, in turn, Archbishop of Rheims, of Ravenna, and afterwards Pope, under the name of Sylvester II. (999), repaired to increase his already large store of learning, and he may claim the honour of having imported into Italy the first elements of the natural sciences. Otho of Cremona sets forth the facts relating to medicinal plants with which he is acquainted in a learned poem of fifteen hundred lines; and John of Milan summarised, also in verse, all the medical botany of his century in the "Code of the School of Salerno," a work which is not devoid of importance from a hygienic point of view, but which is very imperfect in its treatment of the natural sciences.

Although the light of science emanated chiefly from the Saracen schools in Spain, it was not extinguished when the empire of the Caliphs was overthrown, and when reviving civilisation was once more threatened with an invasion of barbarism. The Jewish nation picked up the scattered fragments of the sacred arts of science, and divided them between the various countries of Europe, where the rabbis for some time preserved the monopoly of real learning. Physicians for the most part, often favourites and advisers of their sovereigns, and even of popes, they had chairs at the Colleges of Bologna, Milan, and Naples, and they substituted a new mode of teaching for the "Etymologicon" of Isidore of Seville, which had been, since the seventh century, the basis of scientific studies. The natural sciences—amongst others, zoology, mineralogy, and botany—were doubtless represented in this abridged dictionary of human attainments, but Isidore of Seville, at the remote epoch when he wrote, was unable to treat them save in a superficial and illogical fashion, for want of sufficient experience and observation (Fig. 82).

The progress of the natural sciences was not very rapid during the twelfth century, but there might already be perceived, in several writings on those subjects, a tendency to observation of facts, though no one had yet conceived the simple idea of interrogating Nature herself. Botany continued to have the preference of early observers, and medicine was the starting-point of all scientific investigation. Amongst the works which give the best summary of the opinions and principles of science, as to plants, minerals, and animals, useful or noxious, must be mentioned the "Jardin de Santé," compiled by Hildegarde, Abbess of Bingen, as a very valuable collection of receipts to be used in cases of illness. Hildegarde, like many other abbesses of her time, was much addicted to the study of everything relating to the art of healing; she cultivated herself many medicinal plants, and ascertained their respective properties. Thus a great many monasteries (Fig. 83) and convents possessed not only botanical gardens, but also collections of fossils, minerals, shells, herbs, and animals preserved by various processes of desiccation. This was the origin of those encyclopædiæ of the Middle Ages, vast descriptive compilations, full of popular errors, it is true, but at the same time replete with curious and interesting details, which have been published in every language

Fig. 82.—Noah's Ark.—Miniature of a Commentary upon the Apocalypse.—Manuscript of the Twelfth Century.—In the Library of M. Ambroise Firmin-Didot, Paris.

since the twelfth century, and which, with engravings that often explain and complete the text, are buried in the great libraries without having ever obtained the honours of print. Most of these works contain singular revelations as to the nature of plants and of stones, as to the usage and properties of simples, as to the hygienic qualities of various foods, &c. Several special and less voluminous treatises, written by certain doctors of the twelfth century, were alone printed at the close of the fifteenth century. Amongst these latter may be mentioned a moral poem entitled, " Anti-Claudianus, sive de Officio viri boni et perfecti," which was composed at the close of the twelfth century by the celebrated Alain de l'Isle, or de Lille, called the

Fig. 83.—Monks engaged in Agriculture.—Capital Letter in the " Livre de Jurisprudence." Manuscript of the Thirteenth Century.—In M. Ambroise Firmin-Didot's Library, Paris.

Universal Doctor, and which contains, with a general table of arts and sciences, a number of very sensible remarks on natural history.

The savants and philosophers of this epoch who had a taste for natural sciences were but commentators and compilers, but the thirteenth century produced observers, the first of whom were those whom the Crusades and a passion for Eastern travel took into distant and hitherto unexplored lands, where everything they saw was strange and unknown. Observations, imperfect as they no doubt were, resulted from these voyages, in which the curiosity was continually being stimulated by the sight of novel objects; and the natural sciences profited largely by the expeditions, whether political, com-

mercial, or what not, which were undertaken in Asia and Africa. The
Mendicant Orders, Franciscans and Grey Friars, Dominicans and Preaching
Brothers, whom the Church sent forth as her representatives, contributed in
no small degree to these triumphs of natural history (Fig. 84). A Grey
Friar, John de Plano Carpini, sent by the Pope upon a mission to a Tartar

Fig. 84.—St. Francis of Assisi talking to the Birds.—Miniature from a Psalter of the Thirteenth
Century.—In the Library of M. Ambroise Firmin-Didot, Paris.

chief (1246), was the first Christian who penetrated into the savage regions
beyond the Caspian Sea; another Grey Friar, Guillaume Picard, sent by
St. Louis to the residence of another Asiatic chief, wrote a detailed account
of his voyage (1253); Pierre Ascelin, sent by the Pope into Mongolia, and
Guillaume de Rubruquis, also sent by St. Louis into the depths of Tartary
(1253), were alike monks of the Franciscan Order. These travellers, in

relating their journeys, did not merely record what struck them the most in the way of plants, animals, and stones; they brought back to Europe specimens which might be of use to science, and serve to correct anything incoherent or exaggerated in what they had written. The most celebrated Indian explorer of the thirteenth century, Marco Polo, the Venetian, who passed more than twenty years in those then unknown lands, and who penetrated as far as China, has left a very curious account of his long journeys, in the course of which he relates all that he saw or heard. Natural history occupies a large place in his story, which but too often testifies to his ignorance and credulity. (See below, chapter on *Geographical Sciences.*)

The most prominent botanists of that period, always in regard to the materia medica, were: two Englishmen, Gilbert and Hernicus Arviell, who travelled, the one through Europe, the other through Asia, to study plants and prepare treatises on botany; Simon de Cordo, called Simon of Genoa, who had undertaken a herborising expedition into the islands of the Archipelago and to Sicily, and who, borrowing largely from the Greek and Arab writers, compiled a Botanic Dictionary; and Jean de St. Amand, Canon of Tournay, who proceeded experimentally to his discoveries in therapeutics, and devoted a remarkable work to the research of the medicinal properties of a certain number of simples. But the most learned and experienced of these botanists of the thirteenth century was Peter de Crescenzi, or de Crescentiis, born at Bologna in 1230, a man of mark both in regard to birth and fortune, who had a great predilection for agriculture and horticulture, and who, adding to his own observations all that the ancient authors and those of the Middle Ages had written about the vegetable productions of nature, compiled a sort of agronomical encyclopædia called "Opus Ruralium Commodorum." This great work, replete with information, judicious advice, and excellent practical notions, was translated into several languages, and especially into French, by order of King Charles V., and called "Livre des Prouffits champestres et ruraux."

Peter de Crescenzi treated but one side of natural history, but three of his contemporaries, Vincent of Beauvais, Albertus Magnus, and Arnaud de Villeneuve, entered upon the study of this science in a spirit of observation which embraced all its aspects. They were, in fact, astrologers, alchemists, theologians, and physicians first; naturalists afterwards. Vincent of Beauvais, a Dominican monk, who had translated the story of the voyage of John de Plano Carpini in Great Tartary, became enamoured of those distant expeditions, which he looked upon as confirmatory of the strangest tales of antiquity related by Pliny. These fables he consequently embodied in his enormous encyclopædia, the "Speculum Naturale," not omitting any of the superstitious errors of his time. According to him, the mandragora was of the same shape as the human body; the winged dragon was capable of flying off with an ox, and devouring it in mid-air; the Scythian lamb, a sort of animal-plant, was attached to the ground by a stem and by roots; and

Fig. 85.— "How Alexander fought the Dragons and a species of Beast called Scorpion."— Miniature of a Manuscript of the Thirteenth Century, No. 11,040.—In the Burgundy Library, Brussels.

the tree of life, or the weeping-tree, was to be found, like a living allegory, in the harems of the East. Vincent of Beauvais related wonderful stories about the basilisk serpent, repeated the old legend of the tenderness of the pelican towards her young, spoke of the never-ending flight of the phœnix, and declared that in Scotland the fruits of certain trees, when they fall into the water, produce black ducks of the species termed black divers. (See the chapter on *Popular Superstitions*.) This shows that natural history was still in its infancy in the reign of St. Louis (Figs. 85, 87, and 95).

Albertus Magnus, the illustrious Albert de Bollstadt, was not, perhaps, more learned than Vincent of Beauvais, but he was a greater logician, and ought not to have been subjected to the insult of being credited with the authorship of a wretched rhapsody called the "Secrets of the Great Albert," and of several similar productions, which, though equally unworthy of him, were even more read than some of the most learned books which he really did write.   But, in response to the aspirations of science in the Middle Ages, he had written treatises upon the properties of plants, stones, and animals, which were afterwards disfigured and misrepresented by shameless charlatans. Arnaud de Villeneuve, whose learning has, without sufficient grounds as it seems, been compared to that of Albertus Magnus, had to submit, like the latter, to a blundering and unfair interpretation of his doctrines.   He had studied in the schools of Italy and in that of Montpellier before coming to teach, in the University of Paris, medicine and botany, philosophy and astrology.   This was the first time that lessons in natural history were taught concurrently with theology and medicine.   The immense number of hearers lent still greater notoriety to these lessons, in which the professor boldly declared that the most solemn mysteries of the Catholic faith were to be explained by the teachings of natural history and experimental physics. Scientific teaching so opposed to the dogmas of the Church excited the alarm of the Inquisition, and Arnaud de Villeneuve was accused, not of impiety or heresy, but of sorcery and magic.   It was only through the special protection of Charles of Anjou, King of Naples and Sicily, that he was enabled to leave France without appearing before the tribunal of the Inquisition, and he sought a refuge at the court of this French prince, who retained him as physician.   Arnaud de Villeneuve found at Naples and Palermo, where he had established his residence, greater facilities than he would have enjoyed elsewhere for completing his studies in natural history, for this science appears to have been specially favoured at the court of the kings of the house of Anjou, as at that of the kings of the house of Arragon.   After the Sicilian Vespers, Arnaud de Villeneuve quitted the service of Charles II., and attached himself for the rest of his life to the court of Frederick II., who, more than any other sovereign of his time, favoured the study of the natural sciences.   This king of the Two Sicilies had Aristotle's "History of Animals" translated into Latin; he went to great expense in forming a collection of the rarest animals for his royal menagerie from Asia and Africa; and the "Treatise on Falconry," which he found time, amidst the political anxieties of his reign, to compose himself, shows that he was very well versed in everything relating to birds of prey.

The study of natural sciences had become more general and complete by the beginning of the fourteenth century, though observations from nature were not yet given the preference over the ancient descriptions to be found in the Greek, Latin, and Arab authors. The difficulty of recognising under its Arab name a plant described by Dioscorides also led to endless confusion. Thus, for instance, Matthew Sylvaticus of Mantua, who possessed a superb botanical garden at Salerno, had great difficulty in putting the right names to his plants and ascertaining their specific qualities; for, though he knew Greek, he was ignorant both of Arabic and Hebrew, and hence

Fig. 86.—"How Alexander fought the Dragons with Sheep's Horns upon their Foreheads."— Miniature of a Manuscript of the Thirteenth Century, No. 11,040.—In the Burgundy Library, Brussels.

arose the absurd errors in his nomenclature. The writings of Dino del Garbo, the Florentine; of John Ardern of Newark, the Englishman; and of several other botanists were almost valueless for the same reasons. But James Dondi and his son, John dall' Orologio, who worked in concert about the middle of the fourteenth century at a perfected Codex of the materia medica, lived at Bologna, and studied only the native plants, which they have described with great precision and accuracy in their book on Simples, written in Latin, with the title of "Liber de Medicamentis Simplicibus," and translated into Italian as the "Herbolario Vulgare." Another book, inferior to the above in every respect, but very much better known, was that of Bartholomew Glanvil, an English monk, who compiled, for the benefit of the wealthy, an encyclopædia of natural history, filled with popular stories and a mass of worthless erudition. This singular work, written in Latin—it was styled the "Liber de Proprietatibus Rerum"—had a great reputation so late as the sixteenth century; it was translated into French by Brother Jean Corbichon, under the amphibological title of "Propriétaire des choses," at the request of King Charles V., and it was one of the works most frequently published in different languages when printing was first invented. A like honour was reserved for the treatises which Albert of Saxony, Bishop of Halberstadt, had imitated after the analogous treatises of Aristotle and of Albertus Magnus, and which enumerated the more or less problematical properties of plants, minerals, and animals (Fig. 88). In the fifteenth century a light shone upon the darkness of the natural sciences, and this light was the art of designing, by which a precise and unvarying form was given to the objects described. A German of the Rhine provinces, whose very name has been forgotten, conceived the idea of executing a work of natural history, embellished with paintings intended to illustrate the writer's descriptions. This book, entitled "Das Buch der Natur," was in reality an abridged translation of Martin de Cantimpré's Latin work, "De Rerum Natura;" but it contained a description of various animals, trees, and shrubs, represented by figures, which in their drawing and colouring were very true to nature. This book earned him such great celebrity that it was one of the first books on natural history which the printing-press multiplied throughout Germany as early as 1475, when the first edition appeared at Augsburg. Wood engraving, was henceforward the handmaiden of printing, and they combined in offering to the eyes and to the mind some elementary notions of the natural sciences. Printing, which, driven from its mysterious sanctuary by the siege and sack of Mayence (1462), had made its way, with its typographers and engravers, into the great cities of Italy, stimulated the rivalry of philologists and savants in bringing to light the literary productions of ancient Greece and Rome. Aristotle, Theophrastus, Dioscorides, and, still more, Pliny, at once found translators, commentators, and editors. As early as the year 1468 John Spire published at Venice an edition of Pliny; the following year the German printers, Sweynheim and Arnold Pannartz, published at Rome a new edition, also in folio, revised and corrected by the great philologist, Andrew, Bishop of Aleria. Two years afterwards a French printer settled at Venice, Nicholas Jenson, published an edition

not inferior to either of the above.   The Greek texts of Aristotle and Dioscorides were not published until the beginning of the sixteenth century; but as

Fig. 87.—The Marine World according to the Conceptions of the Middle Ages.—"How Alexander
lowered himself into the Sea in a Glass Barrel."—Miniature of a Manuscript of the Thirteenth
Century, No. 11,040.—In the Burgundy Library, Brussels.

early as the year 1476, the "History of Animals," so long neglected, or, to
speak more correctly, eclipsed by the philosophical treatises of the illustrious
peripatetic of Stagira, was translated into Latin by Theodore Gaza.

The numerous treatises and large works on natural history printed in the
fifteenth century show how eagerly this science was studied.   Those of
Albertus Magnus, whether really written by him or only attributed to him,
had an immense circulation.   The encyclopædic compilation of Bartholomew
Glanvil, " De Proprietatibus Rerum," notwithstanding its deficiencies and
errors, was reprinted ten times in Latin and in French, while it was being
translated into English, Spanish, and Dutch, to appear almost simultaneously
at London, Tolosa, and Haarlem.   The excellent work of Peter Crescenzi
(" Ruralium Commodorum Libri XII."), which obtained the honour of passing
through fifteen or twenty editions before the close of the fifteenth century,
was also translated into several languages.   These large folios did not, of

Le chien de mer est une beste en la mer qui sa nourrisson
prent et sur la terre et en mer · naige en la mer côme ung
poisson et vault terre côme une beste·

Fig. 88.—The Sea-Dog.—Fac-simile of a Wood Engraving in the "Dyalogue des Créatures"
(Gouda, Gérart Leeu, 1482, in folio).—In the Library of M. Ambroise Firmin-Didot, Paris.

course, reach the country-people, to whom some knowledge of natural history
was indispensable ; and this knowledge, which they had acquired by practice
and tradition, was popularised by the miniatures of the calendars placed in
the frontispieces of books of devotion (Fig. 89), and by wood engravings,
which also ornamented these calendars.   The same subjects were also illustrated in a quantity of almanacs, the most celebrated of which is the
" Compost et Kalendrier des Bergers."

The usefulness of plates in a book upon natural history was so generally
recognised (Fig. 90) that no book upon botany appeared without some wood
engravings, which were not always, as may well be supposed, very true to
nature.   It was at this period that a Lubeck burgomaster called Arndes went

to Palestine, taking with him a draftsman who was to sketch for him the plants which grew in the Levant. But as the drawings which he brought back were not accompanied by any text description, a Mayence doctor, one

Une fois lan faict bon ses brebis tondre.
En la saison/sans du cuir escorcher.
Car trop souuent/les peult faire morfondre.
Et sans le cuir/layne ne croist sur chair.

Fig. 89.—Sheep-shearing.—Miniature from the "Three Ages of Man," unpublished Poem attributed to Estienne Porchier.—Manuscript of the latter part of the Fifteenth Century.— In the Library of M. Ambroise Firmin-Didot, Paris.

John de Cuba, was intrusted with writing the text after the botanical works of the Arabs; and in this way were perpetuated, at great cost, the ancient errors which hampered the development of science. At the same time it must be said that some very interesting books on Herbalism, enriched with handsome wood engravings, were published at Mayence, Passau, and Louvain —some in Latin, and others in German—before the great works of Arndes and John de Cuba appeared at Lubeck in 1492.

At Venice, too, were being printed with marvellous rapidity the works of the ancient Arab physicians, Avicenna, Avenzoar, Averroes, and Mesué, who treated of natural history in its relation to medicine; and these publications only served to excite hostility against the Arabists, who had copied Pliny with all his errors. A learned professor of Ferrara, Nicholas Leoniceno, took this opportunity of attacking the Arabic school and its admirers, of whom he said, "These people never saw the plants of which they speak; they steal their descriptions from the works of preceding authors, whose meaning they often distort: this has led to a veritable chaos of erroneous denominations, the confusion being further increased by the inaccuracy of the descriptions." In this literary war, which showed how very imperfect was the knowledge of natural history at the time when Pliny's work was being so widely disseminated by the printing-press, Leoniceno was unjust towards the great Roman naturalist, and this he was made to comprehend by the celebrated Venetian humanist, Ermolao Barbaro, in a reply in favour of Pliny. The latter, in correction of the faults to be found in Pliny's work, published a book entitled "Castigationes Plinianæ," but that writer's "Natural History" was for the time discredited in most of the schools in Italy.

Taking advantage of this discredit, which increased the demand for the works of Aristotle, Theophrastus, and Dioscorides, the Aldi, skilful Venetian printers, brought out the original and hitherto unpublished texts of the Greek naturalists. Aldus Manutius had himself revised, after the ancient manuscripts, these priceless works, which were so anxiously scanned by the lovers of antiquity. They published at about the same time other modern works upon natural history, amongst them being several treatises of Georges Valla upon plants, and a Botanic Lexicon after the Greek authors. The study of botany was also in great favour amongst French savants. A Parisian printer, Pierre Caron, published, about 1495, "L'Arbolayre," a new herbal dictionary, illustrated with a great many wood engravings; and this work, extracted from the medical treatises of Avicenna, Rhazes, Constantine, Isaac, and Platéaire, was reprinted, with the title of "Grand Herbier en François," by six or eight Paris publishers. Botany seemed to hold the first place in natural history, and the discovery of America by Christopher Columbus in 1492 gave a fresh impetus to the study of the flora of that great continent.

The precious metals were at first the only articles of importation, but it was soon found that the materia medica might be greatly increased by the vegetable growth of the New World, and the disinterested love of science induced several learned men to cross the ocean. Italian, German, Spanish, and Portuguese naturalists applied themselves with zeal to examining and

Fig. 90.—River Fishing.—Fac-simile of a Wood Engraving in a Latin Edition of Pliny (Frankfort, 1584, in folio).

testing the numerous productions of this newly discovered land. Other naturalists, passing by the marvels of the American continent, devoted their attention to Asia, which they explored to more purpose than their predecessors had done. In presence of a nature absolutely new and unknown, the first naturalists who visited America were obliged to abandon the teaching of the past, and rely upon the results of their own direct and personal observations. This brought about a complete revolution in science. Travels really useful for purposes of natural history became general. Jean Léon, surnamed the African, visited Egypt, Arabia, Armenia, and Persia, noting with great care the various characteristics presented by the three kingdoms.

Peter Martyr (Pietro Martire d'Anghiera), while on a diplomatic mission in the East, verified upon the spot, book in hand, the statements of Aristotle, Theophrastus, and Dioscorides; John Manardi, a doctor of Ferrara, herborised in Poland and Hungary; and Jacques Dubois, the Amiens doctor, surnamed Sylvius, travelled all through France, Germany, and Italy in order to study nature.

Gradually the taste for scientific travel became general, and bore its natural fruits. Valuable collections of natural history were formed, exotic plants were acclimatised, and animals domesticated. Horticulture became a practical science; to kitchen and fruit gardens were added pleasure-grounds; and it was a Metz priest, Master François, who invented the "herbaceous ingraftment," the secret of which has only recently been recovered. The culture of many new plants gave still further development to botany, which had its special chairs in most of the leading Universities; and those of Ferrara, Bologna, and Padua had the advantage of being filled by Ghini and Brasavola. The best botanists were the doctors, whose main object was to extend the domain of the materia medica, and who all published large books written in Latin and replete with engravings: Otho Brunfels, of Mayence, his "Herbarum Vivæ Icones" (1530-36); Euricius Cordus, of Cologne, whose son Valerino became one of the greatest botanists in Germany, his "Botanologicum" (1534); and Leonard Fuchs, a Bavarian, his "Commentarii Insignes" (1542). It would be impossible to enumerate here all the works on natural history, on botany more particularly, which appeared during the first half of the sixteenth century in Germany, Holland, and Italy, and which testify to the vigorous growth of the new science. It must, however, be said that, out of the countless cosmopolitan travellers who went to the West Indies in search of fortune, one only, Gonzales Fernandes of Oviedo, brought back with him the materials for a really important work on natural history. This work he entitled "La Historia general y natural de las Indias" (Seville, 1535, in folio), and it contains a very accurate description of the animals, trees, shrubs, and plants of Southern America.

√ France, whose artists had enriched so many liturgical and religious manuscripts (Fig. 91) with paintings of flowers, birds, butterflies, and insects, very readily took part in the study of natural history. Charles Estienne, anatomist and botanist, one of the most distinguished members of the family of Parisian printers which conferred so much renown upon the name of

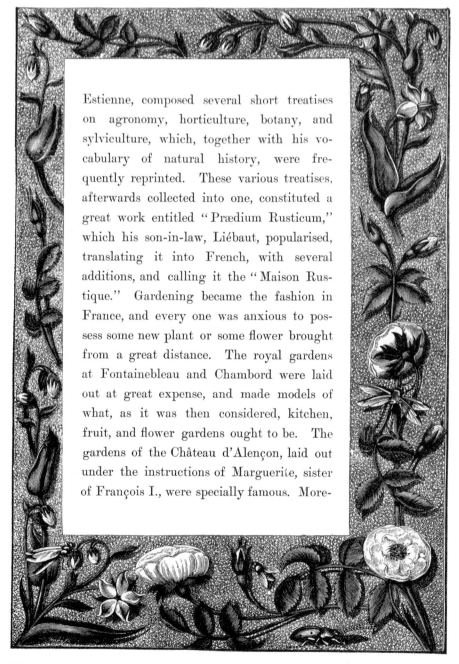

Estienne, composed several short treatises on agronomy, horticulture, botany, and sylviculture, which, together with his vocabulary of natural history, were frequently reprinted. These various treatises, afterwards collected into one, constituted a great work entitled "Prædium Rusticum," which his son-in-law, Liébaut, popularised, translating it into French, with several additions, and calling it the "Maison Rustique." Gardening became the fashion in France, and every one was anxious to possess some new plant or some flower brought from a great distance. The royal gardens at Fontainebleau and Chambord were laid out at great expense, and made models of what, as it was then considered, kitchen, fruit, and flower gardens ought to be. The gardens of the Château d'Alençon, laid out under the instructions of Marguerite, sister of François I., were specially famous. More-

Fig. 91.—Border of a Page in Manuscript of the Fifteenth Century, "Vie de St. Jérôme."—In the Library of M. Ambroise Firmin-Didot, Paris.

over, princes and prelates, nobles and plebeians, seemed to take an interest in horticulture : the greater was political agitation, the greater seemed the attractions of country life. Cardinal de Châtillon had magnificent plantations at Maillezais, of which place he was bishop ; and François Rabelais, during his stay at Rome, sent him various kinds of seeds and plants which were imported into France for the first time, and became indigenous. The two leading statesmen of this period, Cardinal du Bellay and Cardinal de Lorraine, also deserve mention in the history of gardening, for they encouraged the pursuit of botany, and sought repose from the cares of state, the one at the Abbey of St. Maur, and the other at the Château de Meudon, where they passed their time amidst the trees and flowers. At this period there were no public botanical gardens in France, like those of Passau in Bavaria, and of Pisa and Florence in Italy, though Jean Ruel, Dean of the Paris Faculty and physician to François I., explained in his valuable work, "De Natura Stirpium" (Paris, 1536, in folio), the necessity of creating such a garden for the teaching of practical medicine.

The era of Transatlantic voyages, which followed the discovery of America, was a very fruitful one, and the maritime voyages of discovery and conquest were succeeded by scientific voyages. Distant lands, drawn closer to Europe by the ties of commerce, were opened for the researches of science. The first facts of natural history, collected from beyond the seas, both from East and West, from Mexico and Brazil as from China and Japan, were due to the Jesuits, who have left us true and interesting accounts of the countries into which they carried the standard of Christianity. Valuable information was also given by the diplomatic agents in foreign countries. Busbecq, who was the ambassador of three German emperors in Turkey, took with him the learned naturalist of Sienna, Andrew Mattioli, to assist him in his botanical researches. Pelicier, French ambassador at Venice, had as his secretary and physician the learned Guillaume Rondelet ; and Cardinal du Bellay, ambassador of François I. to the Holy See, attached to his suite the great Rabelais in a similar capacity, who, however, has not left us any of the works he may have composed during his travels in Italy. Guillaume Rondelet, on the other hand, published several works on Ornithology and Ichthyology. A French naturalist still more celebrated, Pierre Belon, who accompanied Cardinal de Tournon in several of his diplomatic missions, was supplied by him with the means of travelling in Palestine, Egypt, and Arabia, where he completed and revised two monographs which he had in preparation upon birds and fishes; and these two works he published upon his return from his travels (1551 and 1555), with illustrations which he had himself made after nature, but which were not all of them accurate.

Two men of genius—one a German, George Agricola, the other a Swiss, Conrad Gesner—divided supremacy at that time in the domain of natural history. The first occupied the position in regard to mineralogy which the latter held in botany and zoology. George Landman Agricola, born at Chemnitz, in Saxony, in 1494, had studied in the Universities of France and Italy; while Gesner, born at Zurich in 1516, had been educated in the schools of Paris and Montpellier. Agricola at first practised medicine, and distinguished himself by his experiments in regard to what was called *chemical medicine.* The study of chemistry led up to that of mineralogy, and he devoted his whole time to the latter science, exploring the mines of Bohemia and Saxony. It was in this way that he acquired a profound knowledge of everything relating to the working of metals. In his works on Mineralogy the chemical part is treated with as much precision and learning as the docimastic part. These great works, translated into different languages, and of which several editions were printed, earned for him more reputation than profit, as he employed all his means in making costly researches and experiments. Conrad Gesner did not attempt to rival Agricola upon the field of mineralogy, turning his attention more specially to the study of animals and of plants. He was, in reality, the originator of scientific botany. Classing the plants by genus and kind, he was the first to discover the means of recognising each genus and kind by examining the organs of fructification. In this way he discovered more than eighteen hundred new kinds. His intention was to publish a work upon the natural history of the whole world, and his erudition would have enabled him to complete this immense task had his life been spared, but he only lived long enough to write the first four books of his "History of Animals" (1551, 1554, 1555, and 1558), which comprised the viviparous and oviparous tribes, the birds and the fishes. His pupils, Gaspard Wolff and Joachim Camerarius, were his executors, and they published the incomplete materials which he had left behind him in regard to the vegetable kingdom, the serpents, and the fossils. Gesner, who passed nearly all his life in his study at Zurich, was in permanent communication with the principal travellers of his day, such as André

Thevet and Pierre Gilles; with the leading naturalists, such as Rondelet, Belon, and Aldrovandus; with the greatest botanists, such as Dalechamp, Maranda, Adam Lonicer, and Rainbert Dodoens, surnamed Dodonæus. The books of Gesner may, therefore, be looked upon as the store in which were deposited all the facts and discoveries in natural history during his day.

Gesner's works show that at this period science, notwithstanding the want of classification which militated against an harmonious and complete conception of the work of nature, had reached a very advanced stage. All that remained was to submit the mass of information to a philosophic and methodical classification. Thus, in that part of his great work which Gesner published himself, after ranging the animals alphabetically, with their Latin names followed by those used in different languages, he describes them minutely, indicating their origin, their varieties, their habits, their diseases, their utility in domestic economy, industry, medicine, and arts, and quoting, in reference to each, the different passages which he had extracted from ancient and modern authors. Belon, although less erudite than Gesner, attempted to class the birds according to their instinctive habits, and in some cases according to their external appearance; but he had no settled system, and his most ingenious suggestions failed to bring to his knowledge the unvarying order of natural laws in the formation of species. Rondelet went even further than Gesner and Belon, as he attempted to ascertain by comparative anatomy the analogies and differences of species, but he did not succeed in establishing a general and systematic plan in zoology. Botany was much further advanced than the other branches of natural history, for Gesner not only discovered the elements for the classification of plants, but the conscientious researches of a number of excellent botanists advanced further and further the frontiers of a science which embraced the whole vegetable world. Though henceforward the method of observation was the only one admitted in scientific matters, the books of the ancient naturalists were translated and commentated, and Aristotle, Theophrastus, Dioscorides, and Pliny recovered full authority.

There was, however, a man of genius who, knowing nothing of Greek or Latin, and devoid of all regular education, discovered the fundamental bases of nature, which were only recognised three centuries later, and who, as far back as the sixteenth century, established the principles upon which repose geology, physics, and natural history. This was a humble labourer in

Périgord, called Bernard Palissy, who, at the age of five-and-twenty, left his native village, where he had been earning a scanty living as a potter, and started on a journey, staff in hand and wallet on back, through France, Germany, and Holland, practising different manual trades — at one time glazier, at another geometer, and at another designer. Wherever he went he studied the topography of the district, the irregularities of the ground, the course of the streams, the mines, and the natural productions and specialities of the country. He questioned the inhabitants as to the objects which attracted his attention, and so acquired for himself a scientific education by the sole force of his own intelligence. After five years of wandering, in the course of which he learnt, to use his own expression, "science with the teeth," he returned home and settled in Saintonge. While continuing his trade of surveyor and painter on glass, he sought to discover the secret of making enamelled pottery (Fig. 92), similar to that which Italy manufactured with so much skill, and which was much in favour at every court in Europe. Palissy worked at this scheme for ten or twelve years before discovering the coloured enamel which he required to cover the pottery. He thus equalled those whom he had copied, and he soon surpassed them by making

Fig. 92.—Table Ornament, from the Palace of the Bishop of Lisieux.—Enamelled Pottery of the Sixteenth Century.—In the Collection of M. Achille Jubinal.

vases and dishes which were decorated with figures of flowers, herbs, shells, insects, and reptiles. Palissy, whose earthenware was very highly esteemed when it appeared at the French court, placed himself under the protection of the Constable of Montmorency, and obtained the title of "Inventeur des rustiques figulines du roi." (See in the volume on "Arts," chapter on *Ceramics.*)

He was summoned to Paris by order of the King, and Catherine de' Medicis gave him a workshop in the gardens of the Tuileries. It was then that he described, in a course of public lectures, the result of his discoveries and his theories on natural history. Referring to this, he wrote, "I dis-

Fig. 93.—Mark of Barthélemy Berton, printer at Rochelle, upon the Title-page of the "Discours admirables," by Bernard Palissy, published at La Rochelle in 1563, small quarto.

played placards at the corners of the streets, in order to assemble the most learned physicians and others, promising to explain to them in three lectures all that I knew in regard to fountains, stones, metals, and other bodies. And in order that the audience might consist only of the most learned and those most anxious to instruct themselves, I stated in my placards that no one would be admitted except on payment of a crown; and this I did to see what could be advanced in opposition to my views, knowing well that if I made any false statements they would infallibly be caught up." We do not, unfortunately, possess any further particulars as to these conferences at which thirty-two *most honourable and learned* persons took part, in addition to many others not so distinguished.   Palissy, however, asserts that his statements were not once questioned.   He repeated his lectures every year, from 1575, with increased success, and in 1580 he published his great work, which was, no doubt, a résumé of his public lectures, entitled " Admirable Discourses," &c. (see Fig. 93).

Fig. 94.—The Vegetable Kingdom.—Mark of Guillaume Merlin, Bookseller at Paris, in the middle of the Sixteenth Century.—The design of this typographical mark is attributed to Jean Cousin.

It is only since Palissy's time that geology has obtained a recognised place in science.   He stated that the " petrified fish discovered in the rock had been born there at a time when the rocks were only water and mud, which became petrified simultaneously with the fish;" but these views were

not generally recognised as true until the time of Cuvier and Brongniart.
Palissy was two or three hundred years in advance of the epoch in which he
lived, for he asserted that when the fossils were formed men and certain
kinds of animals did not exist; he distinguished between the water due to
crytallization and the water of vegetation; he laid down the laws of the
affinity of salts in the development of stones and metals; he investigated
the origin of clouds, of springs, of earthquakes, of mineral or spring waters,
and of potable waters; he started, in fact, the great questions of natural
philosophy, of organic chemistry, of mineralogy, and of agronomy. Yet

Fig. 94a.—Mark of Charles Estienne, Printer at Paris, in the First Edition of his Work entitled
"Prædium Rusticum."—(See page 125.)

Bernard Palissy exercised little influence upon the science of his day, and he
was not looked upon as more than a skilful potter.

It is true that this period of civil and religious wars was not very favourable to the silent meditations of science, but the naturalists—more especially
the botanists—careless as to what was going on in the political world, saw
nothing and heard nothing of what passed outside their studies (Fig. 94).

Towards the close of the sixteenth century there were two savants who
discovered the true principles as to the classification of plants. Matthias
Lobel, born at Lille in 1538, but who, after several long botanical expeditions,
settled in England, first of all arranged them into families—such as the
grasses, the orchids, the palm tribe, and the mosses—and compared the mint
tribe and the umbelliferous plants. Andrew Cesalpin, professor of botany at

Pisa, compared the process of generation in animals to the seed of plants, distinguishing male plants by their stamen, and considering the plants which yielded seed as female. He further divided plants into fifteen classes, with male and female genders in each. To Cesalpin, therefore, belongs the honour of having invented the first system of botany, a branch of natural history which was studied very eagerly, and the development and progress of which were materially assisted by the numerous exploring expeditions all over the globe (Fig. 94*a*).

How important were these conquests of science may be gathered by examining the two thousand six hundred wood plates in the "Histoire générale des Plantes," written in French, after the notes of Jacques Dalechamp, and the two thousand five hundred plates in the botanical treatise of the Alsatian Jacques-Théodore Tabernæmontanus, written in German, and published in 1588-90. At that time the rage was for bulky volumes with abundant illustrations, especially in regard to natural history ; and yet, when Dr. Francis Hernandez was ordered by Philip II., to whom he had been acting as physician, to collect in one volume all the animal, vegetable, and mineral productions of Mexico, he could not find during his lifetime a publisher who would engrave the twelve hundred figures which he had had painted at a cost of sixty thousand ducats. The engravings and publications on natural history which Théodore de Bry and his sons executed at Frankfort had more success when they came out in the splendid collection known to bibliographists as the "Grands et Petits Voyages."

Fig. 95.—The Phœnix rising from his Ashes.—Fac-simile of a Wood Engraving in the Latin Edition of Pliny (Frankfort, 1602, in folio).

MEDICAL SCIENCES.

HRISTIANITY, as might be expected, exercised a great and immediate influence upon the practice and the science of medicine. Christ healing the sick by the laying on of hands, restoring sight to the blind and making the lame to walk by an appeal to God, and raising the dead to life in the name of the Father, seemed to intimate to the world that prayer and faith were the best remedies against human ills.

Medicine and its indispensable accompaniment, the art of surgery, underwent, subsequently to the death of Hippocrates, transformations due to the rival sects of dogmatism and empiricism, without making any real progress. Men of intelligence, but too hampered by scepticism or materialism, such as Themison of Laodicea and Soranus of Ephesus, founded a new doctrine called Methodism, which made the science of medicine rest upon the analogous and mutual relations of the organic affections to one another. This doctrine, which took no account of anatomical studies, admitted only two principles or causes of illness, *strictum* and *laxum*—that is to say, the contraction and the relaxation of the tissues; and the invariable course of treatment was either to relax the tissues which were too contracted, or to contract those which were too relaxed. The methodists had no idea of the action of the mind upon the morbid state of the human body.

It was the philosophy of Plato, renewed and revived in the schools, which inspired the doctrine of pneumatism, which attributed to the soul (πνεῦμα in Greek) a considerable part in the diseases of the body as well as in all the acts of human existence. Pneumatism, adopting the formulæ of the peripatetics, and based upon precise data of anatomy, in time gave birth to eclecticism, which was professed by Athenæus of Cilicia, Agathus of Sparta, Philip of Cæsarea, Aretæus of Cappadocia, and, lastly, by Galen, who was the greatest of the eclecticians. Galen, born at Pergamus in the year 131 B.C., studied in the school of Alexandria, and it was there that he learnt to argue with much talent against the already discredited methods, from out of the elements of which, duly sifted and selected, he created the eclectic system, founded upon anatomy and observation. His encyclopædic spirit, the success of his teaching, the excellent results of his scientific journeys, the diversity and the variety of his writings, caused him to be looked upon as nothing short of an oracle when, upon coming to Rome, he became the physician of the Emperor Marcus Aurelius. The sympathies of that monarch for the Christians were undoubtedly shared by Galen, who was as well versed in the Bible as in the books of Plato. He was an anatomist in his early career, but he specially distinguished himself afterwards as a physiologist and psychologist. No doctor, before him, had formed any conception as to the extent of Divine action upon the least important of human affairs: he defined and comprehended the part of the soul beneath its corporal covering, but without pronouncing as to the question of its immortality. This ingenious definition of the πνεῦμα, the part which he assigns it in the sensorial functions, the difference which he distinctly asserts between the nerves of feeling and those of motion, and his division of the forces of the body into three kinds—vital, animal, and natural—are so many touches of genius, which, though but mere glimmers of truth at first, afterwards shone out as bright lights and resplendent truths. According to Galen, the health of the body depended upon an equal and uniform mixture of solids and liquids, and its illness from their disproportion and inequality. Consequently, a clever physician should always foresee illness, by judging as to its immediate or remote causes, its predisposing or accidental causes. Galen was in advance of his time; his ideas as to inflammations, loss of blood, intermittent fevers; his system of antipathies and sympathies, of indications and counter-indications, appertain not less to physiology than to pathology and therapeutics, and show how superior he was to his contemporaries and predecessors.

Yet, after his death, the doctrines of Hippocrates again obtained prevalence, though the materialist tendencies seem to be directly opposed to the spiritualism of the Christian faith. The latter, however, did not disown these theories in medico-philosophic science; and the early monks, who were physicians of the body as well as of the mind, began to transcribe the aphorisms of Hippocrates, the principal treatises of Galen, and the vast repertory of a Greek physician, Cœlius Aurelianus, who had taken up and commentated all the books of the methodists. In these times of trouble and uncertainty, professional teaching had no other sources of knowledge. The cities of Athens, Rome, and Alexandria still had schools of philosophy which attracted a motley crowd of professors and students, and any one was admitted, whether Greek or Arab, Gaul or Roman, Christian or Jew; for the only restriction upon complete freedom of instruction was that the laws of the state and the prevailing religion should not be attacked by the teachers or their pupils. To this may be traced in the philosophy of that day, as it was called, a strange amalgamation of Eastern reveries and scriptural traditions, of pagan superstitions and Christian legends. The most intelligent men of that time believed that "famine, death, foul air, and epidemics are caused by evil spirits, who, enveloped in a cloud, flit through the lower regions of the atmosphere, to which they are attracted by the blood and the incense offered up to the false divinities. But for the odour of the sacrifices, these spirits would not exist. It is to them alone that are due the wonderful cures attributed to Æsculapius" (Fig. 96).

When these ideas were held by the most talented men of the time, it is not astonishing that the common herd should have sought relief for bodily ills in practices of magic and piety, having recourse to talismans, and placing implicit confidence in certain words, formulæ, figures, and cabalistic signs, the effect of which was, as they believed, to exorcise the evil spirits and obtain the assistance of the good spirits.

As the temples of Æsculapius, Hygeia, and Serapis were closed—and these divinities were altogether neglected by the end of the fourth century—Christianity opened its churches and its monasteries to the sick, who received there gratuitously the best attention that charity, still very devoid of science, but animated by the precepts of the gospel, could offer to the indigent. The wants both of the body and the soul were ministered to. The first leper-houses, in which were treated not only leprosy, but the other skin diseases which were so frequent at that day, were erected close to the church. The hydropathic treatment, which was in accordance with the Christian as it had been with the Hebrew faith, became general under the combined influence of religious symbolism and hygienic principles. Many mineral sources and fountains which, though they had lost the patronage of the local divinities, were not the less crowded at fixed epochs, were placed beneath the tutelary

Fig. 96.—Celtic Monument discovered at Paris, beneath the Choir of Notre-Dame, in 1711. (According to several archæologists, the *bas-relief* represents the Gallic Æsculapius.)

protection of various saints, to whom popular opinion attributed a special action in the cure of diseases.

In the beginning of the fifth century the practice of medicine, like that of surgery, which was not yet a distinct branch, continued to be free, without any authorisation being required. There were even women who, like the Druidesses of the Gauls, treated the sick. Charmers, unconscious, no doubt, of the occult forces which they set at work, proceeded by means of magnetism to cure, or at all events to relieve, neuralgic pains; country bone-setters were very expert in remedying fractures and dislocations of the limbs; and numerous oculists, impostors of the worst kind, who had learnt while serving in the army what little they knew about ocular diseases, made large sums of money

by scouring the country with their lotions and quintessences. But at the
bottom of all this popular medicine lurked the most outrageous empiricism.
Yet the authorities of the large towns engaged municipal doctors, who, to
judge by the inscriptions on their tombs, were not devoid of ability, and
rendered considerable service. The public teaching of medicine followed the
fortunes of the Roman empire, and migrated from Rome to Byzantium in
the reign of Constantine. Yet the barbarians, in their repeated invasions,
did not destroy the schools at Treves, Arles, Bordeaux, and Marseilles.
Alexandria and Athens more especially continued to be luminous centres of
intellectual labour, though Greek medicine, which alone was taught there,

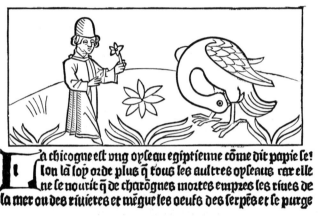

Fig. 97.—The Stork its own Doctor, as testified to by Papias.—Fac-simile of a Wood Engraving
in the "Dyalogue des Créatures" (Gouda, Gérart Leeu, 1482, in folio).—In the Library of
M. Ambroise Firmin-Didot, Paris.

had embraced theories derived both from dogmatism and empiricism, which
continued to prevail throughout the Middle Ages.

Oribasius of Pergamus, physician to the Emperor Julian the Apostate,
was, at the close of the fourth century, one of the last representatives of
pagan science: his writings, in which he had summarised the labours of
many Greek physicians, were adopted by the sect of Nestorians, who cultivated
more particularly philosophy and medicine. The Nestorian school of Edessa
soon eclipsed the school of Alexandria, and shared the renown attaching to the
Athens school; but as at Edessa the propagation of Nestorianism was mixed
up with scientific teaching, the school suffered from the persecution which
the Eastern emperors, Theodosius II. and Leo the Isaurian, waged against the

heresy of Nestorius. The professors whose orthodoxy was not in conformity with that of the Greek Church were deprived of their salaries by a decree of Justinian, who at the same time wrought the final ruin of the Athens school.

The chairs of philosophy and medicine were not, however, altogether untenanted in the East, for the Arab schools were still in existence, though their teaching did not go beyond a few books of Pliny the Elder, of Dioscorides, of Aristotle, and of Galen, very imperfectly translated from Greek or Latin

Fig. 98.—Physician, from the "Danse Macabre," Guyot Marchant edition, 1490.

into Syriac, and then retranslated into Arabic with a multiplicity of errors (Fig. 97). The school of Alexandria had ceased to be more than a shadow of her former self, the lessons of the masters of science were forgotten, and all that she possessed was a few rhetoricians, who, instead of confining themselves to a careful observation of causes and effects, commentated apocryphal and ridiculous books, and applied themselves to the discovery of useless or insensate solutions. Thus, for instance, they discussed why the hand has five

fingers instead of six ; why such and such an intestine is of one shape more
than of another ; why the human head is round, &c.   In the meanwhile the
monks of Mount Lebanon and the ascetics of Mount Atlas, in obedience to
the rules of their order, worked incessantly at the translation and copying
—committing many blunders, unfortunately—of the early texts relating to
the theory of medicine, in order that the information possessed by the ancients
might not be lost to the Christian world.

Amidst all these obscurities of science, a few illustrious savants formed
bright exceptions.   Thus Aëtius, of Amida in Mesopotamia, was to the fifth
what Alexander of Tralles was to the middle of the sixth century.   The
former, a Greek physician, collected, under the title of " Tetrabiblos," the
observations and doctrines of his predecessors, completing and elucidating
them with great judgment.   For instance, his work contains a very plausible
theory upon fever, a detailed description of the principal diseases of the eye,
and a series of very precise descriptions of the functional disorders caused in
the organism by various morbid complaints.   His therapeutics in cases of
acute disease are based upon the principles of Hippocrates, and prove that he
possessed real learning, enriched by experience and refined by excellent logic.
Amongst other things, Aëtius advocates a regular diet and care in the selection of aliments ; he points out the good effects of fresh air and cold water in
cases of angina and in pulmonary complaints.   " May the God of Abraham
and of Jacob," he exclaimed when preparing one of his remedies, " give to
this medicine the virtues which I believe it to possess ! " (Fig. 98.)

After Aëtius comes Alexander of Tralles, whose medical reputation
was very great in the sixth century.   No Greek doctor since the days of
Hippocrates had equalled him with regard to practical science, professional
sagacity, and literary merit.   He had made himself acquainted with all the
facts which had been observed and collated before his time ; but he did not
allow himself to become the slave of any scientific authority, or to be seduced
by any doctrine, recognising no other guide than his own experience.   He
possessed to a supreme degree the art of diagnosis, and he laid down as a
principle that no decision should be arrived at, as to the treatment of a case,
until the specific and individual causes of the disease have been carefully
sought out and considered.   His views upon melancholia and gout, his dislike
of violent aperients and the abuse of opium, his preference for laxatives in
cases of dysentery and for emetics in cases of intermittent fever, testify both

Fig. 99.—View of the Cathedral of Cordova in its present state.

to the independence and accuracy of his observations, and show that he knew how to apply with advantage the most conflicting theories. He was the first to resort to bleeding from the jugular vein, and to use iron filings in certain affections of the blood.

In the seventh century the Jewish doctors endeavoured to possess themselves of the teaching of medicine in the East, forming at Damascus and Constantinople scientific assemblies, in which all real learning was lost in the obscurities of cabalism. The East, always a land of illusions and fancies, was only too accessible to the superstitious ideas implied in the magical and supernatural treatment of disease. This mixture of error and truth is nowhere more noticeable than in the Koran, a compilation which is as much scientific as it is religious, and to which doctors from the schools of Alexandria and Dschoudisapour (the town founded by Sapor II.) must have contributed in the name of Mahomet, for this code of Islamism contains, with regard to physiology and hygiene, some very remarkable views and excellent principles summarised in the shape of aphorisms which often remind one of the language of Hippocrates. It is worth while mentioning here that, long before Mahomet's time, the Arab doctors, who were also poets, legists, and philosophers, had their share in the sacerdotal influences which contributed to the civilisation of the Eastern races. Thus, when the conquests of Mahomet had been consolidated with the sword, the native and foreign doctors residing at Irak found greater security and protection from the Mussulmans at Bagdad and Bassora than from the Emperors at Byzantium.

Paul of Ægineta was, in the seventh century, the last personage of note belonging to the expiring school of Alexandria. This Greek doctor, whose pathology was based upon the principles of Galen, Aëtius, and Oribasius, also had a system of his own for the treatment of different diseases, such as ophthalmia, gout, and leprosy, which latter was spreading with frightful rapidity. He inclined more towards methodism and eclecticism than towards empiricism. One of his contemporaries, named Ahrun, who was not probably a student of the Alexandria school, though he afterwards practised medicine in that city, where he was a Christian priest, published a judicious treatise upon various epidemics, such as scurvy and small-pox, which latter disease had just made its appearance and was spreading rapidly, three centuries before the Arab doctor, Rhazes, gave a more detailed description of them.

The celebrated schools which had been founded at Bagdad, the new capital of the Caliphs of the East, and at Cordova (Fig. 99), the new capital of the Caliphs of Spain, were simultaneously illustrated, at long intervals, by Mesué the elder, John Damascenus or Serapion, Leo the Philosopher, Rhazes, and Ali, surnamed the Magician, the last mentioned of whom apparently embodied all the medical science of the Arabs, which reached its apogee in the tenth century by appropriating to the climate and to the customs of the country the principles of Galen, and basing his system upon a mass of observations which he continued up to the age of a hundred. Greek medicine had undergone a complete metamorphosis through its gradual fusion with that of the Arabs, just as pathological questions varied in their object and character under the influence of the new habits and requirements of modern civilisation.

In the West medical science was still very backward, though it had not to contend, as in the East, with a religious fanaticism which forbade all kinds of drawings, even those necessary to a scientific description of the diseases of the human body, and which punished as a crime the dissection of a corpse. The reason was that it had no protectors since the disappearance of the last of the Goths in the eighth century, and it was scarcely taught at all in the schools of Southern Gaul. The monastic orders had monopolized the practice of medicine, and, as a natural consequence of the sacred mission intrusted to them by their founder, they attempted to combine remedies for the body with remedies for the mind. Prayer, holy water, the touching of relics, and pilgrimages to holy places were the general accessories of monkish therapeutics, which relied upon Providence for the cure of the sick, upon whom, however, every care and attention was lavished. The monks also possessed a number of pharmaceutical receipts which were in daily use, though they were derived rather from tradition than from science ; they were likewise acquainted with the medicinal properties of herbs, which they used freely for wounds and sores.

It was not till the close of the eighth century that there was a regular course of medical instruction, and it was organized at Monte Casino and Salerno, in the kingdom of Naples; and the principles of the teaching imparted there were drawn up in the shape of aphorisms, which remained known long after the schools themselves had disappeared. At this epoch many ecclesiastics—Italian, French, Belgian, and German—commissioned by the Holy See as Apostolic Legates, went to England, Scotland, and Ireland,

and founded schools there, which in a short time contributed to the spread of science in France, Belgium, and Germany. (See Chapter I., *Universities.*) Medicine continued, as before, to be one of the branches of philosophy.

When the municipal régime arose upon the ruins of the empire of Charlemagne, when the spirit of independence and isolation gave laymen a share with ecclesiastics in civil functions, a struggle of interest and vanity commenced between these two distinct classes, which composed society at that time. The monks soon saw that if they were to retain their monopoly

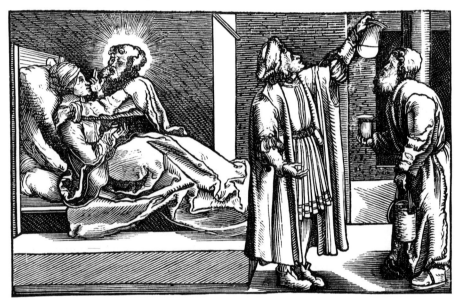

Fig. 100.—Cure through the Intercession of a Healing Saint.—Fac-simile of a Wood Engraving attributed to Holbein, in the German Translation of the "Consolation of Philosophy," by Boethius, Augsburg Edition, 1537, in folio.

in medicine, threatened by the laymen, they must extend their knowledge both of medicine and of surgery; and the consequence was that as physicians they made great progress. The monastic rules laid down the study of the "De Re Medica," a treatise by Celsus, who was styled the Latin Hippocrates. Moreover, numbers of monks and priests left their cloisters and dioceses to wander through the land, devoting themselves to the relief of suffering humanity. Of these were Thieddeg, doctor to Boleslas, King of Poland; Hugh, Abbot of St. Denis; and others. The illustrious

Gerbert d'Auvergne, who became pope under the title of Sylvester II., had in his early life professed philosophy and practised medicine.

It is no doubt true that the clerks who had taken monastic vows, or who had been ordained priests, abstained, as a rule, from practising surgery; but they were often present at the serious operations effected by their lay assistants. In such cases they confined themselves to the part of consulting surgeons; but though they abstained from dipping their hands in blood, they performed in certain urgent cases such simple operations as incisions and blood-lettings; they treated dislocations and fractures of limbs, and dressed the wounds inflicted in battle. Leper hospitals had long since been established all over Europe. There was an almshouse open in every monastery, in every large church where canons lived in common under the conventual régime. There is reason for believing that several monasteries in the diocese of Metz, and especially those of Paderborn and Corbie, which were famous for the philosophical and medical teaching imparted there to students from all lands, furnished their pupils with the means of putting their theory into practice in hospitals attached to the religious establishment. Here were trained the physicians and surgeons who travelled all over Europe without discarding their monastic attire, to fulfil their mission of charity by practising medicine and performing ordinary operations of surgery. It was from conventual hospitals, too, that were recruited the men and women who devoted themselves entirely to tending the sick. There were also a number of matrons and elderly women who belonged to a sort of corporation, which was specially employed upon obstetric medicine, at that time forbidden to men.

The renown of the medical schools of Monte Casino and Salerno continued to increase. The Emperor Henry II. repaired to the monastery of Monte Casino to be treated for stone. Most of the sick who came three sought merely to touch the relics of St. Matthew, the patron saint of the convent, and those of other healing saints (Fig. 100); but they found there, to second the intercessions of these saints, the material attentions of a religious community which had made a serious study of medicine, and which possessed a hygienic code in accordance with the teaching of experience and of common sense. The touching of relics was, nevertheless, looked upon at this period as one of the most effective means of cure, and it is not to be wondered at that the Kings of England and of France, who had been anointed with the holy oil at their consecration, should have believed that they had the power of healing, by the imposition of hands, various maladies, such as goître, king's evil, white tumours, &c.

The empirical method, which was current in the West during the eleventh century, was not the same as the philosophical medical treatment taught in the celebrated schools of the East, but in the practice of which there were many singular contradictions. The Arabic mode of treatment was, so to speak, speculative. Yet the illustrious Avicenna (born at Chiraz, in Persia, about 980), whom his contemporaries surnamed the *Prince of*

Fig. 101.—A Leper House.—Miniature from the "Miroir Historical" of Vincent de Beauvais. Manuscript of the Thirteenth Century.—In the Arsenal Library, Paris.

Doctors, was educated in the school of Bagdad; and his immense reputation, which won him access to the courts of several Asiatic sovereigns, is a proof of the talent with which he practised his art. Amongst the numerous works in Arabic which he left behind him, that entitled the "Canon," a medical encyclopædia, which testifies to the erudition and sagacity of the author, was translated into Latin, and served as a basis of teaching for six or seven centuries. The followers of Avicenna spread the doctrine of their master with great success, amongst them being Harun the Jew, who was one of the first interpreters of the "Canon" in Europe; Mesué the younger, whose treatise on the Materia Medica, disencumbered of the subtleties of the Arab school, contains ingenious deductions drawn from the external aspect of each plant ; Ishak ben Soliman, who collected some very sensible observations upon dietetics ; and Serapion the younger, a Greek doctor, whose writings embodied some entirely novel suggestions as to the use of medicaments. Moreover, the Arabic system of medicine, in passing from the schools of the East to the school of Cordova, underwent many changes. Thus the Spaniard, Albucasis, who was at once an anatomist and physiologist, did not implicitly accept the often contradictory authority of Galen and Avicenna. He laid down as a principle that medicine and surgery should lend each other mutual assistance, and he invented surgical instruments of a most formidable kind. These instruments were of iron ; for, in opposition to the prejudices of the age, according to which every metal had some special property analogous to the different operations in surgery, he maintained that iron only ought to be employed. He therefore attacked the disease with fire and iron, resorting to cauterization with a degree of boldness which was often successful, and practising the difficult operation of bronchotomy, or incision of the windpipe, which modern science again resorts to in certain cases of croup.

The numerous hospitals founded during the eleventh century were rendered all the more indispensable on account of the Crusades ; and monks, hospitallers, and hermits created upon the routes leading to the Holy Land fresh refuges for pilgrims in distress. The Johannists and the brotherhoods of St. Mary and St. Lazarus devoted themselves to the mission of charity in the East ; in France there were the brothers of St. Antony and of the Holy Ghost ; and throughout the civilised world the heroic chevaliers of St. John of Jerusalem, or the Templars, whose countless establishments combined the triple character of conventual church, almshouse, and fortress, and who, attired in a dress both military and monastic, wore a mantle similar to that seen in the statues of Æsculapius, as a sign of the double mission, beneficent and warlike, which they had sworn to fulfil, at the risk of their lives, in the hospitals and upon the field of battle.

Each of these religious congregations gave itself over, either by its origin or by the character of its rules, to the treatment of certain special diseases. The Order of St. Antony, for instance, treated the terrible inflammations of the bowels and the dysenteries known under the generic name of

St. Antony's fire; the Johannists and the brothers of the Order of the Holy Ghost devoted themselves to the cure of the great epidemics of pestilence so frequent at this period; the Lazarists possessed sovereign remedies against leprosy, small-pox, pustular fever, &c.; the Templars tended more particularly the pilgrims, travellers, and soldiers afflicted with ophthalmia, scurvy, severe wounds, and dangerous sores. The Hospitallers were assisted by various corporations of women, and, at a time when regular doctors were so

Fig. 102.—A Ward in the Hôtel-Dieu, Paris.—Fac-simile of a Wood Engraving of the Sixteenth Century, in the Frontispiece of a Manuscript Register, entitled, "Pardon, Grace, and Privileges granted by the Archbishop Patriarch of Bourges and Primate of Aquitaine, to the Benefactors of the *Hostel-Dieu*, Paris."—In the Burgundy Library, Brussels.

scarce, they were very useful as substitutes. Hildegarde, Abbess of Rupertsberg, who was more than eighty years of age at her death (1180), organized a school of nurses who rendered great service in the hospitals. Abelard, in his letters to the nuns of the Paraclete Convent, urged them to learn surgery for the benefit of the poor. In most of the great religious communities there were public rooms for bathing, dressing the wounds of, bleeding, and cupping the indigent sick (Fig. 102). In Italy the Bishop of Salerno and the Abbot of Pescara devoted themselves to the material relief of human suffering. The learned have often sought to discover whether in the Middle Ages there existed such a thing as military surgery properly so called. It is true that no allusion is made to it in history until the fourteenth century, but in the most ancient chronicles mention is continually being made of some monk or clerk as accompanying the army; and it may be assumed that he was a *mire*, or *physician*, or *barber*, according to the terms then used, whose duty it was to tend the wounded and care for the sick. It is impossible, in fact, to suppose any warlike expedition taking place without some one more or less skilled in surgery forming part of it; and it is easy to understand that the first military surgeons were ecclesiastics, as the Church had a virtual monopoly of the science of medicine. In course of time the urban and municipal associations, which had obtained from the feudal lord their communal rights, sought to free themselves from the vassalage imposed by the Church. This was how the barbers were promoted to the rank of subordinate surgeons, and in every town of any importance a certain number of men were paid a fixed salary, and undertook, in return, to attend the poor, and follow to the wars the man whom the commune had to furnish at the bidding of the lord of the soil. In many foreign countries, such as Holland, Italy, and Germany, even more than in France, the populous and wealthy towns engaged in the public service, and at a comparatively small cost, one or more surgeons, nearly all of whom had been educated in the monastic schools, and who were, therefore, well fitted for what were then called works of mercy. Of these was Hugh of Lucca, who, appointed physician at Parma, received but a lump sum of six hundred livres for his services as long as he lived. This was the origin of the *Stadts Physikus* in Germany, and of the salaried surgeons and physicians in France, who, after having been for two centuries the rivals of the monks in medicine, were at last enabled to practise without let or hindrance, and to form civil corporations, to which the Crown granted certain privileges and statutes.

From the reign of Alexis I. (1081) the Emperors of the East accorded their protection to the literary and scientific studies which flourished in their empire far more than they did in the West. Though they had no particular fondness for medical sciences, the latter were held in high esteem at Bagdad and Constantinople; but the philosophical character of the art was disfigured by the shameless devices of astrology and quackery. During the reign of Manuel Comnenus, from 1143 to 1180, Conrad II., Emperor of Germany, having been wounded in the Crusade, and not having in his army a surgeon able to cure him, was obliged to put himself under the care of the Greek doctors at Byzantium, and he doubtless acted under the advice of the Emperor Manuel, who prided himself upon his knowledge of medicine and surgery. It was the Emperor Manuel who afterwards dressed with his own hands the wounds of Baldwin II., King of Jerusalem; and he was noted for his adroitness in bleeding, and for his discovery of potions and ointments which had the reputation of being very beneficial. Unfortunately the superstitious ideas of his time made him the blind slave of astrology.

At about the same period the schools of the Iberian peninsula produced

Fig. 104.—Counter-Seal
of the Faculty of Medicine, Paris
(Fourteenth Century).

Fig. 103.—Seal of the Faculty of Medicine,
Paris (Fourteenth Century).

From the Collection of Seals in the National Archives, Paris.

three men of genius: Ebn-Beithar, a doctor and naturalist, most of whose works have been lost; Abenzoar, who, with no other guide than observation and method, practised medicine, surgery, and pharmacy with the greatest success, and whose "Taisyr," a vast compendium of contemporary science, translated into Latin, long enjoyed a well-merited reputation; and, lastly, the famous Averroes, who, at Cordova, publicly taught philosophy, juris-prudence, and medicine with such boldness and independence that he was obliged to fly from Spain to Morocco, where, notwithstanding some further proceedings, he was able to compose a remarkable commentary upon the writings of Aristotle (1217) The Jewish and Mahometan schools of Cordova and Granada were so famous in the regenerated world of arts and sciences that the neighbouring nations also created schools which attempted to rival them. Thus as early as the twelfth century the schools of medicine at Montpellier and Paris (Figs. 103 and 104) acquired a certain celebrity, just as in Italy, a little later, the schools of Bologna, Modena, Ferrara, Milan, Naples, Parma, Padua, and Pavia became famous. The quickening sap of university teaching began to flow through the veins of every European nation.

The Papal bulls ordering the establishment of the Faculties at Montpellier, Salerno, and Paris settled the discipline to be observed by the students and the hierarchy amongst the masters by the creation of new degrees and dignities. But though to study medicine or surgery in the Universities of Italy and Sicily it was still necessary to be a clerk—that is to say, an ecclesiastic and tonsured—this rule soon fell into disuse at the schools of Montpellier and Paris. Nevertheless, to obtain the rank of *Master Physician* or Doctor at the Faculty of Montpellier, the candidate must be a clerk, and must have undergone an examination before masters or doctors selected from the staff of the college by the Bishop of Maguelonne ; to obtain the degree of Surgeon a similar though less difficult examination was required, but the candidate need not be a clerk. The barbers, who did not quit the faculties of medicine, and who merely practised minor surgery, had not to pass any examination, except that which the masters of their corporation made them undergo at the hands of members of their profession.

In the kingdom of Naples any one desiring to practise as a doctor had to undergo five years of medical study and two examinations for his license and doctorate before masters of the school of Salerno, and then to spend a year upon trial. The surgeon, before entering upon his functions, also had to follow a special course of study for a twelvemonth, so as to become familiar " with the anatomy of the human body, without which it is impossible to undertake an operation in safety, or follow up the cure of the sick person after the instrument has been employed."

For some time the medical school of Bologna was the first in the world. It owed its acknowledged superiority to Jacopo Bertinozzo, to Hugo and Theodoric of Lucca, and, above all, to William Salicetti, born in 1200, not less skilful as a surgeon than as a physician, who operated both in the camps, the hospitals, and in many large towns, such as Bergamo, Venice, and Pavia, which latter city employed an experienced practitioner, who was paid out of the municipal funds. The principal objection urged against Salicetti was that for healing sores he resorted too much to cauterization and the knife, instead of applying toxical and medicinal remedies. He was, however, the teacher of Lanfranc, who always respectfully spoke of him as "my master of honoured memory." Compelled to quit his country for political reasons, this celebrated Milanese professor fled into France, and was invited to Paris by his compatriot, Passavant, Dean of the Faculty, and by Pitard, surgeon-in-chief to King Philippe le Bel. After performing several difficult operations of surgery, which won him great renown, he opened a school, which was very numerously attended. It may be said that his teaching brought about a complete reform in French surgery, and his two works, "Chirurgia Magna" and "Chirurgia Parva," became the manual of practical science; for, before his time, this branch of the art, in the hands of ignorant barbers, both in France, Spain, and Germany, was almost crushed beneath the yoke of medical omnipotence. Thus all surgeons, male and female (for many women insisted on being attended by their own sex in certain cases), were compelled to give an undertaking that they would limit their labours to *handiwork ;* that they would not give any consultation or administer any internal remedy without the advice or the permission of a physician. The surgeon was free to operate as he pleased, but he could not give an opinion or write a prescription. Moreover, in very grave cases, important operations were not left to the decision of the patient, or even to that of the practitioner, however eminent he might be. The permission either of the bishop or of the feudal lord was necessary, and the operation was invariably preceded by a solemn consultation in presence of the friends and relatives of the patient. These exaggerated precautions are all the more surprising, for while the civil and religious authorities seemed to be so particular with regard to operations performed by eminent surgeons, they scarcely interfered at all with the minor operations performed by barbers or hospital nurses. Moreover, the leading surgeons would have considered it beneath their dignity to perform in unimportant cases. At the end of the thirteenth century they did not condescend to operate themselves in cases of puncture for dropsy, of stone, of hernia, or of cataract, and they even disregarded the study of internal diseases as unworthy of their profession.

The genius of Lanfranc was instrumental in bringing about a better state of things. He says, in one of his books, " The outside public believe it impossible for a man to be proficient both in medicine and surgery. But a good physician must know something of surgery, and a good surgeon cannot afford to be ignorant of medicine ; it is, therefore, necessary for a medical man to have some knowledge of both these sciences." Under the influence of

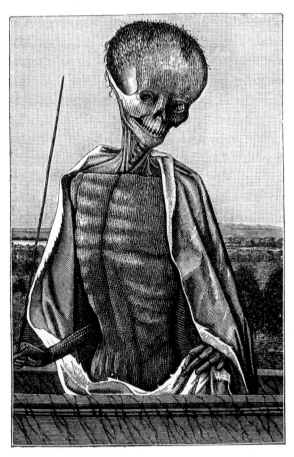

Fig. 105.—Doctor Death.—Miniature from a " Book of Hours " of the Sixteenth Century.—In the Library of M. Ambroise Firmin-Didot, Paris.

these sensible ideas, surgical science rose in the Paris Faculty to the level of the highest literary teaching, and was as well taught as in the best medical schools of Italy and Spain, to which French parents no longer thought it necessary to send their children. The Faculty of Paris was considered to be equal to all requirements, and it was only a few young surgeons who came for some weeks to Bologna, where the great anatomist Mundinus and his successor, Bertreccius, practised dissection before an attentive assemblage of practitioners from all parts of Europe (Fig. 105).

Another set of professors belonging to the Jewish race, less brilliant and more narrow in their teaching than those attached to the schools of Paris and Montpellier, also enjoyed a certain celebrity in towns where the fanaticism of the people against the Jews had been quelled by the authorities. From the Carlovingian times, Metz, Mayence, Strasburg, Frankfort, Troyes, and Avignon had maintained chairs, from which the rabbis, who were looked upon by the Jews not merely as ministers of religion, but as the best advisers on earthly matters as well, taught, after the glossology of cabalism and the Scriptures as commentated by the Talmudists, the Hebrew language, philosophy, moral philosophy, hygiene, and medicine.

From the time that Lanfranc founded the St. Cosmo College at Paris, surgery disencumbered itself more and more from its original barbarism. In 1311 Philippe le Bel enacted that all surgeons in the kingdom should pass an examination before the new surgical college, the members of which, honoured with the confidence of the King and his ministers, caused great umbrage to the Faculty of Medicine. This was the beginning of the long struggle between the long-robed and the short-robed doctors (Fig. 106). The faculty would not confer its degree of Bachelor upon students until they swore never to practise surgery, and continued to exact from them the oath of perpetual celibacy. The faculty also obtained from King John (1352) a decree prohibiting any one who was not an apothecary, student, or mendicant monk from practising medicine. These measures were taken with a view of protecting the honours of the profession, but they proved far less effectual than the labours of Guy de Chauliac (1363), author of the " Grande Chirurgie," who, in his double capacity of physician and surgeon, raised the reputation of the medical body to a very high pitch.

Upon the other hand, the affiliation of Charles V. to the brotherhood of St. Cosmo increased the pride of the surgeons, who were so injudicious as to exhibit towards the barbers as much intolerance and contempt as the physicians had shown towards themselves. The master barbers, "hampered in their calling" by the surgeons, appealed to the King, who received their appeal very favourably, and exempted them from doing duty as watchmen, upon the ground, as the royal decree put it, that "the barbers being nearly all of them in the habit of practising surgery, great inconvenience might arise if they were absent from their houses when sent for during the night."

The surgeons, who continued to encroach upon the domain of the physicians, but who were none the less jealous of their own privileges, subjected the barbers to so many vexations that the authorities, tired of being continually appealed to in order to settle some dispute between the two corporations, formally defined the respective rights of both parties. The

Fig. 106.—The Physician.—Designed and engraved in the Sixteenth Century by J. Amman.

decree of October 3rd, 1372, empowered the barbers " to apply plasters, ointments, and other appropriate medicines for bruises, apostemes, and other open wounds, not of a character likely to cause death, because physicians are men of great estate and very expensive, whom the poor are not able to pay." From this period, then, there were three distinct classes of persons exercising medicine in its different stages : the long-robed practitioners, *mires* or *physicians*, representing the Faculty of Paris ; the short-robed *surgeons*, who formed a corporation under the patronage of St. Cosmo and St. Damianus ; and the barbers, entitled to carry a sword, who formed a business corporation, and, to use the technical expression of the time, filled the "office de barberie, sans conteste."

This rule applied to all France, except to the provinces of Burgundy and Lorraine, in which there were the *great barbers* and the *little barbers.* The latter, who were mere adventurers, travelled on foot, with their small wallet and light purse, from village to village, to sell their antidotes and drugs, while the *great barber*, sworn surgeon, called upon his patients, attired in a long robe trimmed with fur, and bestriding a hackney, the tinkling of whose bells announced his arrival a long way off. This master surgeon, often accompanied by an assistant and several servants, carried in his case five or six kinds of instruments; to wit, scissors, nippers, a sort of probe called *éprouvette*, razors, lances, and needles. He also had five sorts of ointment, which were at that time looked upon as indispensable : the *basilicon*, which was considered a maturative remedy ; the *apostles' ointment*, for quickening the vitality of bad flesh ; the *white ointment*, for consolidating the flesh ; the *yellow ointment*, for stimulating the growth of proud flesh ; and the *dialtæa ointment*, for subduing local pain. The *great barbers* did even more than this, and Guy de Chauliac says, " I never went out on my visits without taking with me several clysters and plain remedies, and I gathered herbs in the fields, so as to treat diseases in a proper manner, winning thereby honour, profit, and many friends."

Guy de Chauliac, who was appointed physician to three popes at Avignon, Clement VI., Innocent VI., and Urban V., was, moreover, very particular as to the conditions under which a surgeon should be allowed to practise. He insisted that a surgeon should be " well educated, clever, and of good morality ; bold when he saw his way clear, prudent in doubtful cases, kind to his patients, gracious towards his colleagues, modest in giving an opinion, chaste, sober, pitiful, and merciful ; not greedy of gain, but receiving a modest remuneration, according to his labour, the means of the patient, the result of the illness, and his own dignity."

It was creditable to French surgery that such honourable sentiments should have been expressed at a time when in neighbouring countries, and notably in England, human credulity was being so scandalously imposed upon by the most ignorant of characters. For instance, an English surgeon called Goddesden had two sorts of prescriptions, one for the rich and another for the poor ; he sold at a high price to the barbers a so-called panacea, which the latter sold again at a large profit, and this panacea was simply a mixture of frogs pounded up in a mortar; he pompously advertised infallible and secret remedies, in which he placed so little confidence that he took care to exact payment for them beforehand (Fig. 107). In one of his books there is a

Fig. 107.—Interior of a Doctor's House.—Fac-simile of a Miniature from the "Epistre de Othea," by Christine de Pisan.—Manuscript of the Fifteenth Century.—In the Burgundy Library, Brussels.

short chapter upon *disagreeable* diseases, as he terms them, which work their own cure, and, therefore, bring no grist to the doctor's mill.

Several great epidemics, the terrible effects of which are alluded to by Guy de Chauliac and his contemporary Petrarch, had caused great consternation throughout Europe, and gave rise to the idea of establishing a medical police for all countries.   The idea was a happy one, but, carried into execution under the joint supervision of the ecclesiastical, the municipal, and the University authorities, the scheme was imbued with the prejudices of that time.   Thus lepers continued to be kept in a state of isolation as in the twelfth century, and the ceremonies by which they were deprived of their rights as citizens were maintained.   The well-known black plague, one of the greatest scourges that ever devastated the world, and which originated in the Asian marshes in 1348, after a long succession of earthquakes and heavy rain, ravaged Italy and France, spreading from thence to Germany, England, and Holland.   The country districts were depopulated and converted into deserts.   In the towns this plague raged with such intensity that Venice lost

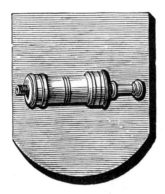

Fig. 108.—Banner of the Apothecaries of St. Lo.—Symbolic Arms of the Corporation.

Fig. 109.—Banner of the Apothecaries of Caen.—Symbolic Arms of the Corporation.

a hundred, and Strasburg fifty thousand inhabitants.   In many localities ninetenths of the population perished in a few months.   The best medical advice was powerless against an atmospheric poisoning, the effects of which often proved fatal in the space of an hour, and the municipal authorities thought to arrest it by large fires which were lighted at the cross roads and in the squares of the towns.   The Church, by order of Clement VI., pope at Avignon, endeavoured, as at the period of the plague which ravaged Italy and decimated the population of Rome in 1254, when Innocent IV. was pope (Fig. 110), to inspire the people with courage, by means of processions, sermons, and public prayers.   The Holy See granted plenary indulgence to all those who, by tending the sick, exposed themselves to almost certain death.   Few medical men were found to face the danger, and the priests alone ventured to approach the dying, and offered them the last consolations of religion.

Public sanitary measures do not date, however, from this period of general calamity, but from a somewhat later epoch, when the outbreak of various local epidemics caused great apprehension as to the return of the black plague. The closing of houses, streets, and even quarters in towns where the disease had raged, the drawing of a sanitary cordon round the

Fig. 110.—Portrait of Innocent IV., elected Pope in 1243.—Fresco Painting upon Gold Ground, in the Basilica of St. Paul, Rome.

places infected, and, what was still more important, the scientific investigation of the causes of the disease, the cleansing of the sewers and the streets, the purifying of the drinking water, the transfer of the needy sick to some place outside the walls, and the practice of burying the victims of epidemic in quicklime, testify to the prudent precautions of the administration. The paving of streets, which had been abandoned, or at all events much neglected, since the fall of the Roman empire, was one of the logical consequences of this system of general salubrity (Fig. 111). At this period, too, the use of mineral waters again became general, and the doctors recommended to the sick, and especially to those just recovering from an illness, the ancient sources of Néris, Vichy, Plombières, Aix-la-Chapelle, &c., which would have had still more visitors if the roads had been better, and a residence at these thermal stations more secure. Many localities, formerly celebrated for the cure of chronic diseases, became places of pilgrimage; and though these pilgrimages retained their religious character, they were approved of and encouraged by the doctors.

It is mortifying to find that in the principal towns of France, Germany, and Italy the authorities made no effort to arrest the superstitious ideas which prevailed. From time to time the Jews, the lepers, the insane, and the imbecile were accused of poisoning the fountains, the wells, the rivers, and even the air, and they were seized and cast into prison, and often put to death. Sometimes, it is true, these iniquitous acts were attributable to the blind fury of the populace, determined to take what they believed to be justice into their own hands; but in some cases the urban administration took part in the massacre, and became responsible for it, as when the council of the city of Metz ordered the punishment of several lepers, "who were executed for their unworthiness." Moreover, in times of epidemic, the population invariably demanded the extermination of the lepers and the Jews.

In the meanwhile the rivalry was going on at Paris between the surgeons and the barbers. The former, having exhausted in vain all their efforts to put down the pretensions of the barbers, addressed, in 1390, the following petition to the University:—"We, your humble scholars and disciples, appeal to your venerable authority, to the masters of the Faculty of Medicine" (Fig. 112). The physicians, appeased by this indirect act of submission, promised the surgeons to lend them their support so far as they remained "true scholars." But whether because the doctors of the faculty changed their minds, or because the Crown interfered in the interests of the public, even at the expense of a privileged body, Charles V. did not take part with the surgeons, and by his silence confirmed the professional independence of the master barbers. The surgeons thereupon adopted a better and more dignified way of asserting their superiority. "Henceforth," they declared in their new statutes, "every apprentice shall be able to speak and write good Latin; moreover, he shall be of comely appearance and free

from all deformity: no master shall receive an apprentice who does not
bring letters of recommendation from his former master, and the degree

Fig. 111.—Shops in an Apothecary's Street: Barber, Furrier, and Tailor.—Miniature from the
"Regime des Princes."—Manuscript of the Fifteenth Century.—Arsenal Library, Paris.

of Bachelor, without previous examination, shall cost two gold crowns, instead of a franc." These precautions were evidently taken in order that access to the professorships of St. Cosmo might be limited to students who, by their learning and application to work, would be capable of sustaining the aristocracy of the surgical body against the invading democracy of the barbers. There was, moreover, very ample room for choice, as the College of St. Cosmo comprised only ten sworn surgeons. The number of barbers, upon the other hand, steadily increased, and from forty, in the middle of the fourteenth century, it had risen to sixty at the close. The degree of esteem in which each of the three classes of medical men was held may be gathered from the characteristic fact that when the Paris Faculty appointed physicians, surgeons, and barbers to attend the plague-stricken, it allotted a salary of two hundred pounds-Paris to the first, of one hundred and twenty to the second, and of eighty only to the third.

By the fifteenth century the Arab school of medicine had lost ground, and the sound doctrines of Hippocrates resumed their sway, owing to the successive checks inflicted upon the doctrines of Avicenna, Averroes, and Galen, which fell into disfavour. These latter would have been still more discredited if to the father of medicine had not been attributed the authorship of a mass of works which he never wrote, and if the theosophical ravings of judicial astrology had not taken the place of observation and method. The illustrious Marsilio Ficino of Florence, who was one of the oracles of his day, himself retarded the progress of true science by upholding with the passionate ardour of a Platonist the tenets of a science which was false and misleading.

It is not astonishing, therefore, that medicine should have been subordinated to the occult sciences, especially to astrology. These imaginary sciences opened to inquisitive and restless minds horizons peopled with all kinds of illusions; with them dreams occupied the place of facts, and each individual was supposed to hold a special rank in the universal harmonic system. The destiny of a country or a city, like that of an individual, was dependent upon the motion of such and such a planet. An epidemic was caused by the conjunction of different stars, and as the inherent principle of every illness was in the constellation beneath which the sufferer was born, the doctor's first duty was to seek out the constellation, so as to get a basis for his prognosis. The constellation once discovered, the most remarkable conjectures were drawn from its position and sidereal influences. Hooping-cough—observed for the first time as an epidemic in 1414—and plica, or scurvy of the head, which extended from Poland into Bohemia and Austria, puzzled the sagacity of the astrologers, who sought for the explanation of terrestrial phenomena in signs from above.

While in medicine astrological imposture was invading the domain of practical observation, Italian surgery, compromised by a mass of charlatans, was not nearly so far advanced as French surgery (Fig. 113). Germany, not

Fig. 112.—Beadles of the Three Faculties of Theology, Jurisprudence, and Medicine at the University of Pont-à-Mousson.—From the "Funeral of Charles III., Duke of Lorraine" (1608), Copper Plate engraved by F. Brentel, after Claude de la Ruelle.—In the Library of M. Ambroise Firmin-Didot, Paris.

less backward in medical science, manifested an equal degree of contempt for bath-keepers, shepherds, and barbers, all of whom were prevented from forming corporations, or marrying into any family not engaged in their trade. Surgical art was at an even lower ebb in Germany than it was in Italy, as a proof of which it may be mentioned that Matthias Corvinus, King of Hungary, in order to be cured of an old wound, was obliged to convoke all the barbers of the Holy Empire, and promise them rich rewards if they would come to his court. Hans Dockenburg, an Alsatian barber, restored him to health (1468); but there is nothing to show that this accidental cure, effected no doubt by empirical means, in any way increased the reputation of the German barber-surgeons (Fig. 114).

There was an equal scarcity of able practitioners and learned professors in England, where the surgeons were merely manufacturers and vendors of plasters and ointments. When Henry V. invaded France in 1415, the only

Fig. 113.—An Operator.—Designed and engraved in the Sixteenth Century by J. Amman.

surgeon he had in his camp was Thomas Morstede, who was with difficulty induced to accompany the army, bringing with him twelve assistants. In a second expedition, undertaken by the same prince, the corporation of London surgeons could not supply as many even as twelve volunteers, and the King was compelled to authorise Thomas Morstede to press into his service as many surgeons as the army required, and as many artisans as would be necessary for making and repairing surgical instruments. The best operators were to be found in France, and the celebrated Balescone of Florence professed and practised surgery at the school of Montpellier.

After thirty years of apparent concord between the surgeons and barbers of Paris, the quarrel broke out afresh. Upon the 14th of May, 1423, the surgeons obtained from the provost of the city an order " forbidding generally all persons, of whatsoever estate or condition, who are not surgeons, even of barbers, from exercising or practising surgery." This order was proclaimed, to the sound of the trumpet, at all the street-corners; but the barbers appealed to the provost, who, upon the 4th of November, 1424, withdrew his own decree. The surgeons, having appealed, but in vain, to the Parliament, resolved not to visit any patient who had been attended by a barber. But

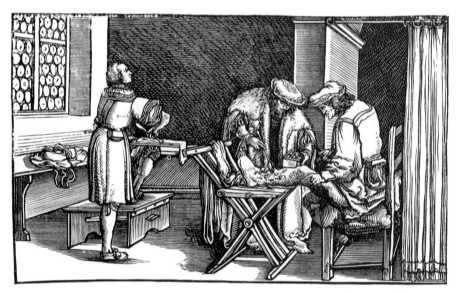

Fig. 114.—A German Surgeon.—Fac-simile of a Wood Engraving, attributed to Holbein, and taken from the German Translation of the "Consolation of Philosophy," by Boethius, Augsburg Edition, 1537, in folio.

the barbers shortly after this obtained formal recognition of the rights which they had been so long insisting upon, for Colonet Candillon, first barber and valet of the chamber to a regent and two kings of France, was invested with the title of *maistre et garde du mestier*, with the right of delegating his authority in the principal towns of the kingdom to lieutenants, who were to have the exclusive right of inspection over all the barbers. The latter formed at this period a numerous association, to become a master of which it was necessary to pass an examination before a jury appointed by one of the lieutenants of the chief barber. Each new master barber obtained "a letter sealed with seals" from the chief of the corporation, in exchange for a sum of five sous, and he also paid two sous six deniers for a copy of the annual almanac, in which were recorded the days of the year favourable for bleeding or the reverse.

The St. Cosmo surgeons, not caring to carry on the struggle against the barbers, especially after one of them, Oliver le Daim, had become the favourite of Louis XI., sought to obtain the title of students of the University of Paris, together with the privileges, franchises, liberties, and exemptions attaching thereto. The University granted their request, but upon condition of their following the lectures of the doctor-regents of the Faculty of Medicine. Thus the surgeons were once more placed beneath the sway of the physicians, while the barbers, unrestricted in the exercise of their profession, obtained one of the sixty banners distributed by Louis XI. to the corporations of arts and trades of the capital (Figs. 115 to 120). Nor was this all. The surgeons, forgetting that the speciality of their art was manual work, abandoned to the barbers cases of incision, dislocation, and fracture, confining themselves to writing prescriptions or *recipes*, which, according to the University statutes, appertained to the masters of the faculty, and not to the surgeons.

This constituted the final triumph of the plebeian over the aristocratic surgeons, and henceforth the barbers formed the most active and useful section of the surgical body. They were to be met with, the lance or bistouri in their hands, not only, in times of peace, in towns and villages, but, in time of war, in the wake of armies and with expeditions to distant lands. But for them there would have been no such thing as military surgery. The intestine quarrels of the doctors did not get beyond the faculties, and, notwithstanding their irreconcilable differences of opinions and systems, the science of medicine was implicitly confided in by the public both in France and Italy. Most of the doctors continued to be in the fifteenth, as they had been in the fourteenth century, superstitious worshippers of the Arabic astrology, and blind imitators of their ignorant and empirical predecessors. They attributed to the seasons, to the lunar periods, and to the hours of the day and the night a direct action upon the humours of the human body. The general belief was that the blood rose, during the daytime, towards the sun, and descended into the lower extremities at night; that at the third hour the bile subsided, so that its acrid qualities might not be mixed with the course

Fig. 115.—Banner of the Corporation
of Physicans at Amiens.

Fig. 116.—Banner of the Corporation
of Physicans at Vire.

Fig. 117.—Banner of the Corporation
of Physicians in the Mayenne.

Fig. 118.—Banner of the Corporation
of Surgeons at Caen.

Fig. 119.—Banner of the Corporation
of Surgeons at Le Mans.

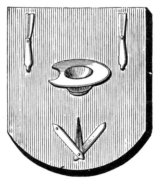

Fig. 120.—Banner of the Corporation
of Surgeons at Saintes.

of the blood, and that at the second hour the atrabilis, and, in the evening, the
phlegm, subsided. Proficiency in astrology implied proficiency in medicine

at a time when Tarenta the Portuguese, Jacques de Forli, Cernisone of Parma, Mengo Biancheli of Faenza, and Bencio of Sienna, were still teaching Arabic scholasticism in the chairs of Montpellier, Pisa, Padua, Pavia, and Bologna. It was at Padua that the Professors Guainer, Bartholomew Montagnana, and Michael Savonarola were the first to denounce the prejudices and ravings of astrological and cabalistic medicine.

The mere list of medical works published from the discovery of printing to the close of the fifteenth century is sufficient proof that medical teaching was exclusively Arabic throughout Europe. The Latin translation of Avicenna was printed at Milan in 1473, at Padua in 1476, and at Strasburg somewhat earlier. The translation of Mesué had appeared at Venice in 1471, and was reprinted almost simultaneously in five or six other cities. But the works of Hippocrates did not see the light until 1526, and the original text of Dioscorides and Galen was not printed in France or Italy till the beginning of the sixteenth century. The treatise of Celsus alone met with any favour from the antagonists of Greek and Roman medicine. Upon the other hand, the leading professors resorted freely to the printing-press as a means of diffusing their own writings.

The illustrious Antonio Benivieni, at the close of the sixteenth century, succeeded in substituting for the fanciful dreamings of the Arab school the pure doctrine of Hippocrates; he commentated the books of the early authors, basing his themes upon the investigations of anatomy—and even of pathological anatomy—which he proclaimed to be the only rule of medical art; and his labours were continued by his pupils, John of Vigo and Berengario of Carpi. The former published a work entitled "Practica in Arte Chirurgica Copiosa" (Rome, 1514, in folio), which went through twenty editions in thirty years, and was translated into French. His precepts were everywhere treated as oracular, but he comes down to posterity, unfortunately for his reputation, as the originator of the system of cauterizing wounds inflicted by firearms with boiling oil—a barbarous practice which, believed to be effective for destroying the venom of the wounds, inflicted infinite torture upon thousands of patients for more than a century. Berengario raised the Bologna school from the discredit into which it had fallen, and his excellent treatise upon Fractures of the Skull entitled him to the esteem of his learned successors.

Germany was throughout the Middle Ages an easy prey to astrologers, wandering Jews, raw apothecaries, and all the other satellites of ignorance and superstition (Fig. 121). There were, however, several eminent men in some of the imperial towns, such as Strasburg, Frankfort, and Hamburg,

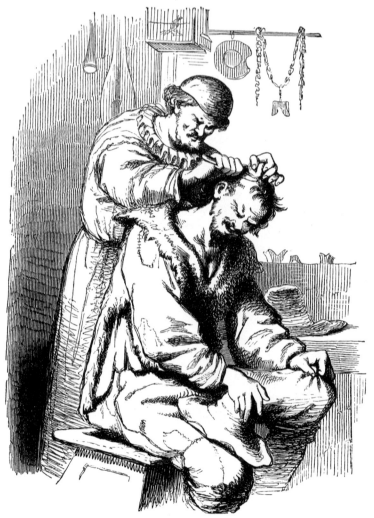

Fig. 121.—A Charlatan performing an Operation.—Fac-simile of an Engraving by Wael (Seventeenth Century).

and in the studious cities of Switzerland. The plain barbers, in many cases, became very proficient, owing to the great experience they acquired. At the same time, Jerome Brunswich, Jean Gersdorf, and Roeselin obtained a great reputation at Strasburg by their practical skill, and by their books, which latter were translated into Dutch and Italian.

Up to the sixteenth century the medical science of the Middle Ages, dominated or absorbed by the Arabic school, was opposed to the renovating tendencies of the teaching body. Tradition, routine, and prejudice were too strong for them; and a love of the supernatural, and vague aspirations after

Fig. 122.—Portrait of Claude of France, Daughter of Louis XII., Painted by Clouet (Sixteenth Century).—In the Collection of M. Double, Paris.

the unknown, retarded the general revolution, which advanced slowly but inevitably. At the dawn of the sixteenth century nothing was ready for a great scientific reform; the medical art only subsisted, so to speak, amidst ruins, surrounded by scattered fragments and materials which had no architect, while the masons who were to be employed in erecting a new edifice had no sheds to work in. Everywhere doubt and credulity were paramount. Rabelais, with his sceptical laugh, was a living satire upon the degenerate and corrupted art in a society which was aspiring after a complete and thorough transformation. Sceptics of another kind were to be found in Henry Cornelius Agrippa of Nettesheim, who, while contending against certain philosophical errors, sought to substitute for them theurgy and magic; or in Paracelsus, who, notwithstanding his splendid intellect, conceived it possible that a hybrid alliance might be formed between cabalistic mysticism upon the one hand, and medicine and occult sciences upon the other. The scientific faith by which his genius was inflamed was not shared by his contemporaries, Argentier, Rondelet, and Joubert, who were powerful to attack ancient theories, but feeble to raise new ones upon their ruins. Each man erected a system of his own, which, after exciting momentary attention, collapsed, and left not a vestige behind it. A few, however, had the good sense to content themselves with philological labours, with translating, revising, and commentating the works of Hippocrates, Galen, and the masters of Greek and Roman medicine; and amongst this select band may be mentioned Thomas Leonicenus, Gonthier d'Andernach, Fuchs, Jacques Houlier, and Louis Duret.

The great doctors of that period, those who devoted themselves to their work from pure love of science, remained poor, and with difficulty made a living out of their profession. They did not practise medicine so much as study the malady and the patient. Moreover, as there was no tariff of doctor's fees, they sometimes received the most inadequate recompense for their labours. Paracelsus sued a canon of Bâle, whom he had cured, for the stipulated fee of one hundred florins; but the judge awarded him only six florins. When the patient was of a generous disposition, the doctor came off better; and the best paid of all were those who attended upon the sovereign and the court. Honorat Picquet, physician to Louis XII., attended his daughter, Claude of France (Fig. 122), during a severe illness, which he was fortunate enough to cure, and Queen Anne of Brittany, her mother, rewarded him with a fee of three hundred crowns in gold. François I., who afterwards became the husband of the Princess Claude, did not forget this almost miraculous cure, and when he founded the Royal College he created a chair of medicine, which was almost always filled by a Frenchman.

Switzerland produced a whole series of learned physicians, who added numerous treatises to the long list of works on medicine. Conrad Gessner, Jacques Ruff, and Guillaume Fabrice conferred renown upon the schools of

Lausanne and Berne, while the Universities of Leipsic, Ingolstadt, and Wittemberg, awakening from their long slumbers, and taking the Italian schools as their models, recovered their ancient renown with anatomists and doctors such as Cannani, Cesalpino, Fallopio, and Eustachi. Wherever there were several doctors, they formed a homogeneous and compact body, solidly constituted, and jealous of their rights and privileges; for though the

Fig. 123.—Andrew Vesalius.—Wood Engraving, after the Design of J. de Calcar, Pupil of Titian. In the Library of M. Ambroise Firmin-Didot, Paris.

doctors quarrelled amongst themselves, they would not allow any one else to interfere with their prerogatives.

While the Universities of Salamanca, Alcala, Henarez, Toledo, Valencia, and Coimbra regained, so to speak, the success which the Arabs and the Jews had accomplished during the Middle Ages, there arrived upon the medical stage of France, which is always in the van of progress as of revolution, the famous founder of anatomical science, Andrew Vesalius (Fig. 123), born at Brussels in 1514, Brissot, Fernel, Sylvius, and Ranchin. But the

barber's art was almost simultaneously illustrated by Ambroise Paré, born i
Laval in the beginning of the sixteenth century, who, occupying the mos
humble position upon his arrival in Paris, soon exchanged his rough barber's
stall upon the Place St. Michel for the Louvre, and who, Huguenot as he was,
was enabled, through the favour of several kings, to reform, or rather to
create afresh, the art of surgery by associating it with medicine.

Fig. 124.—Banner of the Corporation of Apothecaries in the Mayenne.

CHEMISTRY AND ALCHEMY.

Diocletian burns the Books of Chemistry.—Haroun Al-Raschid protects the Sacred Art.—Geber, one of the first Chemists.—Rhazes.—Chemistry in honour amongst the Saracens.—Avicenna, Serapion, Mesué.—Albucasis and Averroes.—Morienus the Solitary.—Albertus Magnus and Gerbert.—Vincent of Beauvais.—Raymond Lulli.—The Lullists, or Dreamers.—Arnauld de Villeneuve.—Roger Bacon.—Invention of Spectacles.—Alchemy in the Fifteenth Century.—J. B. Porta, the Italian.—Origin of the Rosicrucians.—Paracelsus.—George Agricola.—Conrad Gessner.—Cornelius Agrippa.—The Story of Nicholas Flamel.—Alchemy engenders Metallurgy.

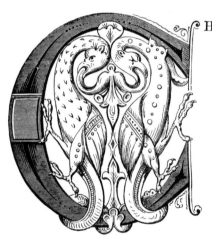

HEMISTRY, which in the first centuries of the Christian era had no practical application, consisted merely of a few vague and entirely speculative theories, and was confounded with physics, under the appellations of *divine art*, *sacred art*, and *sacred science*, in the incoherent mass of transcendental propositions which made up high philosophy. The word *chemistry* (from the Greek χημεία, *chymia* in Latin), used for the first time by Suidas, a lexicographer of the tenth century, at first meant an alloy of gold and silver. Suidas mentions, in this connection, that the Emperor Diocletian, irritated by a revolt of the Egyptians against the laws of the empire, had all their books of chemistry committed to the flames, so as to punish them for their rebellion by preventing them from carrying on the lucrative business arising out of the melting and working of precious metals (Fig. 125). In another part of his Lexicon he states that the Golden Fleece, which the Argonauts went in search of, was but the ancient *papyrus* in which was contained the secret for making gold.

Without attaching overmuch importance to these dim traditions, they are worth recording, because they seem to be the starting-point of chemistry in ancient times. It may be added that a manuscript work of Zosimus, a Greek historian of the fifth century, mentions the Χῆμα, an apocryphal work, in which the giants, sons of the children of God (the descendants of Seth), who are represented in the Book of Genesis as intermarrying with daughters of the race of Cain, registered their discoveries in the arts and the extent of

Fig. 125.—The Gallic Vulcan.—After a Celtic Monument discovered beneath the Choir of Notre-Dame, Paris, in 1711, and now preserved in the Cluny Museum.

their scientific knowledge. According to Scaliger, it was from the "Chema" that the mother science derived its name of chemistry.

It is misleading, however, to quote, as has been done, the evidence of a Greek romance, the "History of Theagenes," composed in the sixteenth century, though it has been ascribed to Athenagoras, who is said to have written it about 176 A.D. The chemical operations described in this apocryphal novel merely serve to show that, in the first century of the Christian era, the

Greeks were acquainted with the hermetic science, the origin of which has been traced back to the mythical Hermes (Fig. 126), and which was afterwards termed *alchemy* (by the adjunction of the Arabic article *al* to the Greek word χημεία), when the sacred art, the art of the philosophers of the school of Alexandria, transformed under the influence of Mahometan civilisation, began to spread throughout the ancient world.

The Bagdad academy, founded by the Caliph Al-Mansour, rivalled in lustre with the Christian school of Dschindisabour. The Caliphs Haroun Al-Raschid, Al-Mamoun, and Motawakkel gave a great impetus during the ninth

Fig. 126.—The Alchemist Hermes.—After an Engraving by Vriese.

century to the sciences of observation, to the experimental methods, and consequently to physics and chemistry. In a few instances men of superior intelligence shook themselves free of the purely theosophical views which had too long influenced, to the exclusion of all others, the Eastern philosophers, and sought in chemistry for something higher than the chimerical transmutation of metals.

Two men of great scientific repute appeared in the East early in the eighth century: these were Al-Chindus, who, by a series of ingenious experiments, was one of the first to discover the secrets of nature, and the

celebrated Geber (Fig. 127), or Yeber, a native of Mesopotamia, who discovered and analyzed red oxide and the deutochlorure of mercury (corrosive
sublimate), nitric acid, hydrochloric acid, nitrate of silver, &c. Al-Chindus
gave special attention to the arts of magic; but Geber, whose works,
translated into Latin, are still extant, notably the "Summa Perfectionis" and
the "Liber Philosophorum," laid down the true principles of chemistry, in
his researches on the fusion, the purifying, and the malleability of metals.
After this great chemist, whom Roger Bacon calls the *Master of Masters*, and
who deserved to be the oracle of chemists in the Middle Ages, we must
come down to the beginning of the ninth century for the next work of
importance on chemistry, which was the book of the great Arab doctor,
Razi, or Rhazes. This encyclopædia mentions for the first time, as belonging
to the materia medica, orpiment, realgar (a compound of arsenic and
sulphur), borax, and certain mixtures of sulphur with iron and copper, of
mercury with acids, and of arsenic with various substances hitherto unknown,
or at all events not used. It is with no little surprise that we read of
Rhazes recommending to doctors the use of various alcoholic preparations and
animal oils, such as oil of ants, which modern chemists claim as remedies of
their own invention. "The secret art of chemistry," says Rhazes, who
wrote a treatise on this science which has become extinct, "is nearer possible
than impossible; the mysteries do not reveal themselves except by force of
labour and perseverance. But what a triumph it is when man can raise a
corner of the veil which conceals the works of God!"

The learned M. Emile Bégin, whose writings on chemistry furnish us
with material for this chapter, states that, from the Middle Ages downwards,
the science of chemistry has been guided by experimental analysis. He says,
"From Schal, the model experimentalist, to Galen, how many important
discoveries, original and fertile ideas, and valuable applications have issued
from the chemist's crucible! How many lives have been spent over it!
How many laborious minds have investigated the mysterious relations
established between organic and organized matter, and the internal combinations of matter with itself! The truth, it must be added, has been blurred
with many superstitious beliefs and wild fancies." At this remote epoch
nearly every savant was more or less of a dreamer. Almost as a matter of
course, Rhazes's great work, translated into Latin, with the title of "El Hhawi,"
a vast pharmaceutical repertory completed by a man of genius who looked at

science from the healing point of view, was not, from its very character, calculated to give us a complete idea of the chemical knowledge appertaining to the epoch at which he wrote it. We can merely guess that this knowledge was in a pretty advanced stage; but the applications of chemistry to metallurgy, to docimacy, to the arts of luxury, and to various kinds of industries, such as the melting of metals, the fabric of warlike weapons, the decoration of edifices and furniture, &c., all are buried in the tomb of so many generations of artists who have left no other trace of their existence than a few of their productions. We can learn less from history in this respect than from an attentive study of the museums of Spain and Sicily, in

GEBER.

Fig. 127.—The Alchemist Geber.—After an Engraving by Vriese.

which are preserved many art monuments which testify to the marvellous skill of the Saracens and the Moors.

The "Canon" by Avicenna, the works of Serapion the younger, and of Mesué (see the chapter on *Medical Sciences*), contain, however, some interesting details as to chemical operations, which show that there was gradual progress, and every now and then a discovery of importance. Mesué says that in the middle of the ninth century certain principles had been recognised as to the analytical classification of the bodies which compose organic matter. Albucasis, a savant of the eleventh century, and a student in the Arab school at Cordova, who, after rising to the highest rank as physician and surveyor, was not above preparing his own remedies and instruments, heralded, by the independence of his ideas and their practical applicability, a new era for science, amidst the misty subtleties of Islamism. Avenzoar and Averroes were the principal apostles of this luminous doctrine, which seemed destined to illuminate in a short time the whole scientific world. Unfortunately the human intellect was easily dragged out of its depth in the Middle Ages. The investigators and inventors, such as the learned Morienus, who fled from Rome into the deserts of Egypt (Fig. 149), had great difficulty in steering clear of the shoals of experimental science in a century when the operations of what was called the *art of fire* were confounded with magic. Their labours in chemistry and metallurgy might have caused them to be condemned as sorcerers.

The Court of Rome deserves praise for its good sense in that, disregarding popular superstitions, it summoned from his cell a humble Dominican monk, afterwards Albertus Magnus, to make him master of the Sacred Palace, and subsequently Bishop of Ratisbon (1260). But, as we have already said (see the chapter on *Philosophical Sciences*), this philosopher monk, after he had been made bishop, wearying of earthly greatness and pomp, abandoned them without a sigh for the exclusion of the cloister, in order to pursue in silence his favourite scientific researches. This was why he was believed to be in communication with the powers of darkness, and it was said that he was guilty of magic, and that he made gold. People came from all parts to see him and question him as to the abstract arts of chemistry. His recipes were in great request, his manuscripts were copied by the thousand, and posterity, which has forgotten all about the monk and bishop, and which does not read his numerous philosophical works, still repeats with honour the name of the *Great Albert*.

It must not be imagined that the princes and sovereigns of the Middle Ages looked at the interests of science from as lofty a point of view as many of the popes. Nevertheless, a French king, whose venerated memory was mercilessly aspersed by the philosophers of the last century, Louis IX., employed as tutor for his children a Dominican monk, the Pliny, the Varro of the Middle Ages. This was Vincent of Beauvais, the wonderful encyclopædist, who lived, so to speak, amongst the ancients at a time when their most splendid works were despised and reviled. Vincent of Beauvais was accused of sorcery because he avoided the idle discussions of the schools, in order to work in his laboratory in the St. Chapelle yard. The high intelligence of the King, and the piety of his mother, Queen Blanche, were scarcely enough to shield their learned protégé from the most absurd accusations. At midnight people often used to creep along the quays of the Seine to see whether they could get a glimpse, reflected in the river, of the magic furnaces in which Master Vincent was supposed to evoke his familiar spirit.

At about the same period there was much talk of another monk, the alchemist Raymond Lulli (born at Palma, in the island of Majorca), who, after a long and eventful life of wanderings and adventures, came to a tragic

Fig. 128.—The Alchemist Raymond Lulli.—After an Engraving by Vriese.

end, being stoned by the populace of Tunis in 1315. A recent attempt has been made to prove that amongst his numerous works on philosophy and theology, those which treat of alchemy should be ascribed to another savant almost his contemporary, and bearer of the same name. But it was precisely these works which had made the reputation of the theologian of Majorca. A thousand absurd stories were related of this singular man, and it was said that he would have been prosecuted as a sorcerer by the Inquisition, unless he had succeeded, by the help of Edward I. of England, in coining six millions of false money, with which the English monarch promised to undertake a fresh crusade against the infidels. Raymond Lulli (Fig. 128) left behind him numerous disciples, who were termed *Lullists* or *dreamers*, and who made a cunning use of the sad end of their leader, just as the Court of Rome seemed inclined to accord him the honours of beatification. Concealing beneath the prestige of black magic their attempts at chemical experimental-ising, the Lullists propagated a report that the soul of the blessed martyr appeared at certain hours of the night, and confided to his neophytes the secrets of heaven, especially touching the divine art of transforming into fine gold the commonest of metals. The Lullists enjoyed considerable credit all over Europe, and although it might have been supposed that this sect, owing to its occult and mysterious practices, would have incurred the rigour of the ecclesiastical and civil laws, the clergy and the magistrates exhibited no little tolerance towards the eminent men belonging to it. The mysterious meetings of the Lullists were surrounded, especially in Germany, with much solemn formality, being held at night, in wild and uninhabited regions, and, if possible, near iron or copper mines (Fig. 129), where the ruggedness of the soil and the bareness of the landscape were in harmony with the arcana of the great work. It is believed that the Brothers of the Rosy Cross, who derived their name from a German gentleman called Rosenkrutz, succeeded the Lullists in the fifteenth century.

A contemporary of Raymond Lulli, and versed, as he was, in Eastern languages, mathematics, philosophy, and medicine, Arnauld de Villeneuve, a native of Languedoc, also interrogated nature by the analysis of bodies and of substances. He investigated more particularly the mysteries of chemical science as bearing upon medicine, and in this way he discovered the various acids since named sulphuric, nitric, and muriatic. It is said that he was the first person to make alcohol and spirits of wine. Arnauld de Villeneuve was, together with Albertus Magnus, one of the most eminent exponents in the Middle Ages of the experimental art, which, still in a state of confusion, was exposed to the suspicions of the ignorant, and could only be practised under the protection of kings, or in the solitude of the cloister. It is a matter for regret, however, that men of such rare intelligence as Arnauld de Villeneuve and Raymond Lulli should have embraced the opinion and systems of theosophy, which was a source of false and absurd theories that often interfered with the application of the most remarkable discoveries in science.

At the same epoch England had the honour of giving birth to Roger

Bacon (Fig. 130), called the *Admirable Doctor*, who had a narrow escape of paying with his life the crime of being in advance of his age. He passed part of his life in prison. Salvino degli Armati had just invented a new process for making glass of a lenticular shape, and Bacon took up this invention, and, having perfected it, made achromatic glasses and the telescope, thus opening the immensities of the sky to future astronomers. He discovered a combustible substance similar to phosphorus, and with saltpetre, which had hitherto only been used medicinally, he composed

Fig. 129.—The Miner.—Designed and engraved in the Sixteenth Century by J. Amman.

gunpowder. There is no truth in the story of his having been the first victim of his own discovery ; for, though he did not foresee the tremendous consequences arising out of the manufacture of this inflammable mixture, he had assumed that it would bring about a revolution in the art of war. The melting of bells, practised as early as the thirteenth century, suggested the idea of casting cannon (Fig. 131). Roger Bacon had investigated all the sciences, and yet, upon his death-bed, he bitterly exclaimed, "I repent of having laboured so much in the interest of science." Thus from the beginning of the fourteenth century, France, Germany, and England each produced almost simultaneously one of the most illustrious representatives of what was called, in the language of the day, the *great art ;* that is to say, the knowledge of the secrets of nature. Of these three learned philosophers, Bacon possessed the highest abilities and the largest powers of conception, and all three of them attracted numerous audiences to their lectures, for they contrived to invest even the most common subject with interest by their way of treating it. When Bacon described the motion of the celestial sphere and the regular march of the planets ; when he expounded his theory of the physical world, and set forth the laws which regulate the matter and cause the transformation of substances, he was listened to with

Fig. 130.—The Alchemist Roger Bacon.—After an Engraving by Vriese.

admiration and in complete silence, for he was himself convinced by the proofs which he had obtained, and by the great problems which he believed that he had settled, and he communicated his own convictions to his audience. But, upon the other hand, experimental science often borrowed its proofs from the most impudent imposture. Thus Arnauld de Villeneuve showed the Parisians copper plates which he declared that he had just converted into silver, and silver foil which he alleged he could convert into fine gold. The people who witnessed these tricks looked upon them as so many miracles, little knowing that a little nitric acid mixed with water would have destroyed the illusion.

The Inquisition burnt the books on alchemy and magic written by Arnauld de Villeneuve; but, through the intermediacy of Pope Clement V., two of his works, the "Rosarium Philosophorum" and the "Flos Florum," were spared, though modern science has not been able to extract much that is useful from these obscure and diffuse compilations. The encyclopædic writings of Albertus Magnus, piously preserved at Cologne, were not in any danger of ecclesiastical censure, and, as soon as printing was discovered, they were published in several towns of the Rhine provinces. The "Opus Majus"

Fig. 131.—Casting of a Bell, in presence of a Bishop who gives it his benediction.—After the "Rationale Divinorum Officiorum," by William Durand.—Manuscript of the Fourteenth Century.—In the Library of M. Ambroise Firmin-Didot, Paris.

of Roger Bacon found in the library of the Vatican the hospitality which it deserved, and it may be said that this book, dedicated to Pope Clement IV., was a deposit for all the science of the Middle Ages.

Most of the disciples of Roger Bacon, Arnauld de Villeneuve, and Albertus Magnus abandoned the chimerical attempt to effect the transmutation of metals, and devoted little time to operations in the laboratory, and those who continued to practise the experimental method derived scarcely any benefit from the discoveries which they really did make, on account of their absurd efforts to discover the philosopher's stone (Fig. 132).

The first who looked upon the practical side of chemistry properly so called was Gentile Gentili de Foligno, whose treatise upon doses and proportions of medicine may be looked upon as a summary of medical chemistry, which was very complete for the time at which it was composed. Next to him come Antonio Quainer of Pavia, who manufactured artificial mineral waters; Saladin of Ascoli, and Arduino of Pesaro, whose works enumerate the substances having a mineral base which have been discovered by the alchemists.

It is to be regretted that nothing of what related to the labours of the

Fig. 132.—The German Alchemist.—Fac-simile of a Wood Engraving attributed to Holbein, and taken from the German Translation of the "Consolation of Philosophy" by Boethius, Augsburg, 1537, in folio.

industrial arts at this epoch, as in the preceding ones, has been recorded in special treatises, for by this neglect we have lost many ingenious processes, whilst others, which might have been ready to hand, have only since been discovered quite accidentally, and after long and laborious research. More profit would have been derived from consulting the daily note-book of an artisan of that period than the farrago of those who were engaged in the great work ; *i.e.* the search for the philosopher's stone.

Moreover, the alchemists went to work in an unmethodical way, and without any scientific theory. Their systems as to the moral value of metals, as to the existence of an exceptional and indecomposable body, and as to the search for a universal panacea could not lead to any result. They took one by one the substances belonging to the three kingdoms of nature, and treated them by fire and by water; they combined them together, noting carefully the isolated phenomena produced by the chemical operation; and they next endeavoured to connect as far as possible these phenomena with the most extraordinary ideas, and then to give to the products obtained a use in conformity with their external characteristics. If some unexpected revelations issued from the rows of retorts and matrasses which the alchemist was at work upon, they were attributed to chance, which sometimes led to some

Fig. 133.—A Mint of the Fifteenth Century.—Reduced Fac-simile of a Wood Engraving at the base of a Monetary Slip, printed at Louvain in 1487.—In the Burgundy Library, Brussels.

fortunate results in these absurd processes of experimental chemistry. In the fifteenth century the alchemists had, unconsciously in most cases, been the means of disclosing to science, apart from several substances comprised in the materia medica, the existence of bismuth, liver of sulphur, regulus of antimony, and volatile fluorine of alkali. They were expert in distilling alcohol, in volatilising mercury, and in obtaining sulphuric acid by the sublimation of sulphur; in preparing aqua regia and various kinds of ether, and in purifying the alkalis. They also had a scarlet dye for cloth superior to anything of the present day. Several processes in glass-staining—which, though said to be lost, were merely abandoned or forgotten—were invented by glass-blowers and enamellers. In all probability the effects of hydrogen, employed as a light-giving medium, revealed themselves to the alchemists spontaneously; and we know that a German alchemist, Eck of Sulzbach, had ascertained the existence of oxygen, which was not demonstrated by Priestley until three hundred years afterwards.

Alchemy was at the apogee of its celebrity in the beginning of the fifteenth century, notwithstanding the royal edicts against it and the suspicions of imposture entertained concerning its adherents. Not only did sovereigns ask them to supply gold for the mints (Figs. 133 and 134), but the outside public, who put faith in the wonders of potable gold, purchased

Fig. 134.—The Officer of the Mint.—Designed and engraved in the Sixteenth Century by J. Amman.

from them, at an extravagant price, certain metallic mixtures combined with ointments and vegetable juices which were warranted to cure diseases, preserve the appearance of youth, render men invulnerable, produce pleasant dreams, prolong human life, and so forth.

It was at this period that were composed most of the treatises upon alchemy, which were a crude mass of incoherent propositions and wild assertions, a mixture of poesy and insanity, in which all logical ideas were lost amidst a mass of stilted phraseology, but through which breathed a blind but evidently fervent faith. Amidst this chaotic collection of absurdities

Fig. 135.—The Extraction of Precious Metals.—Pieces in the Ceremonial Collar of the Senior Member of the Goldsmiths at Ghent.—Fifteenth-Century Chased Silver, size of the original.

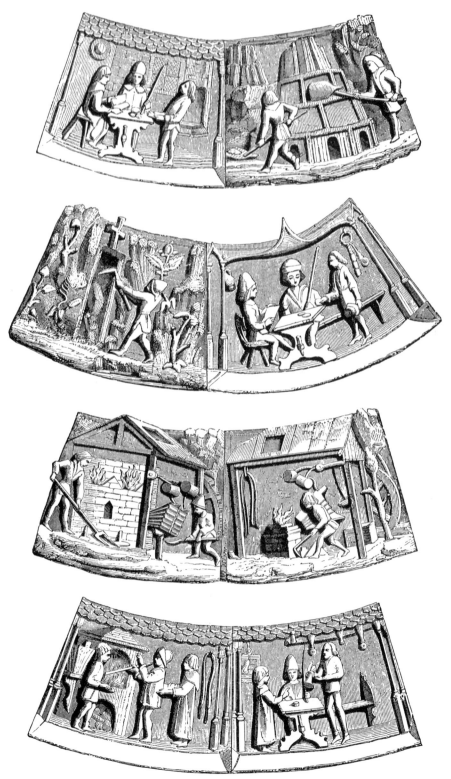

Fig. 136.—The Foundry of Precious Metals.—Pieces in the Ceremonial Collar of the Senior Member of the Goldsmiths at Ghent.—Fifteenth-Century Chased Silver, size of the original.

everything grand or mysterious was attributed by the alchemists to the demons which people the air, fire, and water, to the stars which are superior to the human and to the Divine will, to mysterious sympathies existing between the Creator and his creatures, and to the hybrid combinations of mineral and vegetable substances. The fifteenth century followed, in regard to the arts and sciences, the errors of the preceding age, which was full of grand manifestations, which are to be traced in those wonderful Gothic monuments in which the statuary has represented a mass of figures, sacred and profane, real and imaginary, and which give one the impression of being a book of alchemy, written with a chisel upon stone. And yet, amidst this passion for the strange and the supernatural, there were a few patient and laborious scholars who only devoted themselves to the operations of the laboratory in order to increase the progress of chemistry by logical experiment. Such was the Italian John Baptist Porta, who was the first to allude to the tree of Diana and the flowers of tin, and who discovered the means of reducing the metallic oxides and of colouring silver; or, again, Isaac and Jean Hollandus, makers of enamel and of artificial gems, who have described their process of work with great minuteness and precision; or, again, Sidonius and Sendivogius, who put into execution several new processes for dyeing stuffs.

In 1488 the Venetian Government, following the example of Henry VII. of England and several other monarchs of the time, issued a severe interdict against alchemist practices, but the men who pretended to make gold continued their so-called transmutations. At this epoch it was that the Rosicrucians formed, under the name of *Voarchodumia*, a secret association, the principal object of which was the discovery of gold and silver mines, and, above all, that of the great work (Figs. 135 and 136). In the sixteenth century science began to free itself from the ancient routine of the Middle Ages, and to seek a road in which she might use reason as a staff, and observation as a lantern to her path. And, strange to say, it was alchemy which took the initiative of this scientific reform. Paracelsus (born at Einsiedlen, in Switzerland, in 1493), to whom frequent allusion was made in a previous chapter (*Medical and Occult Sciences*), may be considered the most characteristic type of contemporary alchemists. He represented, so to speak, two men combined in one: upon the one hand, there was the daring reformer who upset all the received ideas of medicine since the days of

Hippocrates, and who, by his incessant experiments, made many additions to the arts ; upon the other, the theosophist—we may even say, the impostor—who pretended that he was one of those privileged beings who receive their knowledge direct from God by mere Divine emanation. This deifying of the illustrious savant contributed to the success of his doctrines ; but he ought, in his own interests, to have held more aloof from men, and lived in a sort of mysterious solitude (Fig. 137). After an adventurous career as a youth, Paracelsus had acquired, at the age of thirty-two, an immense reputation, and his pupils at the University of Bâle, where he filled the chair of

Fig. 137.—The Alchemist Paracelsus.—After an Engraving by Vriese.

medicine, were to be counted by the thousand. The enthusiasm was so great that princes and nobles swelled his cortége, and the people kissed the skirts of his robes and the buckles of his shoes. He had cured eighteen notable personages who were believed to be suffering from incurable diseases, and there was a regular scramble to obtain the elixir supposed to insure indefinite prolongation of human life.

Paracelsus, having probably promised more than he was able to perform, became so unpopular that he was obliged to leave Bâle, and, accompanied by a few faithful followers, to resume his wanderings, the result being that he died in misery in a hospital. Before his time, Henry Cornelius Agrippa of

Nettesheim, philosopher, physician, and alchemist, underwent the same fate at Grenoble (1535), after having been imprisoned at Brussels as a magician. We will not attempt to justify the strange theory which has been called the pantheism of Paracelsus, a theory in which he only pretended to believe to suit his own purposes and strike the imaginations of those who would not, perhaps, have paid any heed to more sober ideas.   But it must be pointed out that in his chemical operations Paracelsus had constantly in view the simplification of the processes resorted to, and the discovery of the elementary principles and of the truly active mediums of nature.   His celebrated *arcana* amount to this, and he says, "The true object of alchemy is to prepare arcana, not to make gold." Starting from this principle, he denounced the tavern-keepers and cooks, who drown the virtue of the best arcana in soups ; the apothecaries, who can only compose insipid syrups and repulsive decoctions, when they have ready to hand, at the bottom of their stills (Figs. 138 to 147), extracts and dyes derived from the best vegetables and minerals.   Paracelsus was equally indignant with the doctors, whose barbarous prescriptions embodied a mass of substances which neutralised each other.   He was very much opposed to the use of correctives added to certain pharmaceutical preparations, especially when these correctives had no natural relation with the preparations used.   He argued that it was necessary to discover the quintessence of plants—the *ether* of Aristotle— and the active principles of organized bodies, isolating them with great care, and using them to avert the different functional disorders of the animal machine.   Bones of the hare, coral, mother-of-pearl, and other analogous bodies, from which he claimed to extract, by chemical process, the arcana, were doubtless used by him for the sole purpose of misleading the inquisitive ; and when he wished to render these mixtures efficacious, he added to them certain potent substances of which he had previously ascertained the influence.

In any event, it may safely be said that, owing to the labours of Paracelsus, alchemy exchanged its speculative for a practical character ; and this is so true that George Agricola (born at Misnia in 1494), who proceeded with greater caution than Paracelsus, effected, without any disturbance or noisy discussion, the auspicious revolution in metallurgy which his ardent contemporary was unable to achieve without a fierce struggle in medicine and the pharmacopœia.   Agricola resided at Bâle, and his sedate temperament was in keeping with the manners of the inhabitants of that business city, while his scientific discoveries could not but please and interest them, when they found it possible to give them an immediate and useful application to arts and industry. From about 1530—at which period Paracelsus had already quitted Bâle—to 1560—that is to say, five years after the death of Agricola

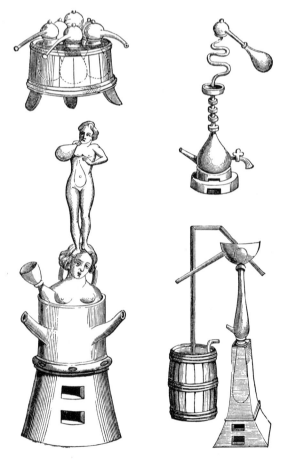

Figs. 138 to 141.—Furnace, Retorts, Stills, and Distilling Apparatus, as used by Chemists and Alchemists of the Sixteenth Century.—After an Engraving by Vriese.

—the printing-presses of Westhmer and Froben were incessantly publishing Latin works, most of them illustrated with wood engravings, in which the father of metallurgic science expounded the results of his long series of investigations.

Henceforth, *chimiastric,* or the art of transforming bodies and substances

from a medical point of view, and metallurgy, or the art of extracting and purifying metals for the use of industry—two sciences having many points of contact and of difference—advanced in parallel lines upon the road of progress. Alchemy, ceasing to be experimental and becoming merely psychological, was abandoned to the study of a few fanatical adherents, and finally disappeared altogether from the enlarged domain of positive science. A history of the conflict between the psychological alchemists and the *chimiastres* (or new chemists) would be a very interesting one, especially if it related how the genius of the Middle Ages gradually lost the ground which it had held for so many centuries; but the place for such a history is not

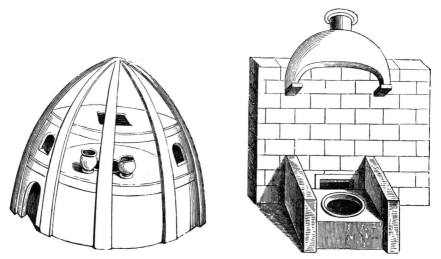

Figs. 142 and 143.—Furnaces, as used by the Chemists and Alchemists of the Middle Ages. After an Engraving by Vriese.

here. We can only summarise the salient facts, deducing from them afterwards the principal consequences. The conflict was fiercest upon the banks of the Rhine. While Graterole, Bracheschus, and Alexander of Suchten sided with the alchemists, and upheld the speculative theories of Avicenna, Gerber, and Raymond Lulli, Conrad Gesner, Thomas Mufetus, and Nicholas Guibert examined the science by the light of the ideas which had inaugurated the new period.

In the meanwhile, Cornelius Agrippa, the sceptic, who from his childhood had been familiar with the mysteries of alchemy, and even of necromancy, was tracing the line which separated science from speculation, and the art from the mere trade made out of it. This was *the art* "concerning which he could say a good deal more, had he not taken an oath of secrecy when he was initiated into its mysteries," which means, no doubt, that he could disclose a good deal of roguery and imposture. He says, "I could show the alchemist fabricating azure, cinnabar, ore, vermilion, musical gold, and other admixtures of colours; I could show the same man committing a regular fraud, forging a Bennet philosopher's stone, by contact with which all

Figs. 144 to 147.—Furnaces and various Apparatus, as used by the Chemists and Alchemists of the Middle Ages.—After an Engraving by Vriese.

other stones are converted into gold or silver, according to the desire of Midas. I would drive such a man out of the country, and confiscate his goods; I would inflict upon him bodily chastisement, for he offends God, the Christian religion, and society." Agrippa, after having promised to keep silence, continues, carried away by his indignation, "It would take too much time to recount all the follies, the idle secrets, and the enigmas of this trade: of the green lion, the fugitive stag, the flying eagle, the inflated toad, of the crow's head, of the black blacker than the black, of the seal of Mercury, of the mud of wisdom, and other countless absurdities of a like kind. As to the science itself, in which I am well versed, and which must not be confounded with the trade made out of it, I believe it to be worthy of the honour which Thucydides says should be paid to an honest woman : that of talking about her as little as possible." Agrippa has also left a very graphic description of the sad condition to which the alchemists of the lower ranks were then reduced, "travelling from fair to fair, in order to make a little money by sale of white-lead, vermilion, antimony, and other drugs used by women for painting the face, drugs which the Scripture calls ointments of lust." These bastards of science stole when they could not earn money, and finally resorted to the coining of false money (Fig. 148). They were, as Agrippa called them, " gaol-birds." Such were the surviving alchemists in France in the reign of François I., and they were far more calculated to discredit the spirit of experimentalising than to bring it into favour amongst the upper classes. The famous Nicholas Flamel had adopted very different means from these, a hundred and fifty years before, to make himself popular amongst the people of Paris. A sworn professor of the University, a philosopher, a naturalist, and doubtless also an alchemist, Flamel enjoyed a reputation for probity which had probably not less to do with his wealth than the cause of the holy stone, so long held in bad repute. People did not stop to inquire whether fortunate speculations or sums of money deposited with him by proscribed Jews who died without heirs and beyond the frontiers of France had increased a hundred-fold the modest savings of the scribe of the parish, St. Jacques de la Boucherie ; the common people, always ready to believe in the supernatural, attributed his large fortune exclusively to alchemy, and long after his death no citizen of Paris would have dared to pass the house of Flamel and Pernelle, his wife, at night without signing himself, so as to keep off the evil spirits which were believed to haunt the abode in which the alchemist concealed his treasure. Yet Flamel, at his death, founded masses for the repose of his soul in all the churches of Paris, and bequeathed his goods to the poor.

The great good fortune of Nicholas Flamel no doubt helped to advance experimental science, but it led thousands of enthusiasts astray, and the search for the philosopher's stone became the mania of the fifteenth century. An ancient author, who did not at all favour the alchemists, says of them,

"Bad coal, sulphur, excrement, poisons, and all kinds of hard work are sweeter than honey to them, until, having consumed patrimony, heritage, and

Fig. 148.—The Alchemist's Laboratory.—After the Picture of Breughel the Elder, engraved by Cock (Sixteenth Century).

furniture, all of which disappear in smoke and ashes, the poor wretches end their days in rags and misery."

Flamel, who died in 1415, carried to the tomb the secret of the great work which he declared that he had in possession, and more than a century and a half elapsed before the doctrine of the Paracelsists obtained a place in the University of Paris. It was only in the reign of Henry IV. that Baillif de la Rivière and Joseph Duchesne, both physicians to the King, and George Penot, a pupil, like them, of the Bâle school, succeeded in attracting attention to the name and the doctrines of the great Swiss alchemist.

This reaction in favour of the chemical system of Paracelsus, though slow and undecisive, was not the less significant. The war broke out afresh between the eclectic chemists and the Paracelsists, and it was amidst this conflict

Fig. 149.—The Alchemist Morienus.—After an Engraving by Vriese.

of the two schools that chimiastrie, against which was ranged the insane spiritualism of the Rosicrucians, those sectaries of mystic alchemy, was able to make its way upon the as yet vaguely defined ground of general chemistry. The two other branches of the science, metallurgy and technical chemistry, owing to the nature of their customary application, did not encounter so many obstacles, and in course of time were protected and encouraged by the governments and local administrations. Venice, which had so long been hostile to the psychological chemists, showed favour to the practical and working chemists, and the same was the case in all the cities and states where commerce throve. The metallurgists demonstrated to the public that they would consult their interests—always the main motive of human progress—by allowing them to construct blast-furnaces, foundries, and manufactories, and in this way they transformed in a few years the whole social system. The savants devoted their attention to metallurgic chemistry, which did in reality make gold in the sense that it extracted mineral matter from all kinds of metals, and submitted the metals themselves to all the changes which they underwent in manufacture. In Germany, for instance, the learned Pole, Tycho Brahe, so famous as an astronomer, spent nearly his whole time in a laboratory with the Emperor Rudolph II., who expended large sums in scientific experiments, but who paid no heed to the philosopher's stone. So, too, in England, Roger Bacon, who has deservedly been called the father of experimental physics, did not think it beneath him to engage in chemical researches; while in France Bernard Palissy, whose labours have already been referred to, did much for technical chemistry.

THE OCCULT SCIENCES.

The Origin of Magic.—The Savants and Philosophers reputed to be Magicians.—Different Forms
of Occult Sciences.—Oneiromancy.—Oneirocritics and Diviners.—Necromancy.—Practices of
the Necromancers.—Astrology.—Celebrated Astrologers.—Chiromancy.—Aëromancy and
other kinds of Divination.—The Angelic Art and the Notorious Art.—The Spells of the
Saints.—Magic.—The Evocation of Good and Evil Genii.—Pacts with Demons.—Celebrated
Magicians.—Formulæ and Circles.—Incense and Perfumes.—Talismans and Images.—The
tormenting of Wax Images.—The Sagittarii.—The Evil Eye.—Magic Alchemy.—Cabalism.
—The Fairies, Elfs, and Spirits.—The Were-wolves.—The Sabbath.—A Trial for Sorcery.

VERY illusion contains a principle,
every false science has its history,"
says M. Ferdinand Denis, in a work
of which we propose to give an analysis.
"To understand as a whole the different branches of occult philosophy,
as it was understood in the Middle
Ages, it is necessary to say a few
words about magic as practised by the
ancients."

To study this vast subject in its primi-
tive sources, it would be necessary to explain the magic formulæ of the Vedas
in India, as handed down to us in the religion of the Hindoos, and to penetrate the systems of Hebraic cabalism. But we need not go back further
than Diodorus of Sicily, who in the time of Julius Cæsar visited the most
distant countries of Asia and Africa, and who tells us of a Chaldean tribe
which composed a sacred caste, devoted exclusively to the study of the occult
sciences, and incessantly seeking to discover, by means of astrology and magic,
the secrets of the future. The same historian tells us that the Assyrians had
their diviners and augurs, to watch the flight of the birds and to offer up
sacrifices to the unknown gods, many centuries before these superstitious

practices had been introduced into use amongst the Romans. Pliny, in his turn, borrowed from tradition a curious chapter upon magic in the time of Homer; and other Latin writers have given us some information as to the practice of magic amongst the Etruscans. This is enough to show that ancient magic, and more especially Eastern magic, was the cradle of the occult sciences in the Middle Ages.

The occult sciences existed, moreover, amongst the ancients, though they were not called by this generic name, which comprises all the forms of the art of divination, notably Astrology and Oneiromancy; all the modes of evoking good or evil spirits, notably Theurgy and Goety; all the material and spiritual communications between the dead and living—that is to say, Necromancy; and all the means of exercising a supernatural and mysterious power by the influence of dreams—that is to say, Sorcery. But when the advent of Christianity changed the face of the world, the first heresiarchs, who had only embraced the new faith in the hope of dragging it down into the chaos of pagan religions, appear to have been the faithful guardians of the dogmas and precepts of ancient magic: these were the Gnostics and the followers of Valentine, Harpocrates, and Basilides, who declared that they were the depositaries of the wisdom of the Eastern theosophists, and who disfigured the Christian worship by mysteries either obscure, obscene, or ridiculous. Thus they added to the ceremonies of the Greek Church a mass of recent practices invented by priests of Buddha or Zoroaster, and which were not devoid of grandeur and solemnity.

It was at the epoch (the third century) when Gnosticism, the sovereign science, flourished in the school of Alexandria, that there appeared two illustrious philosophers—Plotinus, born at Lycopolis in Egypt, and his disciple Porphyrus, born at Constantinople—who in a manner founded the new magical science, and who may be looked upon as the first demono-graphers of the Middle Ages. Plotinus, a thorough Platonist, had studied the philosophy of the Orientalists in Persia and India, before coming to teach mysticism and pantheism at Rome. He embodied in a work entitled the "Enneades"—that is to say, collection of nine books—a whole set of doctrines which Porphyrus completed and commentated, and which contains a selection of the marvellous traditions of the *sacred art* in the East. After them, Jamblichus, born at Tyre in Phœnicia, who also had been educated in the school of Alexandria, discovered a systematic formula for uniting theurgy to magic. Ennapius, Eustathius, and the Emperor Julian himself, accepted the system of Jamblichus, who, in evoking the religious mysteries of ancient Egypt, wrote a sort of gospel for the thaumaturgists and the magicians. Jamblichus may be said to have expounded the physics of the reign of demons, and Proclus the metaphysics.

The revolution which then took place in the neo-pagan philosophy caused

Fig. 150.—Druid carrying the Crescent of the Sixth Day of the Moon, and the Druid Sacrificer. After a Roman Monument of the Second Century.

the aspirations and tendencies of the ardent and inquiring minds, which, after endeavouring to discover the secrets of creation and of terrestrial existence, sought outside of material nature a source of ideal satisfactions which they could not find in the real world, to converge upon the same end. The eyes of the mind were opened, and human intelligence became enamoured of the occult sciences which brought it into communication with the superior intellects of the invisible world. Thus, upon the one hand, there was a scientific movement resulting from the daring speculations of a few savants who endeavoured to fathom the arcana of philosophy ; upon the other hand, there arose and extended amongst the ignorant and credulous populations of Europe an instinctive love for the wonderful, arising out of local legends, a vague desire to march towards the unknown, a feverish impatience to witness terrible evocations of spirits, and a criminal hope of obtaining the intervention of demons, who were credited with the possession of a terrible power, and who became the docile agents of a popular magic more active and dangerous than that of the philosophers of the Alexandrian school. This new magic had its origin not only in the superstitions of Celtic races, but also in the sombre mysteries of Northern mythologies. It was a sort of dark and savage religion, which the people of the North and certain Asiatic hordes had imported into Germany and Gaul (Fig. 150), with their barbarous worship and their hideous gods, scattering terror by their sanguinary rites and magic incantations amongst the primitive inhabitants of these countries, which were still full of the winsome and poetical souvenirs of paganism. It has been said with truth, of one of the most ancient monuments of the Scandinavian language, called the *Hava-mal,* that it contained the germ of most of the superstitious ideas which, by their admixture with the magic theories of the East and of antiquity, brought about the creation of the sorcery of the Middle Ages.

The occult sciences long remained in the shade, and were worked out in silence far from the supervision of the ecclesiastical schools, but under the influence of popular traditions which had preserved the mystic and divinatory formulæ in use amongst the Chaldeans, the Greeks, and the Romans, and which combined with the lugubrious reminiscences of the Valhalla of Odin the graceful fancies of the bards of Brittany. The Middle Ages employed all the elements of the sacred art and of magic sciences borrowed from many different times and lands, linking them with the Mahometan creeds which the Arabs had imported into Spain. As early as the eleventh century there were Saracen schools in the Iberian peninsula, where the occult sciences, which served to unveil the wonders of the supernatural world, were publicly expounded. It was long supposed by the demonographers that the illustrious Gerbert, born at Aurillac in Auvergne, who had completed his studies amongst the Spanish Arabs at the school of Cordova before being elected pope, only owed his election to a mysterious pact which he had made with the demons.

It would be superfluous to refute such a folly, but it may be remarked that two centuries later the Arabic was, so to speak, the key and the first instrument of study for penetrating the mysterious sanctuary of hidden sciences.

This was, perhaps, what brought about the secret introduction into the Christian, and even into the monastic schools, of this language which was so little diffused throughout Europe. Most of the savants who dabbled in these mysterious sciences, which were proscribed and condemned by the Church, learnt Arabic as well as Hebrew and Syriac, a knowledge of which was necessary to become initiated into the mysteries of cabalism. This was why any one who knew Arabic or Hebrew was suspected of magic, and even of

Fig. 151.—" How Alexander engaged in Combat with Men having Horses' Heads and vomiting Smoke from their Mouths."—Miniature of a Manuscript of the Fifteenth Century, No. 11,040. —In the Burgundy Library, Brussels.

sorcery. From the time of Plotinus and Porphyrus to that of Cardan and Paracelsus, no man of eminence could assist the progress of science or make any great scientific discovery without being reputed a magician, or stigmatized as a sorcerer—a fatal appellation which, attached to the name of a noble victim of his love for science, disturbed his repose, often interrupted his labours, and sometimes put his liberty and life in peril. Raymond Lulli, Albertus Magnus, Roger Bacon, Vincent of Beauvais, and many others, after having composed a great number of remarkable works upon scholastic philosophy, could not escape these unjust suspicions and persecutions. The Florentine encyclopædist, Cecco d'Ascoli, whose cabalistic studies had excited the suspicions of the Inquisition, was accused of being in communication with the devil, and burnt at the stake in Rome in 1327.

The occult sciences had spread very rapidly at the epoch when the thirst for knowledge gave an impetus to all the intellectual forces of the Middle Ages. This was the period of the great encyclopædias, which were compiled simultaneously in all countries where the Renaissance of letters was ushered in with more enthusiasm than discretion. These encyclopædias comprised, amidst the vast mass of divine and human sciences, hermetic philosophy, judicial astrology, theurgy, and the other branches of magic; but, notwith-standing this, the occult sciences were not taught *ex cathedrâ;* that is to say, from the chairs of the Universities, over which the religious authorities always exercised an unlimited power of control and suppression. The invention of printing, in the middle of the fifteenth century, all at once conferred upon teaching from books a degree of liberty which oral instruction had never possessed. The occult sciences profited thereby, and, without taking into account the prohibitions and condemnations of the Church, printing brought into full light the doctrines and experimental knowledge belonging to each kind of magic, which had hitherto remained hidden. In most cases these publications did not render the authors or printers liable to any danger, for the Catholic Church was at this period more engaged in pulling down the militant heresies which attacked the dogma and the very essence of religion. Cardan, Paracelsus, Cornelius Agrippa, Jean Reuchlin, and many other psycho-logists, though they were more or less astrologers, demonologists, and magi-cians, were not interfered with for their writings, which, going through several editions, were very widely circulated; but in the beginning of the sixteenth century, certain inquisitors, amongst others Henry Institor and Springer in their "Malleus Maleficorum," denounced the formidable invasion of sorcery, and invoked against its adepts the penal laws decreed by the ecclesiastical authorities. It was only about the middle of this century that the civil power began to proceed against the sorcerers; and it was encouraged, seconded, and urged by the jurisconsults, who seemed fully agreed to punish the insti-gators and proselytes of an illusory science, reputed criminal because it participated in the works of the demons. One of these stern magistrates, Pierre de Lancre, President of the Bordeaux Parliament, boasted in his "Treatise on the Inconstancy of Evil Spirits and Demons" (1610), that he had been more severe on the sorcerers than the Inquisition itself; and his contemporary, the political philosopher Jean Bodin, calmly enumerated in his "Demonomania" (1580) the list of persons who had been handed over to the secular arm as demonomaniacs or sorcerers during the reign of the Valois kings. The magic art was destined to disappear and vanish in smoke when, to use the picturesque expression of Vico, "Curiosity, the mother of Ignorance, gave birth to true Science."

We may now examine in succession the principal theoretical and practical divisions of occult philosophy.

Oneirocricy (that is to say, the explanation of dreams, from the two Greek words, ὄνειρος, a dream, and κρίσις, judgment), or *Oneiromancy* (the divining of dreams, from the two Greek words, ὄνειρος, a dream, and μαντεία, prediction) is of very ancient origin. The Egyptians, the Jews, and the Greeks had reduced the art of interpreting dreams into a regular doctrine. The mystic traditions of this art, which was implanted in all the pagan religions, were all the more readily revived in the Middle Ages, because the Holy Scriptures supplied many instances of prophetic dreams, explained and afterwards fulfilled, which the Church of Jesus Christ naturally accepted as indisputable facts in the history of the people of God. The explanation of dreams did not seem contrary to the Catholic faith, inasmuch as Synesius, who was Bishop of Ptolemais in the fourth century, composed a treatise upon Dreams, in which he endeavoured to sanctify by Christian reflections the belief of the ancients, by making of oneirocricy a science of individual observation, which enabled distinctions to be made between natural dreams, Divine dreams, and dreams caused by the evil one. This triple distinction of the nature of dreams was admitted as a fundamental rule in the oneirocricy of the Middle Ages. However, another father of the Church, Gregory, Bishop of Nyssa, who possessed a surer judgment than his contemporary Synesius, refused to see in dreams more than a momentary derangement of the mind, caused by the recent emotions which it might have experienced. He poetically compared the brain of man during sleep to the string of a harp, which, after emitting its sound, still vibrates after the sound has died away.

Great as were the repugnances of the Church to the systematic interpretation of dreams, the oneiroscopists by profession—those who made of this interpretation, which had been condemned by the popes and the councils, a sacred or diabolic art—exercised their mischievous trade with impunity in the palaces of kings as well as in the towns and in the country. They had

nothing to fear from the civil authorities, and they defied those of the
Church. However, Pope Gregory II., in the eighth century, denounced as
detestable the practice of divination which consisted in seeking auguries in the
visions of the night. The sixth Council of Paris, held in 829, condemned the
art of oneiromancy, as entailing pernicious consequences, and assimilated it
with the darkest superstitions of paganism. These canonical condemnations
did not prevent the art of divining by dreams from being generally practised
in the Middle Ages, either for forecasting the future or for discovering
hidden treasure. The first special treatise on this subject was written by
Arnauld de Villeneuve in the thirteenth century, and was not very widely

Fig. 152.—" How Alexander engaged in Combat with Pigs having large teeth a cubit long, and
with Men and Women having Six Hands."—Miniature of a Manuscript of the Thirteenth
Century, No. 11,040.—In the Burgundy Library, Brussels.

circulated, for the adepts in oneiromancy did not care to spread abroad the
technical elements of an art which they practised as a means of making
money. It was not until the sixteenth century that this process of divination
became general and popular, when the Venice printing-press had published
the "Oneirocriticon," written in Greek, and ascribed to a philosopher of
Ephesus called Artemidorus, who is said to have composed it in the reign of
the Emperor Antoninus. This book, translated into several languages, and
reprinted many times, became the manual and code of the oneiromancers,
though his system did not repose upon any scientific or rational basis. For
instance, according to this system, whoever dreamt that his hair was thick

and carefully curled might anticipate an accession of wealth; upon the other hand, anything wrong with the hair foreshadowed something unfavourable. It was a bad sign to wear a wreath of flowers not in season. In this theory of dreams—borrowed, no doubt, from the East—"the eyes relate to children, as the head does to the father of the family, the arms to the brothers, the feet to the servants; the right hand to the mother, to the sons, and to friends; the left hand to the wife and the daughter." The learned Jerome Cardan, who did not choose to accept these vague and incoherent indications, attempted to establish new laws of oneirocricy, and arranged the dreams in

Fig. 153.—The Vision of Charlemagne.—After a Miniature in the "Chroniques de Saint-Denis." Manuscript of the Fourteenth Century.—In the National Library, Paris.

categories corresponding with the seasons, the months, and the hours during which they occurred. But the common people, little doubting that he was unconsciously reproducing the simpler but more logical system of Pliny in his "Natural History," merely explained the dreams by taking them in their opposite sense, and this was the foundation of a small popular work, which has been frequently revised and renewed since the sixteenth century, "The Key to Dreams."

Oneirocricy might have been to a certain extent harmless, in spite of its superstitious absurdities; but such was not the case with necromancy (derived from the two Greek words νεκρός, death, and μαντεία, divination, or the art of foretelling the future by evoking the dead), a terrible and imaginary science which had earned for its adepts the name of *necromancers*. This

Fig. 154.—The Image of Dame Astrology, with the Three Fates.—After a Miniature in the " Traité de la Cabale Chrétienne," in Prose, by Jean Thénaud, a Cordelier of Angoulême, a Work dedicated to François I.—Manuscript of the Sixteenth Century.—In the Arsenal Library, Paris.

science was all the more believed in during the Middle Ages because it appeared, in the eyes of a superficial observer, to be based upon the authority

of Scripture, through the Witch of Endor whom Saul asked to evoke the
spirit of Samuel. The practices of this art were not in all cases of a solemn
and striking character; for the evocation of the dead consisted sometimes in
merely pronouncing certain phrases, half grotesque and unintelligible, at
night, either in a cemetery or a cellar, by the light of a black taper. In other
cases, it is true, this evocation was surrounded by the most horrible mysteries,
and the necromancer accompanied them by the effusion of blood. A child
was put to death, and its head, placed upon a dish, surrounded by lighted
tapers, was supposed to open its mouth at a given moment, and speak as from
the tomb. Sometimes the necromancer merely summoned up a mute phantom,
which by a gesture or a look replied to the question put to it. It was in
this way that Albertus Grotus, at the request of the Emperor Frederick
Barbarossa, evoked the spirit of his wife, who appeared before him, gloomy
and sorrowful, but still recognisable, and wearing her imperial robes. Necromancy, which must have had its origin in the hypogea of ancient Egypt,
and which has furnished so many terrible stories to the credulity of the
Middle Ages, eventually became fused in sorcery.

Another branch of the art of divination, which flourished in Europe from
the beginning of the Middle Ages to the sixteenth century, was astrology, that
mysterious science which was intimately connected with astronomy, and which
addressed itself to the eyes as well as to the mind, so that the masters of
science consulted the celestial vault as they would an immense book, in which
each star, having received the name and meaning of one of the letters in
the Hebrew alphabet, recorded in indelible characters the destiny of empires
and sovereigns as well as that of the whole human race, which was supposed
to be subject, each man at his birth, to the influence of the planets (Fig.
154). Astrology was the oldest of the occult sciences, for it came from
Chaldea, and was rocked, according to the Hebrew works, in the cradle of the
world. The Jewish nation, which was the natural heiress of this primitive
science, piously preserved the deposit confided to its doctors. One of them,
Simeon Ben-Jochaï, to whom is ascribed the celebrated book of the " Zohar,"
succeeded, according to the tradition of the Talmud, in attaining to such a
degree of familiarity with the celestial mysteries relating to the position of
the stars, that he was able to read the laws of Jehovah in the sky before they
were imposed upon the earth by their Divine Author. It is easy to understand that under the empire of such ideas, higher intellects, deeply interested

in astronomical science, must have modified at their will the science of which they were the boldest interpreters. Hence, no doubt, arose the fondness of the Jews for astronomy, which they resorted to principally for drawing horoscopes and predicting the future. This was why the Jewish astrologers were in such good odour during the Middle Ages. They were admitted into the presence of kings and princes, who loaded them with honours and riches, while the Israelitish race generally was being treated with such great contumely.

The famous Arab geographer Edrisi, who was the favourite of Roger II., King of Sicily, at the close of the eleventh century, owed rather to astrology than to geography the favour in which he was held by that prince, and it has been asserted that the two circular tables of silver which he engraved with great skill for the King were not meant for a terrestrial globe, but for a celestial sphere which reproduced the motions of the stars and their conjunctions from an astrological point of view. It is well known how eagerly, in the thirteenth century, Alfonso X., King of Castile, surnamed the Learned, took counsel with the rabbis in his investigations of astronomy and astrology. Two centuries later, John II., King of Portugal, whom Queen Isabella of Castile called *the man par excellence,* had in his suite a Jew, Master Rorigo, who perfected the astrolabe (Jacob's staff), and who, doubtless, took part in the plans for the great maritime expeditions to the East Indies which his Royal Highness dispatched at about the same time as Christopher Columbus, by the aid of his own knowledge of astronomy, discovered the fourth quarter of the world.

The history of the fifteenth and sixteenth centuries records the doing of a great number of astrologers, who were as famous during their lifetime as they are now unknown, though they composed many curious and some remarkable books. Without recalling the numerous compilers of almanacs and predictions who lived during the sixteenth century, but amongst whom may be mentioned François Rabelais, who had but little faith in astrology, we may cite the names of Luke Gauric, the learned Neapolitan prelate (born in 1476), who drew the horoscope of the cities, popes, and kings of his day ; Simon Pharès, the astrologer-in-ordinary to King Charles VIII., a converted Jew, who has left a manuscript history of the most famous astrologers ; Thiébault, the physician-in-ordinary and astrologer to François I. ; Cosmo Ruggieri, the Florentine astrologer, the confidant of Catherine de' Medicis ;

and the most famous of them all, Michel de Nostredame, otherwise Nostradamus, physician-in-ordiniary and astrologer to Charles IX., who was born at Salon, in France, in 1503, and who died there in 1566. He is the only astrologer whose name has remained popular, and this through his " collection of perpetual predictions," compiled in enigmatic verses, and published under the title of " Quatrains Astronomiques," and which have been reprinted several times under the title of " Prophéties."

Judicial astrology, so called to distinguish it from alchemical astrology and magical astrology, had no fixed rules until the thirteenth century; it had long followed in the wake of astronomy properly so called, but from this time it started upon a path of its own, and adopted many imaginary theories, repeatedly borrowing from the occult sciences certain mysterious and fanciful procedures.

According to the pure theory of the art, the seven planets then discovered, including the sun, formed, with the twelve figures of the zodiac, the totality of the astrological system. Each of these stars or constellations was supposed to govern, by its special influence, either a limb of the human body, or the whole body, or a whole nation, and this bounden relation of the celestial bodies to earthly things extended to all the beings and all the products in creation. " The flowers are to the earth as the stars to the sky," the pseudo-Trismegistus is made to say in the old French translation; " there is not one flower amongst them which some star has not bidden to grow." Albertus Magnus, or rather the anonymous author of the book of " Wonderful Secrets " published with his name to it, tells us that the planet of Saturn presides over life, sciences, and buildings; that wishes, honours, riches, and the cleanliness of the garments are dependent upon Jupiter; that Mars exercises his influence over wars, persons, marriages, and feuds; that hope, happiness, and gain came from the Sun; that love and friendship are under the influence of Venus; that disease, debts, and fear are beneath the influence of Mercury, who is also the planet of commerce; while the Moon causes wounds, robberies, and dreams.

As to the intrinsic qualities of the planetary influences, they were denoted by the planets themselves. The Sun was favourable; Saturn, cold and cheerless; Jupiter, temperate; Mars ardent; Venus, fruitful; Mercury, inconstant; the Moon, melancholy. The days, the colours, and the metals were also subject to the influence of the planets and of the constellations.

But, to draw any kind of horoscope, the first step was to observe with great care what planets or constellations were dominant in the sky at the precise hour when the operation began. The next step was to examine, with the guidance of very complicated calculations, the consequences to be deduced from the positions and conjunctions of the stars (Fig. 155). The most difficult part of the science consisted in determining the *houses of the Suns* and their respective properties. The day was divided into four equal parts: the ascendant of the sun, the middle of the sky, the descending of the sun, and the lower part of the sky. "These four parts of the day were subdivided into twelve distinct parts, which were called the *twelve houses*. Great importance was therefore attached, in drawing a horoscope, to ascertaining in

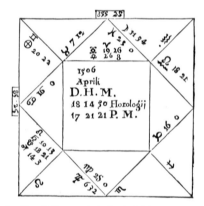

Fig. 155.—Specimen of a Genethliac, or Astrological Horoscope, composed in the Sixteenth Century.

which *house* the stars appeared, especially as these houses of the sun varied astronomically, according to the countries, the time of year, and the hour of the day or night. This is why two horoscopes, drawn by two different astrologers at different places, but at the same moment, would be utterly opposed to one another. But these facts were not taken into account, and the errors and inconsistencies which were always occurring were imputed to the astrologers, and not to astrology, which was never suspected until, disencumbered of all these superstitious follies, it entered the domain of the exact sciences through its fusion with astronomy.

If men sought to interpret the future by means of the sky, just as they had sought to forecast their individual destiny by means of their own dreams, it is not surprising that they should have interrogated their own bodies with a like expectation. From the earliest times the peoples of the East had believed that the broken and multiple lines which radiate from the sutures of the skull are, in fact, the strokes of a mysterious handwriting which contained the secret of each man's individual fate.

The Middle Ages were therefore quite prepared to recognise a symbolical writing of a similar kind in the countless lines, more or less distinct, which correspond with the inflections of the skin of our hand. This speculative science, called chiromancy (from the Greek words χείρ, hand, and μαντεία, divination), had more adepts than all the other sciences of divination, and was eventually merged in astrology, giving rise to a number of systems which have been upheld by savants of unquestionable merit.

The chiromancers cunningly founded their doctrine upon the following passage in the Exodus, which is repeated almost word for word in the Book of Job:—"This shall be as a sign in his hand, and as an instrument before his eyes" (xiii. 9). But the Church would not admit of this futile interpretation of the holy text, and chiromancy was one of the superstitions which she most uncompromisingly opposed. It was not, however, until the beginning of the fifteenth century that this superstition spread from the East into Europe. At this epoch, the Bohemians, who had arrived from the remote regions of Asia (see the volume on "Manners and Customs," chapter on *Bohemians*), brought with them the ancient traditions of chiromancy, and propagated them rapidly in all countries which they traversed. Inquiring minds set themselves to study this new science of divination as soon as it made its appearance. Some of them reproduced, in special treatises with designs and illustrations appended, the types of hands scored with lines or signs favourable or the reverse; others investigated the direct relation between the various parts of the human hand and the celestial constellations. Both had discovered and defined various types of hands: Rumphilius declared there were six types, Compotus eight, and Indaginus thirty-seven, while Corvæus placed the number of different types at a hundred and fifty; but Jean Belot, the curé of Milmonts, afterwards reduced the total to four. There was a long discussion as to whether the right or the left hand was the one from which the horoscope should be drawn. There was an equal difference of opinion as to the meaning of the lines and irregularities of the hand, though it had been subjected to the astrological divisions and subdivisions into which entered the virtues and influences of the planets (Fig 156). Even the colour of the nails and the white spots which are often seen upon them were assigned a special meaning by the exponents of chiromancy, which thus became a very complicated and almost a mathematical science.

In addition to chiromancy, the Middle Ages witnessed the adoption of several modes of divination in use amongst the ancients, and of the revival, in a new shape, of others which were referred to in the books of Greek and Roman antiquity. As in ancient times, there was Aëromancy (the art of divining by the phenomena of the air), Hydromancy, Pyromancy, and Geomancy

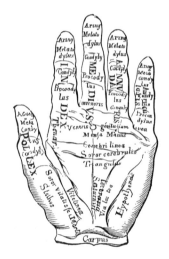

Fig. 156.—Specimen of the Left Hand, with the Lines and their Horoscopic Denominations.

(divining by means of water, fire, and earth). History has often alluded to the fantastic images which the credulity of our ancestors fancied they could see in the heavens when a meteor or the northern light was visible (Figs. 157 to 160). These were looked upon as sinister or favourable presages, according to their character. They also used pitchers filled with water, into which were plunged metallic blades marked with certain tokens, and which, as the water boiled, emitted sounds that the operator comprehended and explained to his listeners. Dactylomancy (from the Greek word δάκτυλος, finger) was practised by means of a ring, in many cases made under the influence of a certain constellation. This ring was suspended by a thread in the centre of an earthenware or metal pitcher, against the sides of which, swinging to and fro, it struck, emitting a number of sounds which were taken to be predictions and oracles. Pyromancy, or the art of divination by fire, varied according to the substances consumed, the smoke of which announced, by its density and colour, what was to be expected of the future. Thus, when a donkey's head was roasted upon live coal, the rotary movement of the fetid vapours emanating from it had a prophetic signification. Geomancy, which served to establish a correspondence between material beings and the elementary spirits, was connected with the sternest combinations of cabalism.

Other processes, which seemed to have a religious character, but which the Church none the less condemned as dangerous superstitions, were also resorted to in the Middle Ages in order to forecast the future. The *Angelic Art*, which consisted in an invocation of the guardian angel, and the *Notorious Art*, which addressed itself directly to God, in order to obtain immediate information as to the future, did not consist of a body of doctrines, but merely of a few prayers and secret ceremonies, by virtue of which the operator believed that he could obtain the Divine Presence. To St. Jerome was actually attributed the authorship of two books in which were indicated the practices of the Notorious Art and of the Angelic Art. Other prophetic books, to which a not less marked importance was attributed, became popular, so generally were they read, towards the close of the fifteenth century. One, entitled "Enchiridion Leonis Papæ" ("The Manual of Pope Leo"), the other, "Mirabilis Liber," attributed to St. Cæsarius, contained nothing to justify these singular pretensions. Moreover, to obtain what were called the *spells of the saints*, a text was taken from the Holy Scriptures and printed in the frontispiece of the book. Gregory of Tours, in his "History of the Franks," relates that he himself practised this kind of divination. In 577, Mérovée, son of Chilpéric, having taken refuge within the basilica of St. Martin at Tours, to escape the pursuit of his father and the vengeance of his step-mother, Frédégonde, entreated the holy bishop to tell him what he had to hope or to apprehend. The Bishop opened the Book of Solomon, and read this verse: "Let the eye which looks at its father be pecked out by the crow." This was a sinister omen. Mérovée did not understand it, and was anxious to interrogate for himself the *spells of the saints*. He placed upon the tomb of St. Martin the Books of Psalms, of Kings, and the

Gospels, and passed the night upon his knees before the tomb. After three days of fasting and prayer, he opened the holy books, and lighted only upon

Figs. 157 to 160.—Fantastic Forms and Figures seen in the Sky in the Sixteenth Century. Fac-simile of Ancient Designs.

passages which foreboded evil. He left the basilica in despair, and soon afterwards perished miserably.

The origin of magic had been religious fervour carried to excess, for

King Solomon was always looked upon by the adepts as the greatest of magicians. Hence came the name of Theurgy (from Θεός, God), which, however, was in many cases much the same as Goety (γόης, enchanter), this latter having for its object the invocation of invisible powers, amongst them being several evil genii (Figs. 161 and 162). Henry Cornelius Agrippa, magician as he was, or believed himself to be, defined the principle of theurgy as follows:—" Our soul, purified and made divine, inflamed by the love of God, ennobled by hope, guided by faith, raised to the summit of human intelligence, attracts to itself the truth; and in Divine truth, in the mirror of eternity, it beholds the condition of things natural, supernatural, and heavenly, their essence, their causes, and the plenitude of sciences, understanding them all in an instant. Thus, when we are in this state of purity and elevation, we know the things which are above nature, and we understand everything that appertains to this lower world; we know not only things present and past, but we also receive continually the oracles of what will happen in the near and in the far future. This is how men devoted to God, and who practise the three theological virtues, are masters of the elements, ward off tempests, raise the winds, cause the clouds to drop rain, heal the sick, raise up the dead." So, according to this Prince of Magicians, as Cornelius Agrippa was surnamed, a magician ought, above all things, to have an ardent and unswerving belief in the assistance of God, in whose name he exercised his celestial or infernal art.

Jesus Christ has said, " Have faith, and ye shall remove mountains." But magic was much earlier than the Christian era, for it is said to have originated with the magi of Chaldea, and to have received the name from them. The demonographers of the sixteenth century asserted that magic had never had any other object than the invocation of demons, and they ascribed the origin of it to Mercury or to Zabulon, who is supposed to be no other than Satan himself. This sinister science was said to have been inculcated and propagated during the life of Christ by one Barnabe Cypriot, who asserted that he drew his doctrines from books of magic, the authorship of which he ascribed to Adam, Abel, Enoch, and Abraham. These wonderful books, which the angel Raziel, the counsellor of Adam, and the angel Raphael, the guide of Tobias, had communicated to men, were said to be in existence in Abyssinia, in the monastery of the Holy Cross, which was founded by Queen Sheba on her return from the visit which she paid to Solomon.

It must not be supposed that the number of adepts to magic has ever been very great; the majority were never more than mere theorists; that is to say, purely speculative savants, who studied in books the mysterious theory of the art of magic. Those who asserted that they put the art of magic into practice alone merited the name of magicians. But the common

Fig. 161.—The Prince of Darkness.—After a Miniature of the "Holy Grail."—Manuscript of the Fifteenth Century.—National Library, Paris.

people, always ready to discover the marvellous side of natural things (Fig. 162), and to place credence in the most mendacious illusions, invariably accused of magic the eminent men who had illustrated themselves by great scientific discoveries. Moreover, any alchemist who was supposed to be in possession of the great work was looked upon as a magician. Thus the famous Arab alchemist Geber, to whom the hermetic philosophers assigned the title of King, was believed to have obtained by magic the power of creating gold; and his numerous works upon occult philosophy, translated into Latin, are said to have been studied by the monk Gerbert, who became pope, with the title of Sylvester II., in 999. Gerbert was a man of vast general learning and a genius, yet he was looked upon as no better than a magician, and even a sorcerer. It was said in the twelfth century that he had possessed a book of black magic, which gave him full power over the hierarchy of demons, and a brass idol which uttered oracles for him; and that this was how he was able to discover treasures even if they were buried in the centre of the earth. Upon the day of his death (April 12th, 1003), however, Satan (Fig. 161) is supposed to have come to claim the debt which the Pontiff had contracted, and the tradition ran that ever after, when a pope was at the point of death, the bones of Sylvester II. were heard to rattle in his tomb.

The accusation of magic, from which even the illustrious Gerbert did not escape, was also levelled during the thirteenth century at the two greatest men upon whom science has set the seal of genius, Albert of Bollstadt, called Albertus Magnus, and Roger Bacon. Both were suspected of holding communication with the demons, and the former, who had endeavoured to expound the Revelation of St. John (Fig. 163), was obliged to resign the bishopric of Cologne, and to shut himself up in a monastery, in order to impose silence upon his accusers; while the second expiated in the dungeons of the Franciscans at Paris the daring of his experiments in chemistry, which were set down to the score of black magic. One of their contemporaries, the celebrated doctor, Peter of Albano, was burnt in effigy by the Inquisition, and died in prison at the age of eighty. Gabriel Naudé says of him, "He had acquired the knowledge of the seven liberal arts, by means of the seven familiar spirits which he kept confined in a piece of crystal;" and what was looked upon as an infallible sign of a pact with the devil, he had the faculty of summoning back to his purse the money he had paid out of it.

Spain, Scotland, and England also possessed about the same period several men of science who were denounced as magicians. In Spain there was Picatrix, whose wonderful feats are attested by the evidence of Alfonso, King of Castile; while Scotland possessed Thomas of Hersildonne, Lord

Soulis, and the philosopher, Michael Scott, who finds his place in Dante's "Divine Comedy." Amongst the English must be mentioned the terrible James Jodoc, who succeeded in "setting" the demon in a magic ring; while all other German magicians are eclipsed by the legendary John Faust, who made a pact with the devil for twenty-four years, and who, at the end of that period, was carried down to hell by the demon Mephistophiles, whom he had taken into his service.

But most of these so-called magicians were men of true learning, who, after exploring the vast domain of science, lapsed into the study of the occult arts. They must not, therefore, be confounded with the sorcerers or enchanters, who paid dearly for their sinister celebrity, and who were

Fig. 162.—Dragons.—After Miniatures in the "Book of the Marvels of the World."—Manuscript
of the Fourteenth Century.—National Library, Paris.

punished with death for their misdeeds. Amongst the latter were Jacques Dulot, who during the reign of Philippe le Bel killed himself in prison, after his wife had been burnt alive; Paviot, surnamed the Butcher, who perished at the stake, while his accomplice, Enguerrand de Marigny, was hung in chains at Montfaucon; Jean de Bar, also condemned to the stake as a necromancer and an invoker of the devil, at the end of the fourteenth century; and, most notable of all, the prototype of the legendary Bluebeard, the execrable Gilles de Laval, called Marshal de Raiz (or Retz), who, in concert with a Florentine sorcerer named Prelati, dabbled in necromancy and magic during his horrible debauches at his castles of Mâchecoul and Chantocé, in Brittany.

The occult sciences had maintained their prestige up to the dawn of the Renaissance; but they were cultivated at that period by men of genius, whose only aim was the love of science, and all of whom came to a miserable end, though they were vain enough to believe that they were in direct communication with spirits and demons. Cornelius Agrippa of Nettesheim, who was generally looked upon as an emissary of Satan, and who was merely a learned expounder of the doctrine of the ancient Gnostics, was always

Fig. 163.—The Angel, holding the Keys of Hell, enchains the Devil, in the shape of a Dragon, in the Pit.—Miniature from a Commentary on the Apocalypse.—Manuscript of the Twelfth Century.—In the Library of M. Ambrose Firmin-Didot, Paris.

accompanied, it was said, by two evil spirits in the shape of two black dogs. Paracelsus, who was believed to have imprisoned his familiar spirit in the pommel of his sword, boasted that he could create dwarfs, whom he animated with his archeus (or principle of heat) as a substitute for the soul, and yet he ended his days in a hospital. Cardan himself, that wonderful philosopher who had studied and dived deep into all branches of sciences, also claimed to possess a supernatural and invisible counsellor, whom he had brought from the planets of Venus and of Mercury, and whom he employed in his operations of astrology and magic. When this mysterious accomplice suddenly deserted him he died of hunger. These great worshippers of science were given to dabbling in sorcery and magic, but they did not turn their supposed intercourse with the beings of the invisible world to an evil purpose.

All the demonographers are agreed upon this point—that to obtain the intervention of Satan in human affairs it was necessary to form a pact with him (Fig. 164). "The pact which the magicians make with the demon," says Martin del Rio in his "Disquisitiones Magicæ," "is the only base upon which all operations of magic stand, so that whenever the magician wishes to do something appertaining to his art, he is expressly, or at all events impli-

Fig. 164.—The Devil, attempting to seize a Magician who had formed a pact with him, is prevented by a Lay Brother.—Fac-simile of a Miniature in the "Chroniques de Saint-Denis."—Manuscript of the Thirteenth Century.—In the National Library, Paris.

citly, compelled to invoke the assistance of the demon." The pact was formed in three different ways: the first involved the performance of various solemnities or ceremonies, in the midst of which the demon appeared in bodily shape to receive the homage of the contracting party; the second consisted in a simple request written and signed by the person who bound himself to the demon; the third, reserved for those who feared to face the demon, was accomplished by the intervention of a lieutenant or vicar, and was termed the tacit pact. All engagements entered into with the demon were based upon impious or wicked promises, which the contracting party had to fulfil under pain of immediate and violent death: these were denial of the Christian faith, contempt for the exercises of religion, *insolvency and bankruptcy to God's com-*

mands, repudiation of all saintly personages, change of baptismal name, horrible blasphemies, bloody sacrifices, &c.

The oath of fidelity, which it was necessary to take to the demon, was always pronounced in the midst of a circle traced upon the ground, accompanied by the offer of some pledge, such, for instance, as a piece of the

Fig. 165.—From the smoke ascending out of the abyss are born scorpions which scourge men. Miniature from a Commentary upon the Apocalypse.—Manuscript of the Twelfth Century. In the Library of M. Ambroise Firmin-Didot.

garments worn by the person taking it. These circles held an important place in all operations of magic, especially in evocations : there were generally three of them, and they were supposed to establish between the evoker and the spirits evoked by him a line of demarcation which the demon could not cross. Vervain, too, together with incense and lighted tapers, was almost always employed. In addition to incense, the magicians and sorcerers also employed a quantity of vegetable, mineral, and animal substances to create smoke, which was believed to act upon the demons, and even upon the influences of the stars (Fig. 165). It is evident that these fumigations, in which belladonna, opiates, &c., were employed, and which produced either giddiness or drowsiness, helped the magicians very much.

The art of magic had regulated the use of perfumes for its professional ceremonies, in accordance with the opinion which held the smoke of odoriferous substances to be a mystic link between the earth and the stars. Thus every kind of smoke was addressed to some particular planet (Fig. 165). To the Sun was dedicated a mixture of saffron, amber, musk, clove, and incense, to which were added the brain of an eagle and the blood of a cock. The Moon received, by preference, the vapour of white poppy and camphor, burnt in the head of a frog, together with the eyes of a bull and the blood of a goose. To Mars was burnt sulphur, mixed with various magic plants, such as hellebore and euphorbium, to which were added the blood of a black cat and the brain of a crow. It may easily be imagined how nauseous was the odour of these horrible mixtures, which ascended in a spiral column of smoke varying in hue, and athwart which the lookers-on believed they could see fantastic shapes. Moreover, the most singular properties were attributed to various substances which were thrown upon live coals. In order to produce thunder and rain, all that was necessary was to burn the liver of a chameleon. This species of witchcraft was practised by a special class of sorcerers called *tempest-raisers*. As late as the sixteenth century James VI. of Scotland had Dr. Fian tortured in his presence, upon the accusation of having raised a storm in which that sovereign nearly lost his life. While the chameleon's liver raised a high sea, the gall of cuttle-fish, burnt with roses and aloe-wood, produced earthquakes. A legion of demons and phantoms might be raised by burning together coriander, parsley, and hemlock, adding to them a liquor extracted from black poppy, giant fennel, red sandal-wood, henbane, and other obnoxious plants. But with all these mixtures it was necessary to observe the laws of sympathy and antipathy which prevail amongst the perfumes, as amongst the celestial bodies, in order to insure the success of the incantations.

The same laws of sympathy and antipathy were to be carefully observed in the preparation of philters, administered for the purpose of inspiring hatred or affection (Fig. 166). These philters, which in ancient times were

believed to have an irresistible effect, were generally composed of hetero-
geneous substances, which the magicians pretended to be able to reduce to
powder by means of various unholy incantations. The sorcerers sometimes
went so far as to use the host, consecrated or not, upon which they traced
letters written in blood. But they more generally employed substances
derived from the three domains of nature, the entrails of animals, the feathers
of birds, scales of fishes, and vegetable and mineral substances. Pulverized
loadstone, the parings of nails, and the human blood served to compose their

Fig. 166.—Marriage of a Young Man and an Old Woman.—Fac-simile of an Engraving in the
German Edition of the " Officia Ciceronis," 1542.—In the Arsenal Library, Paris.

powders, which were mixed with the food or the drink of persons upon whom
these philters were desired to take effect. Some magicians still had recourse
to hippomanes, which was much in favour with the Greek and Roman
enchanters, and which was nothing more than the lump of flesh found on
the head of colts when first foaled. The mandragora, which ancient naturalists
have described as a very wonderful plant, was in still greater renown in
the Middle Ages, and it was made to appear in all the most sinister operations of the magicians. This plant, which grows in the shape of a human

body, and belongs to the Solaneæ tribe, was said to have miraculous and Satanic properties, its origin being ascribed to a gruesome device of the demon.

Philters must not be confounded with the talismans which were in such great vogue during the Middle Ages, and which continued to be in repute until the end of the Renaissance. These talismans consisted of stones or metal plates, bearing astrological figures, and Arabic or Persian inscriptions; they came, in most cases, from the Gnostics of the East, and were intended to place beneath the protection of the celestial powers the persons possessing them. Most of these talismans had been brought into Europe at the time of the Crusades. The sixteenth century witnessed the increase of astrological forms, attention to which would insure the accomplishment of all human desires. Thus, for instance, to those who wished to earn honours and to become great, it was enjoined, " Engrave the image of Jupiter, who is a man with a ram's head, upon tin or upon a white stone, at the day and hour of Jupiter, when he is at home, as in Sagittarius, or in the Pisces, or in his exaltation, as in Cancer, and let him be free from all obstruction, principally from the evil looks of Saturn or of Mars; let him be rapid, and not burnt by the sun; in a word, wholly auspicious. Carry this image upon you, made as above, and according to all the above-mentioned conditions, and you will see things which will surpass your belief." These comparatively harmless superstitions were covered by judicial astrology with the mantle of science.

The magicians resorted to written incantations of a more mysterious character as an accompaniment to the *gemahez*, or quaint stones upon which nature had put some distinctive mark; to the magic phials containing the blood of owls and of bats; to the *hand of glory*, which was no other than the withered hand of a man who had been hung, for discovering hidden treasure; to the magic mirrors, in which were reflected the images of the dead and of the absent; and to the well-known shirt of necessity, made of flax spun by the hands of a virgin, sown during a night in Christmas week, and representing upon the front the heads of two bearded men with the crown of Beelzebub. This shirt was said to render the wearer invulnerable.

One of the most dreaded processes of magic was that of bewitching, the object of which was to compass the death by slow degrees of a person who could not be murdered outright. The first step in this process was to model in clay or in virgin wax an effigy of the intended victim, and the next to kill a swallow, the heart of which was placed under the right arm of the effigy, and the liver under the left. Then the sacrilegious operation began; the body and limbs of the wax or clay figure were pricked with new needles, to the accompaniment of the most horrible imprecations. During the trial of the ill-fated Enguerrand de Marigny, Prime Minister of Philippe le Bel, a magician was brought before the tribunal to declare that he had, at the minister's request, bewitched the King by pricking the magic image which represented him with a needle. The bewitchers had recourse to other processes. In some cases the figure was of bronze, and more or less deformed; it was concealed in a tomb, and left to rust, the rust coinciding with the leprosy which attacked the person bewitched. In other cases the figure was of wax, and was made to melt before a fire of wood and vervain, the progress of the bewitched person to death keeping pace with the melting of his image. In other cases, again, the effigy was made out of earth taken from a graveyard and mixed with dead bones: an inscription in mystic characters completed the bewitchment, and caused the death of the victim within a short time.

Amongst the numerous trials which revealed details of this crime, the most celebrated was that of the Duchess of Gloucester, who was accused of having bewitched King Henry VI. She had instructed a necromancer, a priest named Bolingbroke, with the execution of this act of magic, in concert with a well-known sorceress, one Marie Gardemain, Satan being invoked under the name of *Mill'ouvrier*. The wax figure of the King was found half melted in front of a fire of dry plants which had been gathered in a cemetery by moonlight. The crime being proved, the necromancer was hung, the sorceress burnt, and the Duchess of Gloucester condemned to imprisonment for life. The most notorious bewitchers of the fourteenth century were Paviot and Robert. In the sixteenth century the Italian astrologer, Cosmo Ruggieri, would have been compromised in many such cases but for the protection of Catherine de' Medicis; and it was always believed by the public that the illness to which Charles IX. succumbed eight months after the massacre of St. Bartholomew was caused by bewitchment.

Another piece of withcraft, not less formidable, and very easy to practise, was that of *chevillement* (peg or nail driving), which was also supposed to have a fatal influence upon the person whose death it was sought to compass.

A nail or a wooden peg was driven into a wall, the name of the intended victim being pronounced at each blow of the hammer. The sorcerers of

Fig. 167.—The Alchemist.—After an Engraving by Vriese.—In the Cabinet of Designs, National Library, Paris.

the Middle Ages had other devices for killing people from a distance. Thus, for instance, the *archers*, or *sagittarii*, launched into the air a sharp-pointed arrow, which the demon directed towards a given goal, and rendered invisible. This arrow pierced the heart of the victim at a distance of even seven or eight hundred miles. In the fifteenth century one of these sagittarii, named Pumbert, shot three of these arrows every day, never failing to hit his mark; and his sole object was to make himself agreeable to the devil, who indicated to him the various victims. The inhabitants of Lauterburg, in Prussia, stirred to indignation by his proceedings, eventually fell upon him and murdered him. The device of the sagittarii came from the North, where the inhabitants of Finland and Lapland got rid of their enemies by means of little leaden arrows, which they drew at a venture, to the accompaniment of magic phrases. These arrows went straight to the mark, and left an invisible wound, which invariably proved fatal at the end of three days.

The Middle Ages also recognised the existence of certain magical agents, corporeal and incorporeal, due to the influence of the demon or of familiar spirits. Such was the *evil eye*, a device known from the earliest ages, but inaccurately defined by the demonographers, who do not in all cases attribute its origin to the action of the infernal powers. Nor were the hermetic philosophers agreed as to the nature of the archeus, the architect spirit which labours without ceasing in the cavities of the human body, and which Paracelsus looked upon as one of the active forces of the mind. The most learned men of science, such as David of Planis-Campi and Ambroise Paré, were also believers in the *constellated ascendant*, which participated in all the combinations of the occult sciences, and which manifested itself sometimes as a demon, sometimes as a good angel. According to the learned Ambroise Paré, the astral influence was that which presided at the birth of each individual. These incorporeal agents were therefore supposed to take part in all the acts of the occult sciences, and especially in alchemy, in the practice of which its adepts were incessantly calling to their aid the elementary spirits of the metals, and the evil genii which were invoked in nearly all of the incantations (Fig. 167). These genii and spirits, whether good or evil, are mentioned by name in many of the curious formulæ used in the making of seals (*sigilla*) or magic rings which had a power over demons, preserving the wearers from sudden death, protecting them from illness, and from danger by land or sea, and procuring for them as much money as they required. The Sieur de Villamont relates, in his "Voyages en Orient," that he met at Venice, in 1570, a Cypriot gentleman named Antoine Bragadin, who kept up a princely establishment, and who, by means of his diabolic art, was able to supply the Venetian Senate with five hundred thousand crowns which he had manufactured. This same Bragadin unfortunately went to Bavaria, where he was condemned to the stake ; he obtained, however, by payment of a large sum and by confessing his crimes, the privilege of being beheaded upon a scaffold hung with black, and surmounted by a gibbet covered with copper plates, "which," says a writer of that period, "were typical of the deceptions practised by this coiner of gold."

Fig. 168.—Old-maid Witch.—Fac-simile of a Wood Engraving attributed to Holbein, taken from the German Translation of Boethius's " Consolations of Philosophy," Augsburg Edition, 1537, in folio.

Most of the hermetic philosophers, whether magicians or not, claimed to be in possession of the secrets of the Cabal, which was not, however, identical with the great Jewish Cabal communicated to Adam, according to the rabbis, by the angels after his expulsion from Paradise, and appropriated by the Eastern philosophers in the early ages of Christianity. It was at first a wholly speculative science, which assumed to fathom the secrets of the crea-tion and of the Divine Nature, while the hermetists and magicians merely recognised in the Cabal, as understood by them, the art of causing certain higher powers to act upon the lower world, and so to produce supernatural effects. The main point, therefore, was to discover the names of these superior powers, and reduce them by evocations to a state of passive obedience. This magic Cabal consisted in evocations destined to place man in communication with the invisible intelligences of heaven and earth. According to the belief of the cabalists of the Middle Ages, Ariel, the genius of the sublunary world, had beneath his orders the Princes Damalech, Taynor, and Sayanon; the latter commanded the secondary spirits, the most powerful of whom were Guabarel, Torquaret, and Rabianica. Nanael was the genius of the divine, Jerathel of the terrestrial, and Mikael of the political sciences, while Jeliel presided over the animal kingdom. The other genii, each one of whom had its attributions in the mysterious government of earthly things, formed an innumerable hierarchy of invisible beings, whom the cabalists of the sixteenth century did not scruple to pass in review, designating each by its name as well as by its distinctive quality. Cornelius Agrippa, for instance, boasted that he had registered in his catalogue the names of six thousand intelligences, genii, or spirits, belonging to a great number of categories, and all of which might be evoked by the adepts of the divine art.

The occult sciences had in this way brought within their domain most of the fantastic beings who had been known to popular superstition from the earliest periods under so many names, and as possessing so many different attributions. The fairies were long supreme in the country districts, where they were said often to appear to men without being compelled by magic to emerge from their normal and invisible existence. They were called *favas* in the South of France, *korrigans* in Brittany, *filandières* and *bonnes dames* in the Saintonge and Picardy, *banshees* in Ireland and Scotland, *nornas* in the Northern countries. They were a mixture of human and of divine nature; they were enchantresses or magicians, presiding over the destiny of mortals, sometimes old, sometimes young, beautiful or ugly; they inhabited solitary caves or the snowy peaks of the mountains, or limpid sources or aërial spheres. They were not in much request amongst magicians, who left them to the fancies of poets and novelists. The mysterious beings whom magicians more readily called to their aid were the intermediary spirits who belonged rather to the great family of demons. Amongst these may be mentioned the *estries*, or demons of darkness, who hugged to suffocation the people whom they met at night; the *goblins*, who made their presence felt by harmless antics ; the *follets*, who led the traveller astray by false lights ; the *luitons*, or *lutins*; and the *metallic spirits*, in whom it is easy to recognise the emanations of inflammable gas which produce so many sudden explosions in the mines, and which are known as *fire-damp*.

Demons, too, were the men-wolves and men-dogs, which were very similar to the *ogres*, or *ouigours*, which really existed in the Mongolian hordes, and whose terrible aspect caused them to be the terror of the populations.

The *loups-garous* (Fig. 169), men whom a pact with the devil compelled to assume the face of a wolf once a year, scoured the woods and fields,

Fig. 169.—The Man-dog, the Man-wolf, the Man-bull, and the Man-pig.—After the Miniatures in the " Livre des Merveilles du Monde."—Manuscript of the Fourteenth Century.—In the National Library, Paris.

devouring the young children : like the *vampires* in Poland, the *broucolaques* in Greece, and the *white men* in Provence, they thirsted after human blood. Occult philosophy recognised, in addition, the existence of many other spirits of a more inoffensive kind, whom it comprised under the generic name of elementary spirits, because they inhabited the four elements : *sylphs*, in the air ; *salamanders*, in the fire ; *gnomes*, in the earth ; *ondins*, in the waters.

All the beings of the invisible world were subject to the influence or domination of magic, which always proceeded, though in different degrees, from the works of the demon ; but in the Middle Ages there were various sectaries of this infernal art. The *enchanters*, the *charmers* (male or female),

merely made use of magic words or verses for their charms or enchantments; the *necromancers* and *magicians* added to their incantations a whole
ritual of dark and sinister ceremonies; the *sorcerers* and the *sorceresses*, *stryges*
and *faiturières*, did not hesitate to resort to the most abominable practices
in order to get into direct communication with Satan. The characteristic
difference between the acts of magic and of sorcery is precisely stated in
the following passage from a theological work by Cardinal de Richelieu:—
" Magic is an art of producing effects by the power of the devil; there is
this difference between magic and sorcery, that the principal aim of magic
is *ostentation*, and that of sorcery *mischief*." This definition will explain
how it was that the sorcerers and sorceresses were proceeded against and
punished in the sixteenth century with more severity than the necromancers and magicians had been in the Middle Ages. The enchanters
and charmers were only proceeded against for any specific injuries they
might have caused, and the astrologers who confined themselves to the
astrological art had nothing to fear in the shape of legal repression,
though they were liable to the censures and anathemas of the ecclesiastical
authority.

It was not until the fifteenth century that sorcerers and sorceresses began
to attend the Sabbath, which henceforward became the council of sorcery
and the supreme court of the demon. There is a difference of opinion as to
the true origin of the name and of the thing itself. There were nocturnal
meetings of the sorceresses among all the early peoples, but these were not
the Sabbath, which, when first instituted, was essentially of an obscene and
impious character, obnoxious alike to human and Divine laws. The starting-
point of the Sabbath was, perhaps, what was termed, in the twelfth century,
the *messe des Vaudois*, a denomination afterwards transformed into *mezcle des
Vaudois*. This *messe* was originally a secret meeting of the Vaudois proselytes
of the heretic Pierre Valdo in the mountains of Dauphiny. It was said that
the Vaudois met in this way to assist at magic ceremonies, the object of
which was to destroy the crops and disturb the elements, and that they were
accompanied by devilish feasts and infernal dances, with unintelligible incantations, resembling those of the Jews at their synagogue meetings on the day
of the Sabbath. These mysterious assemblies continued to be held in the
dark, but their aspect and purpose changed when *vaulderie* became synonymous with sorcery, and the heretics had made way for the sorcerers. Hence-

Fig. 170.—The Sabbath: St. James the Elder combating the diabolical Enchantments of a Magician.—Composed by Breughel the Elder. Engraved by Cock (Sixteenth Century).

forward the Sabbath was merely the trysting-place of sorcerers and sorceresses who assembled from all quarters, traversing space with the rapidity of lightning, some mounted upon animals of fantastic shape, or hoisted upon the shoulders of demons, others bestriding the magic broomstick (Fig. 170). It was here that Satan held his assizes, and received the impure homage of his subjects, distributing to novices the mark and sign of the infernal initiation. De Lancre, in his "Treatise upon the Inconstancy of the Demons," says, "The devil, at the Sabbath, is seated in a black chair, with a crown of black horns, two horns in his neck, and one in the forehead, which sheds light upon the assembly, the hair bristling, the face pale and exhibiting signs of uneasiness, the eyes round, large, fully opened, inflamed, and hideous, with a goat's beard, the neck and the rest of the body deformed, the body of the shape of a man and a goat, the hands and the feet of a human being."

The horrors and sacrileges committed at the Sabbath were no merely imaginary crimes; the sorcerers could not impute their misdeeds to credulity or ignorance, and M. Ferdinand Denis says, "All that the wildest imagination can conceive, mythological recollections, fantastic traditions, terrible traditions, form the compound of the court of Satan. Diseased minds invent new crimes, and the strident laugh of the devil encourages the commission of a thousand nameless sins. Beelzebub himself ceases to put on the image of a foul goat." Thus the faggots of the stake burnt throughout the whole of the sixteenth century, and all kinds of torture were applied, without distinction of age or sex, to persons accused of having assisted at the Sabbath and given themselves up to Satan.

POPULAR BELIEFS.

ACTANTIUS, in his book upon the "Divine Institution," says, "Religion is the worship of what is true, superstition of what is false." "All superstition is a great punishment and a very dangerous infamy for men," added St. Augustine. The Council of Paris, held in 829, pronounced very energetically against "most pernicious evils, which are assuredly remnants of paganism, such as magic, judicial astrology, witchcraft, sorcery or poisoning, divination, charms, and the conjectures drawn from dreams." The Provincial Council, in 1466, admitted with St. Thomas that superstition is an *idolatry*. The illustrious John Gerson had already declared that "superstition is a vice opposed in the extreme to worship and religion." At all periods the Church, by the organ of her doctors and her councils, waged war upon superstition, as the good labourer roots up the tares which threaten to choke the wheat. In some cases superstitious beliefs took the form of an exaggeration of faith and an excess of devotion, in which event there was something touching and respectable about them; in others they were due to demonomania, and were the expression of a culpable or absurd credulity. In other cases, again, they had their root in an erroneous or distorted tradition; sometimes, also, they were of a futile and uncertain character, or became a heresy against the Church. In fact, everything in the physical world was made the pretext for superstition.

The Middle Ages teemed with recollections of ancient mythology, and those who may be surprised that such should have been the case, considering the horror in which the religion of the Gospel held everything relating to the errors of paganism, may be reminded that the pagan religions, when they disappeared from off the face of the globe, left behind them a mass of popular prejudices profoundly rooted in men's minds. We may cite, for instance, the address of St. Eloi, minister of King Dagobert, and Bishop of Noyon, to his clergy:—"Above all, I beseech of you, do not observe any of the sacrilegious customs of the pagans; do not consult the engravers of talismans, or the diviners, or the sorcerers, or the enchanters, for any cause, even for illness; pay no heed to omens or to sneezing; do not be influenced by the singing of birds when you hear them in your journeys. . . . . Let no Christian pay heed to the day he leaves a house, or that upon which he returns to it. . . . . Let not any one at the Feast of St. John celebrate the solstices by dances or diabolic incantations. Let no one seek to invoke the demons, such as Neptune, Pluto, Diana, Minerva, or the Evil Genius. . . . . Let no one observe the day of Jupiter (Thursday) as a day of rest. Let no Christian make vows in the temples, or by the side of fountains, or gardens, or stones, or trees. . . . . Let no one perform lustrations, or enchantments upon herbs, or drive his flock through the hollow in a tree, or through a hole dug in the ground. . . . . Let no one utter loud cries when the moon wanes. . . . . Let no man call the sun or moon his master." Thus spoke, in the seventh century, a pious prelate, who boldly attacked the superstitions of his time; and this episcopal exhortation readily explains, and even excuses, a number of strange or monstrous facts which, though of much more recent date, seem to form part of the annals of the grossest idolatry.

The Feasts of the Ass, of the Deacons, of the Kings, of the Buffoons, and of the Innocents, characteristic as they were of the Middle Ages, and very popular with the people at large, especially with the lower clergy, the students, the lawyers' clerks, and the youth of the period, deserve notice, not only because the recollection of them still survives in the local history of certain districts, but because they were the origin of French dramatic art.

When Herodian, Macrobius, and Dionysius of Halicarnassus describe the Saturnalia and the Lupercalia of ancient Rome, they might have been describing these singular festivals of the Middle Ages, which Christianity was compelled to tolerate for a long time, as an inheritance which, though declining to accept, could not be shaken off in a moment. This is how it was that so late as the fifteenth century the feasts of Saturn, Pan, and other pagan divinities were, in spite of ecclesiastical censure, celebrated

Fig. 171.—The Procession of the Bœuf Gras.—Stained Glass of the Sixteenth Century, in the Church of Bar-sur-Seine (Aube).

under denominations which only served to disguise the persistence of the idolatry.

With the Romans the Feast of the Kalends, or of the Saturnalia, began in the middle of December, and continued until the third or the fifth day of January. As long as it lasted public and private business was suspended, and the whole time was spent in banquets, concerts, and masquerades. People exchanged presents very freely, and at the banquets slaves were proclaimed kings of the festival instead of their masters. This period of license was thought to be a reproduction of the reign of Saturn and of the Golden Age. Christianity, whose first followers were selected from the lower classes of society, was unwilling at first to deprive them of a popular festival which no longer possessed a religious significance, and the only change made was to divide the festival into several shorter ones of a day each. Hence arose certain pagan idolatries and reminiscences, to which the festivals of Christmas, of St. Stephen, of St. John the Evangelist, of the Innocents (from December 25th to 28th), of the Circumcision, and of the Epiphany, or of the Kings, gave rise. The Lupercalia, or the feasts of Pan, the god of the country, which the ancients celebrated in February, were also divided by the Christians into two series, the feasts of the Carnival (Fig. 171) and those of the month of May, which were generally restricted to the three Rogation days. The Church was at first indulgent towards these remnants of paganism, merely blaming the abuses which they engendered. The councils and doctors were more severe, but the bishops in their dioceses, the priests in their parishes, and the abbots in their monasteries seemed afraid to oppose these superstitious habits, which still held such great sway.

At first the Feast of the Kalends was called the Feast of the Barbatorii, the reason no doubt being that the actors in these saturnalia covered their faces with hideous beards, which in the language of the thirteenth century were called *barboires*. We do not possess any very accurate information concerning this festival earlier than the twelfth century; but it was known to have been observed not only in cathedrals and parish churches, but in many monasteries and convents. It was invariably the cause of, and the excuse for, the most disgraceful excesses.

The first liturgical work which, under the name of "Liberty of December," describes the strange and indecent proceedings at the Feast of the Buffoons, bears date 1182, and shows that one of the main features in it was an inversion of the duties and rank of the clergy. As a proof of how thoroughly this profane usage had passed into custom, it may be mentioned that though the practice had been several times anathematized by the councils, and though several prelates and sovereigns had laboured hard to extirpate what a French king called "a detestable remnant of pagan idolatry, and of the worship of the infamous Janus," upon the day of the circumcision in 1444 the priests officiated in the churches, some dressed as women, some as buffoons (see Figs. 172 and 173), some as stage-players, others with their capes and chasubles turned inside out. They elected a bishop or archbishop of buffoons, attired him in the pontifical robes, and received his benediction, chanting an indecent parody of the matins. They danced in the choir, singing ribald songs, ate and drank upon the altar,

172.—Buffoon playing the Bagpipe.— From the " Atlas des Monuments de la France," by Alex. Lenoir.

Fig. 173.—Buffoon holding the Bauble beneath his Arm.—After a Miniature in a Manuscript of the Fifteenth Century.—National Library, Paris.

played dice on the pavement, burnt old leather and other foul matter in the censer, and incensed the celebrating priest with it, and after this mock mass they promenaded the streets mounted upon chariots, and vying with one another in grimaces and in insolent and impious remarks.

The ecclesiastical censures and the royal prohibitions naturally remained dead letters at a time when, as Gerson tells us, there were preachers who declared from the pulpit that this festival was "welcome in the sight of God," and when the clergy of Troyes met the remonstrances of King Charles VII. by saying that their bishop, Jean Léguisé, had ordered them to celebrate the Feast of the Buffoons, which was also kept at Sens.

This festival, which the Troyes clergy set great store by, was the same as the famous Mass of the Ass which existed, in different forms, in various towns of France, but the special ceremonial of which, drawn up expressly for the Church of Sens, is still to be read in a manuscript of the thirteenth century preserved in the library of that town. The *rubrics*, inserted in the text of the order of service, enable us to follow the whole proceedings of this mass, which was not celebrated, as has been alleged, in honour of Balaam's ass, but of the ass which was in the stable in which our Lord was born, or of that which He rode when He entered Jerusalem upon Palm Sunday. This singular festival did not, it may be added, cause any greater disorder than that of St. Hubert, when dogs and falcons were brought into the church to receive the priest's benediction, to the sound of horn and trumpet; but there was no idea of profanity on the part of those who did this.

The festival of the Ass was conducted in this wise. A comely animal having been selected, it was conducted in procession through the streets, which were strewn with carpets, and was met by the clergy, chanting, who accompanied it to the door of the church. Here they announced to the people, in Latin verse, "This is the day of gladness. Let those who are of doleful countenance get away from here. Away with envy and haughtiness! Those who celebrate the Feast of the Ass desire to be joyful." The ass was led up to the altar, and then was sung that "Prose of the Ass" which, according to the evidence of a contemporary, given in verse at the commencement of the ritual, brought into relief the talents of the first chorister, and which, far from being a sacrilegious mockery, as the philosophers of the eighteenth century have insinuated, was a simple and pathetic manifestation of the faith and piety of our forefathers. Two of the Latin strophes, with the French chorus, run :—

> "Orientibus partibus,
> Adventavit Asinus,
> Pulcher et fortissimus,
> Sarcinis aptissimus,
> *Hé, sire Ane, hé !*

Hic in collibus Sichen,
Enutritus sub Ruben,
Transiit per Jordanem,
Saliit in Bethleem.
Hé, sire Ane, hé !"

According to an old tradition, preserved at Sens, after the Hallelujah, which was sung several times during the service, all the congregation brayed in chorus in imitation of an ass. Then the choristers, from behind the altar, chanted two Leonine lines, proclaiming that this "is the most illustrious of all illustrious days, the greatest of all the festivals." Lastly, the chief precentor, who had used his voice to the utmost in chanting the "Prose of the Ass," was conducted in pomp to a well-spread table, where he and his acolytes were supplied with a bountiful meal.

The Feast of the Ass, as stated above, was celebrated in several towns of France. Thus we learn by the registers of the Cathedral of Autun that from 1411 to 1416, in the Feast of the Buffoons, an ass was led in procession, with a chasuble thrown over him, and to the usual chorus of, "Hé, sire âne, hé !" sung by lay clerks in masquerade costume. The ceremonial at Beauvais was very similar to that at Sens, and it is clear that the refrain quoted in the preceding sentence was taken by the spectators as an invitation to bray in all tones. At the Feast of the Ass, as celebrated at Rouen, Balaam's ass was introduced into a *show* or review of personages taken from the Old and the New Testament, and composing a sort of mystery-play, interlarded with dialogues in doggerel Latin.

Eudes de Sully, Bishop of Paris, towards the end of the twelfth century, was one of the prelates who tried the hardest to put down these saturnalia, and if his efforts were not crowned with immediate success, he set an example to other ecclesiastics to use their influence in the same direction. The ritual of the Feast of Buffoons, properly so called, has not come down to our own day, but we know that from the beginning of the fifteenth century it was only under the porch, in the churchyard, or upon the open space beyond—that is to say, outside the church itself—that these masquerades took place, and soon afterwards the festival was suppressed altogether. The clerks regarded this ancient tradition as one of their most cherished privileges, and were not easily induced to renounce it ; but while the laity, inheriting, so to speak, the Feast of the Buffoons, formed associations for getting up the mystery-

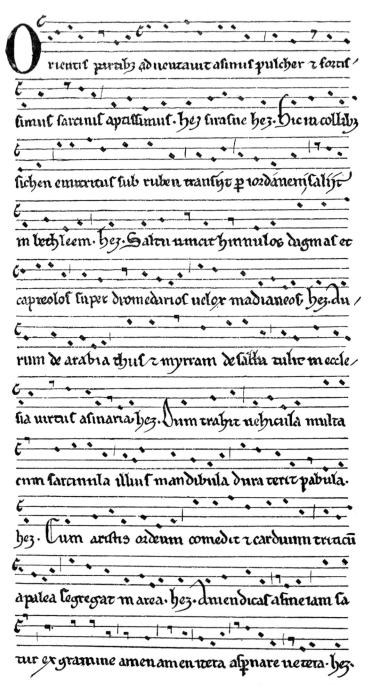

Fig. 174.—"Prose of the Ass," plain.—Fac-simile of the Page of the Ritual of Pierre de
Corbeil.—Manuscript of the Thirteenth Century.—Sens Library.

ORIENTIS PARTIBUS

Fig. 175.—" Prose of the Ass," set to Music with Organ Accompaniment by M. Félix Clement.

plays, the Church gradually withdrew its protection and tolerance of the excesses arising from the "Liberty of December."

It is certain, however, that the election of a Pope of the Buffoons was discontinued before the suppression of the Feast of the Innocents, as the former was considered an insult to the Papacy previously to the election of a Bishop of the Innocents being looked upon as offensive to the episcopacy. It is also worthy of remark that these parodies of elections lasted longer and were more celebrated in the North than in the South. At Amiens, for instance, as late as 1548 there was not only a Pope of the Buffoons, but several Cardinals as well. This pope, elected by the subdeacons, received as the insignia of his dignity a gold ring, a silver tiara, and a seal. His enthronement took place at a banquet paid for by the canons of the cathedral, upon the condition that the servitors of the mock pontiff should abstain from removing the bells from the tower and committing other such pleasantries. The Bishops of the Innocents, elected, consecrated, and acclaimed by the precentors and subordinate officials of the Church, had the right to wear the mitre, staff, and gloves at the ceremonies of the Buffoons; they issued decrees and ordinances sealed with their seal, and also coined lead and even copper money bearing their name and motto.

The learned hold that these pieces of money, which had much analogy with the *sigilla*, or seals, which the Romans offered as presents at the Saturnalia, were used as counters at games of chance, and so became sorts of passes or countermarks to be used at the processions, *shows*, and theatrical representations which the Bishop of the Innocents had the right to organize and have performed by his adherents. These moneys, great quantities of which have been discovered, especially in Picardy, which seems to have been the mother country of the Innocents, are in many cases similar, with regard to the effigy and inscriptions, to the royal and baronial coinage of the fifteenth and sixteenth centuries. In addition to the Latin inscription, *Sit nomen Domini benedictum*, they often bear various French inscriptions, such as, *Monnoie de l'evesque Innocent*, or nondescript mottoes, such as, *Vous voyez le temps qu'il est!* Guerre cause maintz hélas (griefs)—*Bene vivere et lætari*, &c.

The popes and patriarchs of the Buffoons also coined money, but all the pieces which have been preserved are distinguished by two principal characteristics. One of them represents a double head of a cardinal and a buffoon, with the inscription, *Stulti aliquando sapientes.*

We cannot attempt to give even a summary description of the extravagances to which the celebration of the festival of the Buffoons, or of the Innocents,
gave rise in the various localities where they were carried on. At Noyon,
Senlis, Corbie, Rheims, Toul, Bayeux, Rouen, Vienne in Dauphiny, Viviers
in Provence, &c., the reign of Folly was annually proclaimed, and lasted a
more or less considerable period. The processions, the cavalcades, the
mummeries, the parodies of the most solemn actions, and of the most staid
personages, made up this popular festival, which, when it had been excluded

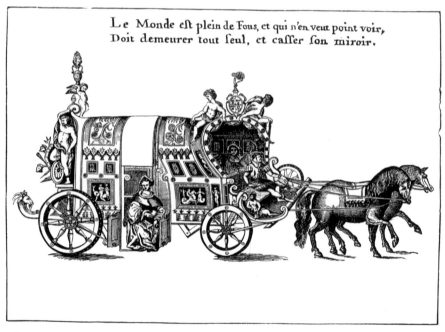

Fig. 176.—Chariot of the *Mère Folle*, which figured at Dijon in 1610.—Fac-simile of a Design
communicated by M. Ruggieri.

from the sanctuary, was kept up amidst debauchery and riot in the highways.
At that period each town had its own special procession or *show :* that of the
Spinet at Lille ; of the *Mère Folle* at Dijon ; of the Prince of Love at
Tournay ; of the Prince of Youth at Soissons ; of the Caritats at Béziers ;
and they were all imitations of the Feast of Buffoons, foreshadowing, so to
speak, the coming of the theatre, for these processions were accompanied
by scenes enacted in dumb-show, or with the accompaniment of dialogue,

comic and serious, which became *mysteries* and farces when they had been set to rhyme by a poet. (See below, chapter on the *Theatre*.)

There was a general effort made, moreover, to form private societies for preserving and perpetuating the traditions of the Feast of Buffoons. The brothers of the Passion, whom Charles VI. allowed to settle in Paris (1402), and to represent the mysteries in a room at the Trinity Hospital, were, in the origin, members of the Church and pious persons who were desirous of letting religion benefit by the unbridled passion for spectacles and masquerades which the Feast of the Buffoons had spread amongst the clergy and the population. At first the ecclesiastical authorities encouraged these plays, as being more edifying than those of the Pope of the Buffoons and the Bishop of the Innocents. The lawyers, advocates, procureurs, and clerks of the Basoche, who remembered the good times of the "Liberty of December," resolved to offer an asylum to the *Folie*, when it was condemned by and banished from the Church. They created the kingdom of Sots and the empire of Fools, electing a prince, whom they crowned with a green cap with donkey's ears, under the name of the *Mère Sotte*. The principal object of this new institution was the representation of *farces* or satires upon the people in authority.

Amongst the provincial societies which carried on the traditions of the Feast of the Buffoons must be mentioned, first of all, that of the *Mère Folle de Dijon* (see Fig. 176), which Philip the Good, Duke of Burgundy, himself founded in 1454, for the sole purpose of putting an end to the scandalous orgies which took place in the churches at the festivals of Christmas, Epiphany, and Rogation Sundays. This society, the practices of which were in complete harmony with the customs of that wine-growing country, consisted of more than five hundred persons of all ranks, and they were divided into two parties, one of infantry (see Fig. 177), the other of cavalry, all of whom wore the fool's cap and *liveries ;* that is to say, costumes which were a motley mixture of yellow, red, or green. The leader of the band, named *Mère Folle*, passed reviews of his army, presided over a mock tribunal, and pronounced mock judgments, which his *procurator-fiscal green* undertook to put into execution. These trials and pleadings, cavalcades and solemn assemblies, brought into relief all the types and attributes of Folly, which have disappeared without leaving the world any wiser ; but the ancient Feast of the Buffoons, when driven from under the vaulted roof of the temple, continued to inspire songs and farces which betokened the birth of some comedy, while the clergy inaugurated the serious drama by histories taken from the sacred books and the legends of the saints. The mystery-plays and farces were, therefore, so much to the credit of the Feast of Buffoons, but there is an interval of three or four centuries between the "Prose of the Ass" and

Fig. 177.—Staff of the Dijon Infantry in 1482.—Fac-simile of a Design communicated by M. Ruggieri.

the scenic compositions of Jean Michel, of André de la Vigne, and of Peter Gringoire. (See below, chapter on the *Theatre.*)

Many instances might be given of popular errors which had their source in the traditions of antiquity, and which maintained the ideas of paganism amidst the most holy and solemn of beliefs; but, at the same time, these errors would not have been sustained had not the credulity of the men of learning helped to propagate them by the creation of a world of fantastic beings (see Fig. 178). Thus, for instance, when Peter the Eater, called *Comestor*, a famous theologian of the twelfth century, in his paraphrase of the Scriptures, arrived at the fourth chapter of Genesis, where Moses speaks of the giants born to the sons of God and the daughters of men, he takes care

Fig. 178.—The Serpent, or the Dragon, and the Behemoth, or the Devil.—Miniature from a Commentary on the Apocalypse.—Manuscript of the Twelfth Century.—In the Library of M. Ambroise Firmin-Didot, Paris.

to state that these giants are of the family of Enceladus and Briareus. The deluge of Deucalion and Pyrrha was borrowed from to furnish certain dramatic incidents in the Deluge of the Bible; the serpent Python and the monsters bred from the slime of the earth (Figs. 179 to 182), in the Greek theogony, were imported into the glossology which the rabbis, those grand masters of superstition, were continually introducing into the elastic frame-work of the Talmud. The Christians were careful not to abandon the emblematic representation of these monsters, which soon became, in the eyes of the people, the multiform personification of the spirit of evil.

There are numerous legends in which the serpent is vanquished by the great champions of the faith. In Phœnicia we find St. George slaying the dragon which was about to devour the daughter of the king of that country; St. Michael and St. Germain arming themselves with the cross to drive out

Figs. 179 to 182.—Monsters born from the Deluge.—After the Wood Engravings in the "Chronique de Nuremberg," printed in 1493, in folio.

the winged serpents which were invading the land of Parisis; St. Romain binding with his stole the *Gargouille* of Rouen (see Fig. 183); St. Martha leading with a string the terrible *Tarasque* which had laid waste the neighbourhood of Tarascon. Thus the serpent took his place in emblazonry with the unicorn, the chimæra, and other marvellous animals. He has his place in history under the designation of Mélusine of Lusignan; he has been the theme of the most wonderful travellers' tales, and is to be found from one end to the other of science, poetry, and art.

It is the serpent, or, to speak more accurately, the devil, to whom is attributed the birth of the grotesque and hideous monsters which descended in a natural order of succession from the giants, pigmies, cyclops, satyrs, centaurs, harpies, tritons, and sirens of mythology (Fig. 191). The fathers of the Church did not venture to call into question the existence of these monsters, whom Pliny and the ancient naturalists complacently admitted into the hierarchy of living things; and the people were all the more ready to

Fig. 183.—The Gargouille.—From the Stained-glass Window representing the " Life of St. Romain," in the St. Romain Chapel, Rouen Cathedral.

accept them as realities, because they attributed their existence to the power of the demon.

It is astonishing that none of those who lived in the Middle Ages, with the exception of a few heroes of legends, claimed to have discovered the earthly Paradise, though learned writers tried hard to define its precise geographical position. If some one of the travellers of the twelfth or of the thirteenth century, such as Benjamin de Tudèle, Jean Plano Carpini, or Marco Polo, had put forward such a claim, it would assuredly have been admitted, inasmuch as many of the Christians of that period, so fertile in wonders, did not hesitate to believe that access could be gained to purgatory, and that Paradise could be seen from afar, without leaving the world of the living. Sorcerers alone were believed to have the power of descending into hell. The entrance into purgatory, whither certain persons claimed to have made their way and to have returned from, was believed to be in Ireland, in an island of Lake Derg. This purgatory, according to the legend, had been discovered by St. Patrick (Fig. 184), guided by Jesus Christ himself, who was said to have left him for a day and night in this "very obscure pit," on emerging from which the saint found himself "purged from all his former sins," in gratitude for which he at once built, close to the pit, a handsome church and a monastery of the order of St. Augustine. After his

Fig. 184.—The Purgatory of Monsignor St. Patrick.—Miniature of a Manuscript of the Fourteenth Century (No. 6,326).—In the National Library, Paris.

death the people came there in pilgrimage: a few rash persons attempted to enter the pit, but they never reappeared. There was one more report brought from purgatory by an English knight named Owen, who, loaded with sins, determined to try the experiment of St. Patrick (Fig. 185), and who was fortunate enough to behold again the rays of the sun, after having arrived at the gate of hell, and seen from afar the heavenly Jerusalem. The story which he told of the strange and wonderful things he had seen in the company of the devils, who refrained from harming him because he incessantly invoked the name of the Saviour, was implicitly believed, and generally referred to throughout the Middle Ages. The monks who kept

watch over St. Patrick's gap showed the doorway of it to the pilgrims who
were attracted to Ireland by motives of piety or curiosity, but the aperture
remained impenetrably closed. Notwithstanding, and though no one ventured
to renew the experiment made by the Chevalier Owen, every nation took
care that it was represented in the stories told of visits to the purgatory of
St. Patrick, so firmly rooted was the belief in it throughout Europe.

A not less famous superstition, which dates from the same period, and
which seems to have been brought from the East after the first Crusades,
is that of the Wandering Jew, as the inhabitants of the country dubbed
every beggar with a long white beard who trudged along the roads with
eyes downcast, and without opening his lips. The story of this accursed

Fig. 185.—Owen, accompanied by Monks chanting the Litanies for the Dead, repairs to the
    Aperture of the Gap, and creeps into it.—Miniature of a Manuscript of the Fifteenth Century
    (No. 1,588).—In the National Library, Paris.

pilgrim was told for the first time to the monks of St. Albans in 1228 by
an Armenian archbishop who had arrived from the Holy Land. Joseph
Cartaphilus was doorkeeper at the prætorium of Pontius Pilate when Jesus
was led away by the Jews to be crucified. As Jesus halted upon the threshold
of the prætorium, Cartaphilus struck him in the loins and said, "Move faster;
why do you stop here?" Jesus, turning round to him, said with a severe
look, "I go, and you will await my coming." Cartaphilus, who was then
thirty years old, and who since then always returned to that age when he
had completed a hundred years, was always awaiting the coming of the
Lord and the end of the world. He was supposed to be a man of great
piety, of few words, often weeping, never smiling, and being content with

the most frugal nourishment and the plainest garments. Moreover, he announced the final judgment of souls, and recommended his own to God. This simple story was well calculated to make an impression upon persons

Fig. 186.—The Tree of Life, or the Weeping-tree, planted in the States of Prester John.
Fac-simile of a Wood Engraving of the Sixteenth Century.

of pious mind, and some singular additions were made to it in Germany. Paul of Eitzen, a German bishop, declared, in a letter to a friend, that he had met the Wandering Jew at Hamburg in 1564, and had a long conversation with him. His name was no longer Joseph or Cartaphilus, but Ahasuerus. He appeared to be fifty years of age; his hair was long, and he went barefoot; his dress consisted of very full breeches, a short petticoat coming to the knee, and a cloak descending to his heel. He was present at the Catholic sermon, notwithstanding his creed, and prostrated himself, with sighs and tears and beating of the breast, whenever the holy name of Jesus was pronounced. His speech was very edifying; he could not hear an oath without bursting into tears, and when offered money would only accept a few sous. The story of his meeting our Lord, as related by Bishop Paul of Eitzen, differed from the original account so far as this, that he was standing in front of his house, with his wife and children, when he roughly entreated Jesus, who had halted to take breath while carrying his cross to Calvary. "I shall stop and be at rest," was the indignant reply of the King of the Jews, "but you will be ever on foot." After this decree he quitted his house and family, to do penitence by wandering over the world. He did not know what God intended to do with him, in compelling him to lead so long this miserable life. In the sixteenth century there was not a town or village but what claimed to have given hospitality to the unfortunate witness of Christ's passion; and yet, whenever his appearance was announced in any place, it was believed to foreshadow great calamities. Thus the Wandering Jew was believed to have been seen at Beauvais, Noyon, and several towns in Picardy when Ravaillac assassinated Henry IV.

Another superstition, not less popular than that of the Wandering Jew in the Middle Ages, may also perhaps be attributed to the same origin; namely, the *Prester John*, a sort of pontiff-king, half Jew, half Christian, who for centuries had governed in India, or in Abyssinia, a vast empire in which the hand of God had collected more marvels than in the paradise of Mahomet (Fig. 186). It was an Armenian bishop, too, who brought to Europe the first story as to the fabulous personage, and many a traveller, chronicler, and poet capped it with still more wonderful details. In 1507 a letter (evidently written ironically by a partisan of the Reformation) was put into circulation, in which Prester John, who entitled himself, by the grace of God, the *Almighty King of all the Christian kings,* after making an orthodox profession of faith, invited Pope Julius II. and King Louis XII. to come and settle in his States, which he described as the most favoured upon the face of the earth. The descriptions which he gave of them were very tempting, and it is even

Fig. 187.—The Reign of Antichrist.—After an Engraving by Michael Volgemuth, in the "Liber Chronicarum," 1493, in folio.—Cabinet of Engravings. National Library, Paris.

said that the Kings of Portugal, Emanuel and John III., went so far as to send several expeditions to India and Abyssinia, to see whether these wonders really existed. According to certain savants rather less credulous, the fiction of Prester John had its origin in the actual existence of a Nestorian leader, named Johannes Presbyter, who in the twelfth century founded a powerful empire in Tartary.

It was by a natural transition that to the Wandering Jew and Prester John came to be attached the personality of the Antichrist who, since the year 1000, had always been expected, and whose long-delayed appearance was to be a prelude to the end of the world. "At the end of a thousand years," said St. John, "Satan will leave his prison and seduce the peoples which are at the four corners of the earth." Basing their arguments upon this prophecy, which they interpreted the wrong way, several early theologians had announced that the millennium would mark the accomplishment of the times. When that date arrived the early Christians at once prepared to appear before God, renouncing all their property, which they gave to the churches and monasteries, and suspending as useless the cultivation of the land and all industrial and commercial pursuits. The *year thousand*, which was expected to be the last of the world, was marked by many threatening signs in heaven and earth—by eclipses, comets, famine, and overflowing of rivers. A contemporary writer has left us a terrible picture of the desolation which then prevailed throughout the entire West. The whole talk was of terrible miracles and unheard-of prodigies. Upon the eve of the day when the *year thousand* was on the point of completion, the whole population crowded to the churches, weeping and praying, waiting in dread expectation for the sound of the seven trumpets and the coming of the Antichrist (Fig. 187). But the sun rose as usual, none of the stars fell, and Nature's laws continued their course. Nevertheless, it was believed that this was only a short respite which God had granted to the world in order that sinners might be converted, and the days, weeks, and months were anxiously counted. It was not until many years afterwards that men's minds were reassured. Even after this the end of the world was from time to time announced and expected, and the coming of Antichrist was believed to be imminent, whenever civil or foreign warfare, famine, epidemics, or moral disorder in society seemed to call him to the earth. In 1600, more especially, it was rumoured that he had at length been born; at Babylon, according to one report; near Paris, according to another. A sorceress, put upon her trial, declared that she had held this diabolical infant upon her knees at a Sabbath, and that he had claws instead of feet, wore no shoes, and could speak every language.

Moreover, prophecies and presages, the ordinary accessories of all historic events of any importance, always had a great hold upon the popular imagination, which was invariably ready to accept mysterious interpretations of the plainest and most trifling facts. Since the decadence of the false gods, the orators of the pagan temples were mute, but this was made up for by the prophecies attributed to the Sibyls, who continued to be held in honour by

Fig. 188.—The Token of Macé Bonhomme, Printer and Bookseller at Lyons.—Taken from the original Edition of the " Prophecies of Michael Nostradamus," 1555, octavo.

the Christians, for it was firmly believed that they had predicted the birth of Christ. The prophecies of Merlin the Enchanter, a bard of the fifth century, were in special favour.

The success of the prophecies of Michael Nostradamus surpassed that of all previous soothsayers. Catherine de' Medicis and her son Charles IX., more superstitious than the least enlightened of their subjects, contributed to their popularity by paying visits to this famous astrologer at the little town of Salon, in Provence, to which he had withdrawn. The courtiers naturally followed their example, and were also anxious to have their horoscopes taken. It was in the stars and the planets, in the revolutions of the sun and the moon, that Nostradamus claimed to be able to read the destinies of men and of nations. He composed, after his pretended astronomical observations, an unintelligible sort of conjuring book in rhymed verse, teeming with hybrid words and foreign names, and he made many additions to it up to the date of his death in 1556. The form of these prophecies (Fig. 188) made it very easy to find them applicable more or less clearly to all the events of history, and this sustained the reputation of the astrologer of Salon long after his death.

But Nostradamus, in his collection of Sibylline oracles, dealt only with the fate of kings, princes, and nations, and he was succeeded by a number of less pretentious astrologers who prepared *genethliatics*, or horoscopes, upon interrogation of the stars, for all those who came to them with money. These astrologers had for competitors the *diviners*, who made it their business to interpret visions and dreams, and who could trace back the origin of their profession to a very remote period. With all ancient peoples, and notably with the children of Israel, dreams were looked upon as anticipated reflections of the future, as divine or diabolical warnings, whether in disclosing without concealment or enigma the things which were destined to occur, or whether concealing beneath a sombre and mysterious veil the spectre of destiny. The Church did not, as a rule, do more than declare that dreams were two kinds— sometimes sent by God, sometimes wrought by the demon. Thus, according to the writers of the period, there was no important event in the Middle Ages, or even subsequently to the Renaissance, which was not announced by a dream.

The day before Henry II. was struck down by the blow of a lance during the tournament, Catherine de' Medicis, his wife, dreamt that she saw him lose one of his eyes. Three days before he fell beneath the knife of Jacques Clément, Henry III. dreamt that he saw the royal insignia stained with blood and trodden under foot by monks and people of the lower classes. A few days before he was murdered by Ravaillac, Henry IV. heard during the night his wife, Marie de' Medicis, say to herself, as she awoke, "Dreams are but falsehoods!" and when he asked her what she had dreamt, she replied, "That you were stabbed upon the steps of the Little Louvre!" "Thank God it is but a dream," rejoined the King.

The death of Henry IV., like that of Julius Cæsar, was, moreover, pre-

ceded and accompanied by presages of many kinds. From one end of France
to the other, there were so many precursory signs of a great event that the
people believed that the end of the world was at hand. At Paris the May-
pole, planted in the courtyard of the Louvre, fell to the ground without being
touched; in the abbey church of St. Denis the stone which sealed the funeral
vault of the Valois lifted itself from its place, and the statues upon the royal
tombs shed tears. Henry IV. himself had gloomy presentiments, which
doubtless arose from the great number of official warnings addressed to him
on this subject. "You do not understand me," he said to the Duc de Guise
on the very morning of his death; "when you have lost me, you will learn

Fig. 189.—Dream of Childeric.—After a Miniature in the " Chronicles of St. Denis."—Manuscript
of the Fourteenth Century.—In the National Library, Paris.

to appreciate me, and that will not be long first." He often remarked that it
had been predicted for him that he would die in a carriage and in his fiftieth
year. After the murder numerous visions, evidently bearing upon this tragic
event, were mentioned: at Douai, a priest, who was dying at the very hour
the crime was committed, had three convulsions, and expired saying, "The
greatest monarch in the world is being slain." In an abbey in Picardy a
nun who was sick exclaimed at the moment of the assassination, "Pray God
for the King, for he is being killed."

Visions, which have often been confounded with dreams, do not occupy less place in history than the latter. They were so frequent in the Middle Ages that the gravest historians mention instances of them without making the slightest reservation. It is difficult to make a choice amongst so many visions combining the elements of terror and mystery, but two may be mentioned which occurred in the first centuries of the French monarchy, and which are very celebrated. First that of King Childeric, who, the first night of his marriage, saw, under the form of various ferocious animals, the whole future of his race; and secondly, that of a hermit in the island of Lipari, who, at the very hour of King Dagobert's death, witnessed in his sleep a deadly combat between the demon and various saints who were fighting for the possession of his soul "over one of the gratings of hell." The demons were vanquished, and the victors carried his soul up to heaven.

In every page of the ancient chronicles are to be found visions and prodigies of a similar kind. There is no lack of phantoms and apparitions wherever the marvellous can be brought in; and there is no fact, futile as it may seem, that is not thought to deserve some supernatural manifestation. As a general rule, a vision was looked upon as unlucky, and this, no doubt, is the origin of the tradition, according to which a spectre always appears to announce the death of the head or of some member of certain illustrious families. There is the legend of the fay Mélusine (Fig. 190), which appeared, uttering loud cries, upon the donjon of the Château de Lusignan, in Poitou, whenever a Lusignan was about to die. But this legend is less terrible than that of the canons of Mersburg, in Saxony, for it was said that three weeks before the death of a canon a strange tumult arose at midnight in the choir of the cathedral, and a grim hand appeared, which struck with great force the stall of the canon who was condemned to die. The guardians of the church marked this stall with a piece of chalk, and the next day the canon, warned of his approaching end, prepared for death, while the chapter made every preparation for his obsequies.

Visions were very often of a public character, and caused consternation throughout a whole town or kingdom. Pierre Boaistuau, François de Belleforest, and other simple-minded compilers of the sixteenth century, have collected in one volume these "Histoires Prodigieuses," and still they are far from having exhausted the subject. Thus, to cite but one instance, after having predicted the numerous prodigies which announced the calamities of civil war, such as apparitions in the heavens of fiery dragons, of gigantic bulls, of pigs bearing royal crowns, of bloody stars, of multiform rainbows, accompanied by several moons and suns, they do not refer to the strange noise which was heard in the air, about the precincts of the Louvre, during the seven nights which followed the massacre of St. Bartholomew, a concert of cries, groans, and screams, mingled with furious imprecations and blasphemies, as if the horror of the massacre was being renewed in the invisible

Fig. 190.—The Fay Mélusine, from whose Flanks springs the Genealogical Tree of the House of Lusignan.—After a Wood Engraving of the "Romance of Mélusine," Augsburg, 1480, in quarto.—In the Library of M. Ambroise Firmin-Didot, Paris.

world. It may be added that these visions were in many instances facts witnessed by thousands of people, such as the showers of blood, of stones, of wheat, and of frogs, ordinary and simple phenomena which were not at the time understood, and the natural origin of which, not having been ascertained by the learned, did not, of course, occur to the public.

We have said nothing as to many other popular superstitions, traces of which still exist, such as the use of magic talismans, amulets, rings, herbs, stones, and the hair of animals (see chapter on *Occult Sciences*), for an enumeration of them would merely serve to display the ignorance of our ancestors, over which it is better that we should draw a veil.

Fig. 191.—The Siren.—Token of Gérard Morrhy, Printer at Paris in 1551.

GEOGRAPHICAL SCIENCE.

 GREAT as was the progress of geographical knowledge after the establishment of the Roman empire, still greater, in contrast, were its decadence and disfavour in the early part of the Middle Ages; that is to say, in the beginning of the fifth century. Geography, in fact, was one of the most useful auxiliaries of the aggressive policy of Rome, directing the march of her expeditions all over the world, and enabling her to acquire useful knowledge concerning the countries which she had conquered. It may, therefore, be said that the science of geography was in general practice during the reign of Augustus. A perusal of the principal writers of that period is sufficient to show how widely spread were the general notions of geography in a society which, being well versed in letters and highly educated, was acquainted with the great works of the ancient Greek geographers, especially those of Eratosthenes (276—194 b.c.) and Polybius (204—121 b.c.), and which used Strabo's Greek Geography as a manual for reading the Latin historians and poets, and as a guide-book for the most distant provinces of the empire. Poets such as Virgil, Ovid, Manilius, and Lucan, and historians such as

Livy and Julius Cæsar, were also geographers; and Pliny the Elder summed up, in his four books of "Natural History," all the results obtained by geographical research, and set forth in a number of works no longer extant.

Pliny often mentioned in his "Natural History" the geodesical operation attributed to Marcus Vipsanius Agrippa, prime minister and son-in-law of Augustus. It was Julius Cæsar who, during his consulship (according to the positive assertion of Ethicus, a geographer of the fourth century), "ordered by a *senatûs-consultum* that the whole Roman world should be measured by men of the greatest ability and endowed with all sorts of knowledge." This vast enterprise, intrusted to four Greek mathematicians and geographers, Zenodoxus, Theodotus, Polyclitus, and Didymus, who had under their orders a staff of geodesical measurers and land surveyors, was completed in twenty-five years. It would appear that Agrippa took the matter in hand, and when it was completed he proposed to construct at Rome a gigantic portico, beneath which he intended to "unfold the map of the world before the eyes of the universe," as Pliny expressed it. The premature death of this illustrious general prevented the execution of this grand project, but the map of the Roman world, with the roads and distances indicated, was deposited in the archives of the Senate (Fig. 192).

Nor was the progress of geography assisted by the victorious armies alone, for the travellers, and still more the merchants, whose vessels, even at that period, conveyed them to the most distant parts and brought back cargoes from the ports of India, did much towards the same end. Under the reign of Nero, two centurions were sent by the Emperor to Ethiopia in search of the sources of the Nile, and this expedition is alluded to by Seneca and Pliny. Previously to this, during the reign of Claudius, a Greek philosopher of Egypt, one Hippalus, had struck out with his vessel from the coast, and ventured across the high seas, starting from the Gulf of Adulis (Aden), and arriving upon the coast of India. Another traveller, named Diogenes, was driven by north winds as far as a large island called Menuthias, otherwise Zanzibar. From this time forward all the coast-line was marked upon the marine maps, but the Erythrean Sea (as the Indian Ocean was then called) was believed to be impassable and full of terrible dangers, though more than one Egyptian or Phœnician sailor had endeavoured to sail across it.

One of these experienced pilots, Marinus of Tyre, carefully collected all the geographical information which he could gather from the maritime commerce of Phœnicia and Egypt, and he used it to prepare more detailed and correct maps than were at that time in use, and to compose a book of geography, which, though no longer in existence, is copied from by Ptolemy. That writer says of him, "Marinus of Tyre, the latest of our contemporaries who has cultivated geography, seems to have done it to some purpose, for it is evident that he has made several additions to the former knowledge

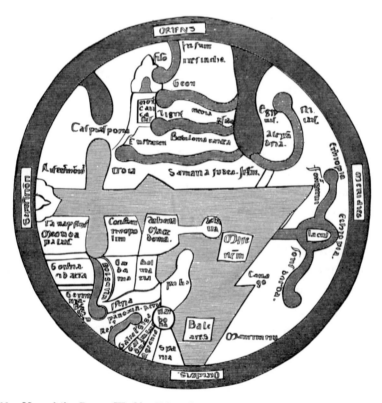

Fig. 192.—Map of the Roman World.—Taken from the "Liber Guidonis."—Manuscript dated 1119 (No. 3,898).—In the Burgundy Library, Brussels.

of this subject, and that he has corrected earlier writings which contained errors that had at first misled him as well as others. This is seen very clearly in his corrections of the Geographical Table." Previously to Marinus of Tyre, a Roman citizen, Pomponius Mela, had written a useful treatise on geography, entitled, "De Situ Orbis," in which he described the countries of the known world, following the circumference of the seas, and beginning with

the Mediterranean; and his treatise, which formed a luminous and rapid summary, was one of the handbooks of geographical study in the Middle Ages.

A Greek geometer, named Claudius Ptolemæus, born at Pelusa, in Lower
Egypt, who was at the famous school of Alexandria in the middle of the
second century, formed an idea of writing a general treatise upon Mathematical Geography after the plan traced by Hipparchus in the year 125 B.C.
He had prepared himself for this task by a long series of astronomical
observations and calculations.   In the second book of his " Almagest " he
wrote, " I intend to mark the longitude and latitude of the principal towns
of each country, to facilitate the calculation of the celestial phenomena
which occur there.   I shall mark by how many degrees, counting from the
meridian, each of these towns is distant from the equator, and I shall
also compute, in degrees counted from the equator, the eastern and western
distance of each meridian compared with that which passes at Alexandria, for
it is after the meridian of that city that I intend to reckon those of the
other places on the earth's surface."   Ptolemæus was more of an astronomer
and a geometer than a geographer; he had not travelled at all, and had,
therefore, no personal experience, while, excepting the astronomical part of
his book, he merely borrowed from his predecessors and contemporaries cos-
mographic materials which he loosely arranged without sequence or comment.
The best features in his work are what he borrowed from the treatise of
Marinus of Tyre, and he says, " I resolved to preserve so much of his book as
does not require correction, and to throw light, by means of the most recent
information, and by a better arrangement of the places on the maps, upon
the obscure points of his treatise."   Ptolemæus unfortunately, while preparing
his list of all the places in the known world, making eight thousand names,
committed the most glaring errors, owing to his having sought to fix the
latitude and longitude of the localities by means of astronomical observations.

The Geography of Ptolemæus, written in Greek (Fig. 193), and doubtless
translated simultaneously into Latin for the use of persons travelling through
the Roman empire, was, in spite of his faults of omission and commission,
consulted as being the most useful guide-book during a long journey.   The
coloured maps appended to it were, perhaps, rectified soon afterwards, upon
new itinerary measurements being taken; for, previously to Ptolemæus, there
existed not only road maps, to which Vegetius refers in his treatise on the
Art of War, under the name of *itinera picta* (coloured itineraries), but

itinera adnotata (annotated itineraries), upon which were marked the day's marches. It was one of these figurative itineraries that the learned Conrad

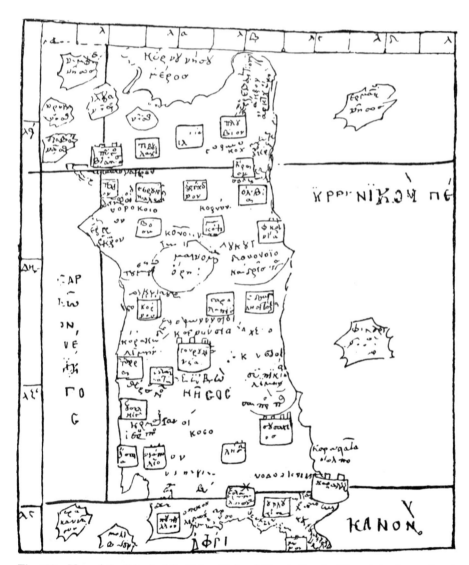

Fig. 193.—Map of the Island of Sardinia.—Reduced Fac-simile of a Map of the Geography of Ptolemæus.—Greek Manuscript of the Twelfth Century, preserved in the Monastery of Vatopedi, Mount Athos.

Celtes discovered in a monastery of Germany, at the end of the fifteenth century, and which his friend Pentinger of Augsburg presented to the

Imperial Library at Vienna (Fig. 194). This precious document, consisting
of twelve maps representing the world as it was known in the third century,
forms, so to speak, the explanatory complement of the tract chart of the
provinces of the Roman empire, which has been handed down to us under
the title of "Antonini Augusti Itinerarium," and which appears to have
been drawn by the geographer Ethicus in the fourth century.

These itineraries and maps, which were sold at Rome and in the principal
cities of the empire, and which must have often been copied as they passed
from hand to hand, were not, in all probability, foreign to the continuous
migration of the barbarian hordes which gradually moved upon Italy
from the different parts of the world, and systematically followed the same
method in order to reach Rome. These invaders, whether coming from the
North like the Lombards, the Suevi, the Vandals, and the Goths; from the
heart of Asia, like the Huns; or from the steppes of Caucacus, like the Alani
or the Heruli, had long been kept in awe by the Roman legions; but, when
once they began to burst the barriers and to advance with sagacious caution
through the Roman provinces which they ravaged (Fig. 195), it was easy to
see that they had selected beforehand the territory which they intended to
occupy, by the way in which they created frontiers and military stations
with not less intelligence than boldness. They did not swerve from the
route which they had traced out, and paid implicit obedience to chiefs who
had been formed in the schools of Athens or Alexandria.

Thus the study of geography was apparently fatal to the empire, because
it demonstrated to its enemies and rivals how vulnerable its very vast-
ness made it, and what facilities were afforded for an invasion by those
splendid military roads which enabled countless hosts to arrive by easy stages
under the very walls of Rome. The Emperors, it is true, endeavoured for
more than a century to stem the tide of invasion, and it is not unreasonable
to suppose that they had all the maps and itineraries which facilitated the
progress of the invasion destroyed. The teaching of geography was not,
however, neglected in the schools, for the historians of the fourth century,
Claudianus, Nemesianus, and Ausonius, the Emperor Julian, Ammianus
Marcellinus, and Macrobius, display very profound geographical knowledge,
which they must have acquired by travel and study. But the special treatises
on geography were very rare at this period, and the only works which are
known to have escaped a destruction which we may assume to have been a

planned one are the Latin "Cosmography" of Ethicus and a few *peripli* (books of circumnavigation) written in Greek.

As soon as the invading nations had formed themselves into kingdoms

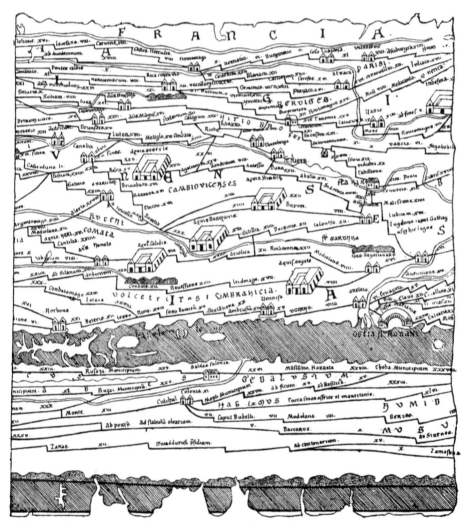

Fig. 194.—Fragment of the Map of Gaul.—Reduced Fac-simile of Pentinger's Map.—Manuscript of the Thirteenth Century.—In the Imperial Library, Vienna.

upon the Roman soil, and their chiefs had become kings rivalling the Cæsars in power, geography resumed its position and reasserted its usefulness. Thus at the court of Theodore the Great, Boethius and Cassiodorus, one born at Rome and the other in Calabria, both of whom rose to the highest dignities in the new kingdom of the Ostrogoths, combined with learning of a very varied kind an extensive and thorough knowledge of geography, which made their services exceedingly valuable. Cassiodorus has disseminated in his "Letters" a mass of valuable information and of interesting remarks concerning places, men, and customs. Boethius himself translated into Latin the books of Ptolemy, so as to put them within the reach of those who did not speak Greek.

In the pagan schools which remained open at Constantinople and throughout the empire of the East, until closed by Justinian in 529, were taught, after the writings of Eratosthenes and Hipparchus, of Strabo and Ptolemy, both cosmography and geography, in addition to simple astronomy—this latter as a guide to the forecast of weather, the variations of the atmosphere, and navigation. Stephen of Byzantium, who lived in the sixth century, composed a large Dictionary of Geography, of which all that remains extant is a dry and useless abridgment. But it may be learnt from the works of the Greek historians of this epoch, especially of Procopius, that geography was considered to be inseparable from history. Thus Procopius and his successor, Agathias, are true geographers. We meet but one Latin geographer in the sixth century, viz. Vibius Sequester, who, in a work dedicated to the nomenclature of rivers, springs, and lakes, seems to have learnt from the poets what little he knew upon the subject. The Christians of Africa still read Syriac translations of the Latin and Greek works on geography by Aristotle, Ptolemy, Pliny, Pomponius Mela, &c., which had been studied after the original texts in the schools of Athens and Alexandria, and these Syriac translations were afterwards retranslated into Arabic, when the Caliphs, successors of Mahomet, had founded Mussulman schools in the countries which they occupied and conquered. Very naturally geography must have had a special attraction for a warlike people which aspired to conquer the world, and to propagate throughout it the religion of the Koran.

The schools of Cordova and Toledo in Spain, as well as those of Bagdad and of Dschindesabour in Asia Minor, accordingly remained open for geographical instruction at a period when geography was no longer taught throughout the West, which was at that time plunged in barbarian darkness.

From the sixth to the tenth century there were but few manuscripts which escaped destruction; all the coloured maps and traced itineraries were, like the images, ruthlessly destroyed by the iconoclasts. The only remaining

Fig. 195.—Arrival at Cologne of the Fleet of the Tyrant Maximus, who revolted against the Roman Emperor Gratian. Some of the Vessels conveyed St. Ursula and her Companions to the number of eleven thousand, who were put to death by the Barbarians whom the Emperor Gratian had dispatched against the hostile Fleet.—Fragment of the "Legend of St. Ursula," painted upon the Reliquary of that Saint, at Bruges, by J. Memling (Fifteenth Century).

notions of cosmography and geography dating from that period are to be found hidden in scholastic encyclopædias, which, like the ark in the Deluge, float here and there amidst the abysses of ignorance. In addition to the encyclopædic compilations of Martianus Capella (470) and Isidore of Seville, there were a few historians who took some interest in geography : the historian of the Franks, Gregory of Tours (about 590), the historian designated as the "Anonymous of Ravenna," and the historian of the Lombards, Paul Warnefrid (780). There can be no doubt, moreover, that Charlemagne had contemplated the encouragement of the teaching of geography, when this science, not then regarded as a handmaid of politics, resumed its rank at the Palatine School directed by Alcuin, who included it, with dialectics, philosophy, astronomy, and arithmetic, in his course of lessons. Yet it was only a very

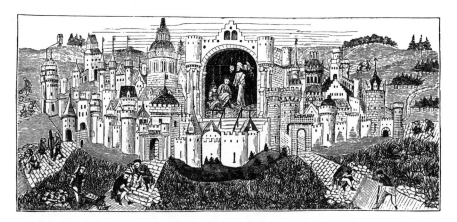

Fig. 196.—Brunehaut superintending the making of the Seven Roads which led from the City of Bavay.—After a Miniature in the "Chroniques de Hainaut."—Manuscript of the Fifteenth Century.—In the Burgundy Library, Brussels.

imperfect and elementary science, for it was confined to the theories of Aristotle, who described the terrestrial globe as being 9,000 leagues in circumference and 2,803 leagues in diameter, while he estimated the sea to be ten times greater than the earth, and asserted that the latter was 1,400 leagues deep from the surface to the central axis, and had an area of 5,000,713 square leagues. Based upon these data, mathematical and astronomical geography could not be other than a chaos of erroneous ideas and misleading traditions.

The genius of Charlemagne, however, extracted therefrom the clever invention of the cadastral measurement, the germ of which is to be seen in the Capitulary Laws of the great Emperor, and which eventually, under the feudal régime, gave the geometrical measure of the area of the soil, while carefully preserving the ancient names of the different localities. By means of this descriptive definition of the limits of fiefs, historical geography recovered, after the lapse of centuries, all the topographical details of the territory of the Gauls during the lifetime of Charlemagne and of his successors. The historians and the poets of this period, of whom but a few are known to us, do not give much information as to the state of geographical knowledge, which, notwithstanding the schools founded by Alcuin, seems to have been

Fig. 197.—Seal of the Town of Dunwich (Thirteenth Century).

very scanty. But it is probable that the knowledge of geography was much more advanced in Great Britain and Ireland, for Alcuin was educated in the monasteries of those countries, as also were St. Columba, St. Gall, Theodore, Archbishop of Canterbury, Scotus Erigena, and other savants who came to France, where they founded monasteries and established chairs for teaching the sciences, and geography was always given a place in their programmes. There was the more need for its cultivation in England, as it was very useful to the traders and fishermen of the ancient port of Dunwich (Fig. 197), in the North Sea.

Alfred the Great, King of the Anglo-Saxons (849—901), who, like Charlemagne, was a sovereign of great organizing powers, took a special interest in these studies, and set an example to his subjects by making himself acquainted, with a view to developing the fisheries and trade, with the islands and coasts washed by the Baltic and the North Seas. Two travelling traders, one a Dane named Wolfstan, the other a Norwegian named Other, wrote an account of their maritime explorations. Wolfstan had explored the Baltic coast, and Other had navigated to the polar seas by way of the coasts of Norway and of Lapland. Alfred the Great, who translated into Saxon the " Universal History " by Orosius, written in the fifth century, added to it, from the accounts given by Wolfstan and Other, the description of an immense extent of country which the Romans had but caught a glimpse of athwart the miraculous stories of a few sailors who had sought to reach the mysterious island of Thule (Iceland), which was looked upon as the extreme limit of the habitable globe. It was owing to him that there were prepared pilots' charts, to enable fishermen to exercise their industry in the remote regions of the Norwegian continent (Figs. 198 and 199), and to establish a carrying trade with all the ports of the Baltic. Geography, in England as in Germany, consisted at that time of a few rudimentary but practical notions. Thus a canon of Bremen composed, in 1067, a brief description of Denmark, under the pretentious title of "Geographia Scandinaviæ ; " while, two hundred years before, an Irish monk, Dicuil, wrote a regular treatise on general geography entitled, " De Mensurâ Orbis " (Concerning the Extent of the Universe), borrowed from the Latin writers, Pliny, Solinus, Orosius, and Priscian, supplemented by some novel remarks upon the northern countries. But this treatise, though it contains an account as to the discovery of Iceland and other interesting facts in contemporary history which the monks had imparted to the author, also contained several errors, but little in the way of commentary. For instance, Dicuil divides the world into three parts, Europe, Asia, and Libya, in which latter he places the source of the Nile, not far from the Atlantic, in the mountains of Mauritania.

There are doubtless but few geographical works during the tenth and eleventh centuries which place the theory of the science in a reliable form, but it may be taken as certain that geography itself was taught wherever education existed. The Greek schools in the empire of the East could not afford to neglect a study which was inseparable from that of history and of philosophy, and geography even became an essential part of politics, as is to be learnt from the treatise composed by the Emperor Constantine Porphyrogenetes for the education of his son, and which bore the title of " De Administratione Imperii." This book, written in the middle of the tenth century, is, in reality, a geographical work, containing a very complete description of Eastern Europe and of a part of Asia. Many cosmographical books, descriptions of travels or of embassies, were written in Greek during the eleventh and the twelfth centuries, but they have not been published. The numerous writers of the history of Byzantium describe the peoples and

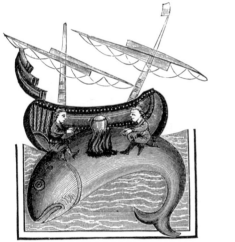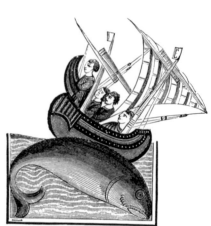

Figs. 198 and 199.—Navigators who have mistaken a Whale's Back for an Island seating themselves upon it to cook their food. The Whale, feeling the fire, plunges to the bottom, and the Vessel narrowly escapes being wrecked.—Miniature from the "Bestiaire d'Amour," by Richard Furnival.—Manuscript of the Tenth Century.—In the Library of M. Ambroise Firmin-Didot, Paris.

states in other parts of Europe with a degree of accuracy and detail which testifies to their being well versed in geography.

It was in Islam that the best geographers of that time were to be found. The Mahometan mind had from the first taken to the study of geography, which made immense progress after the eighth century in all the Arab schools. The Caliph Al-Mamoun, son of Haroun Al-Raschid, was noted for his predilection in favour of this science, and he translated into Arabic the Geography of Ptolemæus, adding to it illuminated maps, which latter fact showed that Ptolemæus's original maps had either been lost or were not reproduced

in the Syriac translation.   From the reign of Al-Mamoun the Arabs measured
an arc of the meridian in order to calculate the size of the earth, and to rectify
the calculations of Ptolemæus as to the measure of the degree of each of the
large circles which were supposed to intersect the earth at intervals of $66\frac{2}{3}$
miles.   The conquests of the Arabs, their trade by land and sea, and, above
all, their religious pilgrimages to Mecca, served at once to enrich their store
of knowledge both as to astronomical, physical, and political geography.
They brought from China the compass, with which the Chinese had been
acquainted from time immemorial, and the use of it at sea unquestionably
led to a total and almost immediate revolution in the science of geography.

The Arabs possessed in the tenth century two learned geographers, Ibn-

Fig. 200.—" How Alexander did battle with the Beast which is very formidable and has three
   Horns."—Miniature from a Manuscript of the Thirteenth Century (No. 11,040).—In the
   Burgundy Library, Brussels.

Haukal and Masoudi, both natives of Bagdad.   The first wrote a geographical,
political, and statistical description of the Empire of the Caliphs, in the preface to which he said, " I have collected all the information which has made
of geography a science interesting to men of all degree."   Masoudi introduced into a large encyclopædic work entitled " Akhbar al Zeman " (the
News of the Time) all the documents which he had collected during twenty-
five years' travels through Asia and Africa; but it would appear that this
work has been lost, and all that remains is an abridgment made by the
author himself under the title of " Golden Prairies," and which itself fills

eight volumes. Masoudi deserves to be surnamed the Pliny of the East. A great number of works on geography in the Arab literature of the Middle Ages might be cited, the best known of which is that by Edrisi, a Spanish Arab, who wrote his book at the court of Roger, King of Sicily, in 1154. It was for this prince, a friend of letters and sciences, that Edrisi constructed an armillary sphere and a terrestial planisphere in silver. (See the chapter on *Occult Sciences.*)

The example of the Arabs was not without its influence upon the renaissance of geographical science in Europe, when the Crusades made a knowledge of geography indispensable. First of all, it was necessary to study all the routes leading to Jerusalem, to prepare itineraries and tract charts for the

Fig. 201.—" How Alexander did battle with White Lions big as Bulls."—Miniature from a Manuscript of the Thirteenth Century (No. 11,040).—In the Burgundy Library, Brussels.

crusaders ; and in these new and unknown lands, into which eager multitudes were about to penetrate, there was nothing to guide them save the untrustworthy descriptions of the ignorant pilgrims who from the fifth century had undertaken the laborious task of visiting the holy places. This led to an improved study of geography in the schools of the West ; and in the monasteries, each of which had its library, the monks set to work at copying the writings of the early geographers, such as Strabo, Pausanias, and Polybius, Pliny, Pomponius Mela, Solinus, and Ethicus. These authors were expounded, commentated, and compared with the less ancient and almost contemporary writers. The famous Abbey of Monte Casino, in the kingdom of Naples, was at that time one of the principal centres of geographical lore. Numerous pilgrims who went to or returned from Palestine halted for a day at this abbey, where they were received with the greatest hospitality, and told the story of their travels and adventures (Figs. 200 and 201) to their learned hosts. It was here that Constantine the African, one of the lights of the school of Salerno, retired, after having, when he left the schools of Alexandria and Bagdad, travelled through Egypt and Asia for twenty-nine years. His wonderful lore earned him the reputation of a sorcerer, but the Duc de Pouille, Robert Guiscard, whose secretary he was, protected him, and he was able to continue undisturbed his medical and geographical works in a retreat where his curious descriptions of the countries beyond the sea lighted up the hours of repose and recreation which the monks of St. Benedict were allowed to snatch from their labours and prayers.

The University of Paris was not yet founded, but the ecclesiastical schools already flourished in the capital as well as in all the important cities which had their bishop. The teaching of geography was limited at that time to a few rudiments, all more or less erroneous, and it was in the Latin classic poets, such as Virgil, Horace, and Ovid, that students got some idea of the facts relating to descriptive geography. Nothing can prove more clearly the ignorance which then prevailed as to the shape of the globe than the rough designs which are to be met with in a few manuscripts of the eleventh century, the authors of which could never have seen Ptolemy's Geography. The geographical descriptions which occur in some of the poetry of the time were much nearer the truth, for the poets of the eleventh and twelfth centuries, such as Ausonius and Venantius Fortunatus, wrote of countries and places which they had seen. It was in this way that Marbodius, Bishop of Rennes, who died in 1123, sketched in his didactic poetry the geography of Brittany, giving it a picturesque character quite in harmony with nature.

There were, however, some few men of genius to whom the general study of science had, even at that period, opened the arcana of astronomical and philosophical geography. Such was the master of Roger Bacon, that man of learning whose real name is not written in the works of his illustrious pupil, and who appears to have been one Mehairicourt, a native of Picardy. Roger Bacon always speaks of him as *Master Peter*. Philosopher, mathematician, and geographer, he had travelled in Europe and Asia before coming to Paris, where he taught Roger Bacon, about 1230, that which no other teacher had the power to impart to him. He had constructed a sphere which imitated the motion of the heavens, and it was through the intermediary of astronomy

Fig. 202.—Plan of Clermont en Beauvaisis.—Beauvais Tapestry (1530), preserved in the Cathedral of that City. Communicated by M. Achille Jubinal.

and mathematics that he grappled with the most arduous questions of geography. Roger Bacon, in the fourth part of his "Opus Majus," devoted almost entirely to the description of the earth, doubtless transcribed without change the lessons which he had received from Master Peter; but he notes the errors of the ancient geographers, refutes the opinions of Pliny and Ptolemy, and brings forward a host of fresh problems which science did not solve till long after his time. Not only did he describe very accurately regions not yet known and scarcely hinted at, but he further maintained that Africa extended very far south, that it had inhabitants the other side of the equator, that the temperature of the pole was endurable, that the Indian Ocean washed the southern coasts of the Asiatic continent, and that the earth was ten times more thickly peopled than was believed to be the case.

At the time Bacon committed to paper, under Master Peter's dictation, these ingenious theories which changed the face of geographical knowledge, Albertus Magnus was propounding to attentive audiences numbered by the thousand, from his chair in the University of Paris, a system of geography stripped of all commentaries, and teeming with errors which he did not erase when he embodied his public lessons in a treatise entitled "De Naturâ Locorum."

Roger Bacon appreciated in the following terms the utility and main object of a science which was still groping its way in the dark:—" Geography, like astronomy and chronology, has its roots in mathematics, inasmuch as it must repose upon the measurement and shape of the inhabited globe, and on the precise determination of latitudes and longitudes. But the carelessness of the Christian peoples is such that they do not know one-half of the globe which they inhabit. Yet the first important points to be settled are the measurement of the earth, the determining of the position of towns (Fig. 202) and of countries, and the adoption of a fixed degree for the longitudes, starting from the western extremity of Spain to the eastern extremity of India. This immense work can only be accomplished under the auspices of the Holy Apostolic See, or of a monarch who would undertake all the costs of the enterprise, by remunerating the savants employed upon it. Moreover, it is impossible to form an opinion of men unless one knows what climate they inhabit, for if the products of the animal and vegetable kingdoms are dependent upon the climate, how much more must this be the case with the manners, the character, and the constitutions of peoples!" Thus we see that Roger Bacon's sagacity and spirit of intuition enabled him to anticipate by five centuries the philosophical results of modern science.

The thirteenth century could not but restore geography to its place of honour, when the Crusades were taking so many people to the East, and when the development of classical study, favoured by the ardour of the students who flocked to the schools of the Paris University, fostered a taste for encyclopædias edited upon the same plan as Pliny's "Natural History." Geography was destined to occupy a permanent place in these vast compilations, and Vincent of Beauvais, who, by order of St. Louis, had intended to present, in a voluminous compilation entitled "Speculum Majus," the compendium of the scientific, historical, and philosophical information of his time, instead of merely putting together all the documents and systems which antiquity furnished him with concerning the history of geography and the description of the universe, sought out the travellers who had visited the countries which he intended to describe, and so obtained fresh information, which, unfortunately, he failed to get revised by a competent critic. Nevertheless, his book is a valuable one, and he deserves great praise for his "Speculum Naturale," in which he treats of the position of the skies, of cosmography and geography, citing not more than a dozen Latin authors.

From this period the accounts of travellers in Upper Asia enabled the inhabitants of Europe to form more accurate and extensive notions concerning this part of the world. The story of Prester John, alluded to in the previous chapter, was the principal cause of these travels, and Pope Innocent IV. and Louis IX. both determined to ascertain what truth there was in these travellers' tales. The Pope accordingly sent two missions into Asia; one confided to monks of the Franciscan order, the other to Dominicans. The first proceeded to Mongolia, and the second to Persia and Armenia. The story of the first mission was written by Brother John de Plano Carpini, who arrived with his companions upon the banks of the Volga. The embassy sent to the Great Khan of Tartary by St. Louis a few years later was of greater service to geographical science, and the Flemish Franciscan monk, Ruysbroeck, generally called Rubruquis, gave many interesting details in the account which he wrote as to distant countries of which he could not ascertain even the name. Yet for another two centuries the existence of Prester John was generally believed in.

Another traveller, Marco Polo the Venetian, who, soon after Rubruquis and John de Plano Carpini, went to seek his fortune in Tartary, and who for twenty years held a high post at the court of the Great Khan, availed himself of his residence and of his excursions in Asia to collect a mass of valuable notes about the geography of the countries which he inhabited for such a long time. Upon his return to his country in 1298, he dictated an account of his journeys to a romance-writer, one Rustician of Pisa, who took them down in French eight years before Marco Polo had them written in Italian. This account, valuable and truthful notwithstanding the great credulity of the author, contained the fullest and best description which then existed of Tartary, Mongolia, Cathay or China, and other parts of Central Asia, and was, so to speak, the first effort of picturesque geography. Marco Polo found many imitators, but none of them equalled him. Travellers in Asia up to the fifteenth century consisted almost entirely of Franciscan or Dominican monks, amongst whom may be mentioned Ricoldi of Monte Croce, John of Monte Corvino, Oderic of Frioul, and John of Marignola; but the most famous of all was an Englishman, John de Mandeville, who, from 1322 to 1356, explored nearly the whole of the known world for the mere pleasure of travelling, and who, after a pilgrimage to the Holy Land (Fig. 203), explored part of Africa and nearly the whole of Asia. The story of his travels, written in English, teems with stories which do not say much for his judgment or powers of discrimination. Several travellers, who had seen fewer countries, displayed better powers of observation and more knowledge of geography, amongst them being Bertrandon de la Brocquière, a Burgundian gentleman, who was one of the last to start with the pilgrim's staff for Jerusalem.

The caravan travellers seem to have stimulated the energies of travellers by sea, and hydrography took its place beside geography. The first navigators who explored the western coasts of Africa were Portuguese. In the beginning of the fourteenth century (in 1315), Alonzo Gonzales Baldaya advanced as far as Cape Bojador, almost within sight of the Canary Islands. The island of Madeira, which an Englishman, Masham, caught sight of in 1344, was not positively discovered till 1417 by Gonzales Zarco, who took possession of it on behalf of his master, John I., King of Portugal. That king's son, Prince Henry, surnamed the Navigator, was passionately fond of maritime exploration, and devoted forty-eight years of his life to it. The object of his expeditions was not merely to discover new countries rich in gold, and offering fresh opportunities for commerce; but, in trying to reach the equator, this enlightened prince had mainly in view the increase of geographical knowledge. The Canary Islands were already known, and the

King of Castile's flag had floated there since 1345, but the Portuguese expeditions advanced as far as the mouth of Rio Grande, and founded establishments at the islands off Cape Verde. In these successive explorations, which lasted half a century, under the leadership of Gil Eanes (1442), of Nuno Tristam (1443), of Alvaro Fernandez (1448), and of Cadamosto (1454—56), hydrographic surveys had been made of about a third of the

Fig. 203.—John de Mandeville, a celebrated English Traveller, taking leave of King Edward III., before his Departure for "beyond the Seas."—Miniature from the "Merveilles du Monde." —Manuscript of the early part of the Fifteenth Century.—In the National Library, Paris.

African coast, as far as the great South Cape. After the death of Prince Henry, João de Santarem and Pedro de Escalona, who had explored the Guinea coast in 1471, crossed the line and opened up the navigation of the southern hemisphere. In 1484 Diego Cam reached the sixth degree of southern latitude at the mouth of the Zaire, and two years later Bartholomew

Diaz, who had ventured out into the ocean, which was still called the *Impenetrable Sea* and the *Dark Sea*, perceived the Cape of Good Hope, or Stormy Cape, at the extreme end of Africa.

These African islands and coasts had already been frequented, for in 1471, when the Portuguese landed in Guinea, they were much surprised to find there a French trading depôt called Le Petit Dieppe, which sailors from Dieppe had founded a century before. These were the same men who knew of the existence of North America a century before Christopher Columbus discovered the Antilles. Moreover, in 1395, the fleet of the brothers Zeno, freighted at Venice by the traders, had crossed the Atlantic under the guidance of a Dieppe pilot, who pointed out to it the northern coast of America; but all these discoveries, due to commercial enterprise and the love of gain, and achieved by daring adventurers, were in no way useful to science, for they were kept secret when they were likely to be beneficial to some branch of maritime commerce, while no importance was attached to them when they resulted in no material gain. It was not until the fifteenth century that navigators began to write an account of their voyages, or to have them recorded by the cosmographers who were generally to be found on board. But these records were either kept secret or were shown to only a very few people, as the navigators looked upon them as property over which it was necessary to keep close watch. Thus the curious voyage of Cadamosto, "Prima Navigatione alle Terre de' Negri" (First Navigation to the Land of Negroes), did not appear until 1507.

These travels were more useful to map-makers than to geographers, for every traveller and navigator found a map indispensable, and after making one for himself, he added to it the result of his own discoveries. Previously to the fourteenth century maps were very scarce, and those which did exist were faulty and incomplete. The oldest general map of the world dating from the Middle Ages is that which Marino of Venice presented to Pope John XXII. in 1321. This map, which appears to be an imitation of the Arab maps, is nothing more than a picture in which the relative position of places and countries is given almost hap-hazard, without any sign of parallels or meridians. A hundred and forty years later, a Camaldulan monk, Fra Mauro, painted upon the wall of one of the rooms in his monastery, in the isle of Murano, near Venice, an immense planisphere, in which he grouped all the known geographical facts of his time. The first marine maps, drawn by Italian, Portuguese, or

Spanish pilots, are not of an earlier date than Marino's map of the world, but they were very numerous in the following century. These charts, which are as a rule remarkable for the excellence of their drawing, are wonderfully accurate, and often contain allusions to celebrated sea voyages, together with

Fig. 204.—Map of the Island of Taprobana.—Reduced Fac-simile of a Map in Ptolemy's Geography, in the Latin Edition of 1492 (Ulmæ, per Leonardum Hol), offered by Nicholas Germain to Pope Paul II.—In the Library of M. Ambroise Firmin-Didot, Paris.

references which enable the reader to follow the phases of these voyages in chronological order, and to ascertain their results. It may safely be said that every pilot was capable of drawing for himself a very minute coast chart of all the seas in which he navigated.

This abundance of charts and maps, especially in countries which possessed a navy, explains how it was that copper engraved maps were almost contemporaneous with printing in movable type, which was invented in 1440, but kept a secret by the town of Mayenne until 1466. The first edition of Ptolemy's Cosmography was printed in folio at Vicenza, by Hermann Levilapis of Cologne, in 1462; but this edition had no maps. Nicholas Denis the Benedictine had, however, composed for Ptolemy's book maps which were engraved on copper by Andrea Benincasa. But in the meanwhile a new set of maps, also intended for Ptolemy's book, was admirably drawn by the printer, Conrad Sweynheym, the associate of Pannartz, who had removed his presses to Rome; and these maps, numbering twenty-seven, in which the letters were stamped with jewellers' punches and hammered, were completed by the Alsacian Arnold Buckinck, to illustrate the edition of Ptolemy which was printed at Rome under the superintendence, so far as the letterpress was concerned, of Domitius Calderini, and which appeared in 1478. Other editions, with maps engraved on wood and coloured with the paint-brush, appeared in succession in Italy and Germany (Fig. 204). The Greek text of Ptolemy was carefully revised by the geographers, who sought to amend and interpret it, in order to improve the Latin translation, which was continually being reprinted by the thousand; for the Greek text was not printed until 1533.

The publication of the Latin translation of Ptolemy was followed by that of several ancient geographers, and these primitive editions testified to the sympathy of the lettered public for geographical science. The Popes Paul II. and Sixtus IV. gladly accepted the dedication of the editions which Conrad Sweynheym and Arnold Pannartz printed at Rome. Strabo, translated into Latin, appeared in 1469; Pliny in 1473; Solinus, at Milan, in 1471, and at Paris in 1473. These works were also reprinted at Venice, where they were eagerly bought up. The study of geography at this period held a large place in the system of public education, and what proves it even more clearly than contemporary evidence is the quantity of small editions of Pomponius Mela which were printed for use in the universities throughout Europe.

There can be no doubt that this profusion of maps and books on geography gave a general impulse to sea voyages and expeditions. The Portuguese, after spending a whole century in their discovery of the western coasts of Africa, prepared to push forward into the Indian Ocean by way of the Cape of Good Hope, so as to extend their commercial, military, and naval power to Asia as well as to Africa. Diego d'Azambuza created in 1481 the first European establishment in Guinea, which had been explored twenty years beforehand by his compatriot Cintra; and Joan Cano discovered Congo in 1484. But the boldest mariners, notwithstanding their possession of the compass, which had been discovered in the twelfth century, would not

Fig. 205.—Discovery of San Domingo (Insula Hyspana) by Christopher Columbus.—After a Sketch which is attributed to him, and in which he is himself made to appear.—Fac-simile of a Wood Engraving of the "Epistola Christoferi Colom," undated Edition (1492 ?), in quarto.—In the Milan Library.

venture across the Atlantic, which was believed to be boundless and full of perils. The pilots, however, discussed amongst each other whether or not a vessel, by steering continually westward, would reach the most easterly islands of the Indian Ocean. This was the idea formed by the Genoese pilot,

Christopher Columbus, born in 1446, and accustomed to the sea from his childhood. He says in one of his letters, " God imparted to me great knowledge of maritime matters, and some knowledge of the stars, of geometry, and of arithmetic. Moreover, He granted me the power to delineate globes, and to indicate the proper position of towns, rivers, and mountains." He was, therefore, a geographer, and still more a chart-maker.

A Florentine astronomer, Toscanelli, showed him a map upon which he had indicated the route to follow in the Atlantic in order to reach the Indian isles, for it was not supposed that there was any land between Europe and Asia. Columbus, as he himself states, only intended at first to " seek for the East by way of the West." The advice of Toscanelli induced him to follow this new route, but it was in vain that he applied to the Republic of Genoa and the King of Portugal for funds to equip his vessels. After eight years of fruitless efforts he obtained from Ferdinand, the Catholic King of Arragon, and Queen Isabella of Castile, three small vessels, with which he started from the port of Palos, in Andalusia, on the 3rd of August, 1492. In March, 1493, he returned to Spain, after having discovered the islands of San Salvador, Cuba, and San Domingo (Fig. 205). Appointed Viceroy of the new lands which he had acquired for Spain, he returned there in the following year, but it was not until his third voyage in 1498 that he discovered the continent and explored the coast of South America (Fig. 206).

The discoveries of Christopher Columbus, whose name did not apparently obtain the notoriety which it deserved in after ages, produced a great effect throughout Europe. The first indications, vague and incomplete as they were, were received with enthusiasm, and the detailed information by which they were followed left no doubt as to the existence of these vast unknown lands. They led to the fitting out of a great number of maritime expeditions, in which science had no part, and the object of which was to take people to what was called the *gold country.* A great impulse, however, was given to geography, and throughout Italy and Spain the principal families devoted large sums to the formation in their palaces of collections of books, maps, and instruments bearing upon nautical astronomy, hydrography, and all the branches of ancient and modern geography. These families, animated by generous motives, spent vast sums in promoting voyages of exploration and discovery to the new parts of the world.

An adroit Florentine adventurer, named Amerigo Vespucci, was enabled, by the munificence of one of these Italian families, to equip a small flotilla, and make several voyages in the seas explored by Christopher Columbus. These voyages were probably undertaken for commercial purposes; but Vespucci gave them the appearance of having been made in the cause of geography by publishing, in the form of a letter, the description of new lands which he claimed to have discovered before Christopher Columbus, to whom he made no allusion. This letter, written in Italian and of which a great many copies were printed, was widely circulated throughout Italy, the

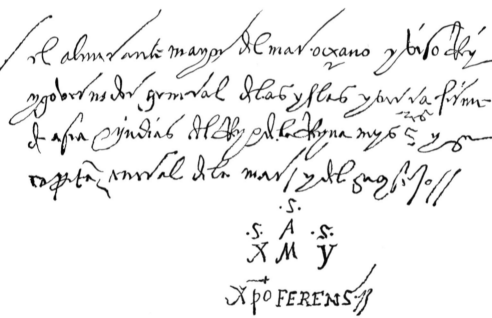

Fig. 206.— Signature at the foot of an Autograph Letter of Christopher Columbus, addressed from Seville to the noble Lords of the Office of St. George, and dated "A dos dias de Abril 1502."—Preserved in the Municipal Archives at Genoa.

inhabitants of which were much pleased at the success of one of their country-men, and at once gave to the New World the name of *America* in his honour. The latter, after the death of Columbus in 1506, continued his voyages along the American coast, and stoutly maintained that if Columbus had discovered the islands of that continent, he was the first to have found the continent itself. His statements were believed, and the name of America was finally given to a continent which he had merely explored in company with several

Spanish, French, and Portuguese navigators, such as Hojeda, Pinzon, and Cabral.

The Portuguese seemed for a time to abandon their expeditions to the New World, being so much engaged in establishing their trading stations upon the west coast as they had already done upon the east coast of Africa. Albuquerque and Vasco de Gama had won for them the islands of Goa and Ceylon, and their possessions upon the Asiatic shores increased rapidly. But their navigators could not long remain indifferent to the commercial current which was drawing all the navies of Europe into American waters, and they entertained the hope of discovering in the new land a passage into the Indian Ocean (Fig. 207). Thus their voyages had a certain scientific tendency, and were calculated to serve the progress of geography. Gaspar Cortereal sought in vain northward this passage communicating with Asia. He entered the Gulf of Labrador, and ascended the St. Lawrence in 1500, where he was stopped by the ice. Three years previously a Venetian trader named Cabotto, settled at Bristol, had attempted to discover in this direction a passage to India, but the only result of his explorations was the discovery of Newfoundland. The intrepid Magellan was more fortunate in his researches along the east coast of South America, and he discovered in southern latitudes the straits which still bear his name, and which opened up an entrance into the South Sea, across which he pursued his voyage to the countless islands of Polynesia (1521). Magellan, though a Portuguese, was in the service of Spain when he undertook this long and perilous expedition, which had such brilliant results for geographical science.

The object of the expeditions of the Spaniards into America, which followed one another in rapid succession, was to take possession of the country in the name of the King of Spain, and to enrich a few adventurers of various nationalities. Diaz de Solis and Pinto discovered Yucatan in 1507, having disembarked at Rio Janeiro; Pontius de Leon discovered Florida by chance in 1512; Vasco Nuñes saw Peru in 1513, and Pizarro conquered it in 1526. These conquests and discoveries were not of any immediate service to geography, for the navigators thought less of studying the country than of working the gold and silver mines; but when naturalists and men of letters, such as Oviedo y Valdes, J. Varezzani, Ramnusio, and other savants went to the country, its geographical features became better known.

King Francis I., who would have liked France to have had a share in the new continent, gave a very conspicuous place to geographical study in the Royal College founded by him. He encouraged most of the voyages undertaken during his reign, amongst which must be mentioned that of Jacques Cartier, who discovered Canada in 1533. Other French travellers

Fig. 207.—Galley of the Sixteenth Century.—After an Engraving by Raphael.—In the Collection of the Fine Arts Academy, Venice.

not less devoted to the cause of science explored both hemispheres, and collected, during their distant pilgrimages, very useful information of a geographical kind; amongst them being Pierre Gilles, André Thevet, and

Pierre Belon, who published excellent Cosmographies on the East; Jean Parmentier and François Nicolay, who visited the two Indies, and brought back much interesting information.   Amongst the most indefatigable of

Fig. 208.—Vow of the first Companions of St. Ignatius in the Church of Montmartre, upon the Day of the Assumption (1534).—Father Pierre Lefèvre, the only priest in the whole Company, is saying Mass.—Picture of the School of Simon Vouet (Seventeenth Century), in the School of St. Geneviève, Paris.

travellers were the companions of St. Ignatius and of François Xavier, who commenced about this time to write the history of their missions in the hitherto idolatrous lands whither they went to preach the gospel (Fig. 208). Geographical publications were in such demand throughout France at this period that the Paris booksellers ventured the simultaneous publication, during the reign of Charles IX., of two enormous compilations taken from the celebrated "Geographia" of Sebastian Munster, and bearing the title of "Cosmographie Universelle," the one by François de Belleforest, and the other by André Thevet, and both illustrated with maps and engravings.

The English and the Dutch did not hold aloof from this passion for discovery and exploration in Africa and America. The Dutch had also sought in a northerly direction for a direct route to the Indian Ocean, but they were driven back by the ice at the North Pole. England, while at war with Spain, sent two fleets, commanded by Drake and Cavendish, to the coast of North America to destroy the Spanish settlements; and Drake, after he had accomplished this task, sailed to Cape Horn, and round it as far as Vancouver's Land, while John Davis had been extending his Antarctic explorations far into the frozen waters of Greenland.

The savants of the Netherlands seem to have acquired the monopoly of the works illustrating the progress in geographical knowledge effected by such expeditions. Abraham Oertel, a Fleming of Antwerp, published in 1570 the first Atlas of modern geography, under the Latin title of "Theatrum Orbis Terrarum" (Theatre of the Terrestrial Globe). Gerhard Kauffman, surnamed Mercator, a native of Rupelmonde, also published in 1594 a large Atlas executed with the utmost precision and elegance, and very remarkable from a mathematical point of view. These two magnificent works soon obtained a great reputation, and the learned Vossius was justified in his declaration that "geography and chronology have become the two eyes of history."

HERALDIC SCIENCE.

 OME have endeavoured to trace back the
use of armorial bearings to almost the
very commencement of human society.
A writer on heraldry has not scrupled to
affirm that the posterity of Seth borrowed
their armorial bearings from the animal
and vegetable kingdoms, and that the
children of Cain painted upon their
bucklers implements of husbandry. Another person attributes their invention to
Noah when he came out of the ark, and
in the sixteenth and seventeenth centuries it was constantly being asserted that
ancient documents had disclosed the arms of Adam, of the first patriarchs, of
the prophets, of the Kings of Jerusalem, of the Virgin Mary, and of Christ
himself.

As M. E. de la Bédollière, in a very luminous treatise upon the origin of
heraldry, remarks, such blunders are not worth refuting. So far from being
contemporaneous with the earliest ages, armorial bearings were not even
known to the ancients. They had their national and hereditary symbols,
such as the Lion of Judah, the Golden Eagle of the Medes, the Owl of

Fig. 209.—Or.   Fig. 210.—Argent.   Fig. 211.—Gules.

Fig. 212.—Azure.   Fig. 213.—Sinople, or Vert.   Fig. 214.—Sable.

Fig. 215.—Purpure.   Fig. 216.—Tenne range.   Fig. 217.—Ermine.

Fig. 218.—Ermines.   Fig. 219.—Vair.   Fig. 220.—Counter-vair.

Metals, Colours, and Furs interpreted by the Engravers of the Middle Ages by means of Marks
and Conventional Signs.

Athens, the Crocodile of Egypt, and the Dove of Assyria, but the devices with which their bucklers were covered were not transmissible from father to son. These figures, which the celebrated warriors of Rome represented upon their arms as the insignia of their warlike achievements, were selected at the bidding of fancy. We may, however, cite, as a unique instance of a patrimonial emblem, the crow which was worn on the crests of their helmets by the descendants of Valerius Corvinus, to whom tradition attributed a singular victory achieved by the intervention of one of these birds of evil omen.

When the age of feudalism set in, it became the custom to distinguish by means of various signs, bright colours being as a rule used, the military shields and insignia, so as to provide rallying-points for the troops during the thick of the fight. These decorative paintings, in which may be discerned the germ of armorial bearings, were at first styled *cognisances*, or *entre-sains*, and they were all the more necessary as the *vantailles*, or eyelets, of the *armet* (closed helmet) quite hid the face of the wearer.

Here and there, in the chronicles of the Middle Ages, are to be found traces of the cognisances, but at the epoch when they first appear in history these different signs, all of a very simple kind, were not used to form the special combinations which afterwards became the exclusive appanage of such and such a family, and which fixed the principles of heraldic science. They were, so to speak, public property, and any one who chose could appropriate them. Master Jean de Garlande, who wrote in 1080 a very curious description of Paris, relates that the "dealers in bucklers, who supplied their goods to all the towns of France, sold to the chevaliers shields covered with cloth, leather, and pinchbeck, upon which were painted lions and fleurs-de-lis." Thus, as late as the close of the eleventh century, the Kings of France had no regular coat-of-arms, and the *shields*, embellished with lions and the fleur-de-lis, belonged by right of purchase to any one who chose to buy them, upon his showing that as a chevalier he had the right to use them.

If the coat-of-arms existed as one of the attributes of nobility, it may be affirmed that the practice had not any fixed and general basis. Heraldic science was in its infancy, and had not even settled the way in which armorial bearings were to be composed, by the use of *enamels*—that is to say, the *metals* and the colours—and of the *plush*, or fur, to form the ground of the shield, in such a way as not to confound them, or place one upon the other. The metals, the *or* and the *argent*, were probably no more than colours of yellow and white. The colours properly so called—blue, red, green, black, and violet—had not received the names of *azure, gules, sinople, sable,* and *purpure,* which were assigned them when emblazonry became an art or a science (Figs. 209 to 220). The images or enigmatic figures which were placed on the coloured or metallic ground of the escutcheon presented little variety, and every one considered himself free to alter their colour and shape as suited his fancy. In any event, the unvarying principle which consists in never placing colour upon colour, or metal upon metal, in a coat-of-arms, was not established during the feudal period. At about this epoch, however, a few coats-of-arms, which at first were mere cognisances, began to become hereditary, amongst them being the cross *voided, chequé,* and *pannetée,* which Raymond de St. Gilles affixed, together with his seal, to a deed dated 1088, and which remained part of the armorial bearings of the Counts of Toulouse; the two *bars* placed back to back which appear in the seal of Thierry II., Count of Montbéliard and of Bar-le-Duc, and which were handed down to his successors; and the *young lions* which the Plantagenets had upon their coat-of-arms in 1127, and which, under the name of *leopards,* are still preserved in the royal arms of Great Britain.

It was in the course of the twelfth century that the armorial bearings increased in number, and this was no doubt attributable to the first Crusade, as may be inferred from the choice of *enamels* used in them. The azure blue, or lapis-lazuli, had just been imported from the East, and its name of *ultramarine* is a reminiscence of the voyage to Palestine. Red got its name of *gules* from the fur trimmings which the crusaders wore round the neck and the wrists, and which were dyed red and purple ("murium rubricatas pelliculas quas *gulas* vocant," says St. Bernard, the apostle of the second Crusade). The enamel *sinople* also received its name from the dye which the crusaders brought from Sinople, a town in Asia Minor.

Several divisions in the shield also recall the time when the chevaliers were fighting "in the miscreant lands:" the *martlet,* a species of bird which emigrates every autumn to warm climates, naturally recalled Jerusalem; the *shell* (coquille) appertains specially to the pilgrims; the *bezant d'or* (a Saracenic or Arab coin) was the ransom paid to the Infidels; while the *cross,* which in every conceivable diversity of shape appears in all the oldest coats-of-arms, announced a participation in the Holy War.

In the thirteenth century the cognisances became in universal use, and henceforward not only the nobles, but towns, villages, and abbeys also, assumed armorial bearings. The cognisances then received the name of *blazon*, the etymology of which gave rise to much debate among the learned, though this debate might have been spared had they noticed that in early French the word *blázer* (to shine, to blaze), of Celtic origin, is often used instead of shield or buckler. Thus the author of the romance "William-the-Short-Nosed," describing a battle in the twelfth century, writes that the assailants crushed the helmets and broke the *blasons* in pieces; and in the not less ancient romance of "Garin le Loherain," which is referred to in another part of this volume, the hero is overthrown by a terrible blow dealt at his *blason* by Chevalier Ivait: in another place, King Amadus, attacking a Gascon, strikes the *buckle*, or central part, of his adversary's *blason*. *Blason*, then, simply means the buckler, the shield, upon which the coat-of-arms was at first displayed. The science of *blazonry*, begotten of the necessity for having some means of distinguishing between so many different signs and emblems, was but the result of studying the various manners in which were arranged the *enamels* and *divisions* which appeared in the coats-of-arms. It was also called *heraldic science*, because it was the special study of the *heralds*, whose functions became of considerable importance in the feudal organization of the Middle Ages. The duties of the heralds are alluded to in the volume on "Manners and Customs" (chapter on *Chivalry*), but it may be added here that these officers of the household, who only obtained their diploma, or commission, after an apprenticeship of seven or eight years in the service of their feudal lord, had over them the kings of arms (Fig. 221), appointed by the sovereign to draw up a list of the nobles and gentry of each province, with their different armorial bearings, for the compilation of a general peerage, which was placed in the custody of the premier King of Arms of France.

Figuring in their capacity of public officials at certain ceremonies, where they received, in accordance with the established custom, many valuable presents, the heralds of arms were, as a rule, men of considerable erudition, incessantly engaged in verifying the titles of nobility and the genealogies, in deciphering the *blazons*, and in establishing generally the true principles of heraldic science. It was they who laid down the laws with regard to the mass of distinctive decorations, the original selection of which had often been guided by ignorance or capriciousness.

They, in the first place, settled the shape of the *shield*. That of the French barons, which was first of all triangular and somewhat slanting, was replaced by a quadrilateral shield, rounded at the two lower corners, and terminating in a point at the centre of its base. The Germanic shield was remarkable for its rounded basis, and for a lateral indentation, which was used for supporting

Fig. 221.—"Fashion and Manner in which the King of Arms displays to the Four Judges the Plaintiff and Defendant, and presents to them the Letters of the said Plaintiff and Defendant, wearing upon his shoulder the Cloth of Gold and the Painted Parchment of the same."— Miniature from the "Tournois du roy René."—Manuscript of the Fifteenth Century.—In the National Library, Paris.

the lance when the man-at-arms, mounted upon his charger, held this lance at rest, covering his breast with his buckler.

Leaving to special heraldic treatises the theoretic description of the different partitions of the shield—that is to say, the lines which divide it into horizontal, diagonal, and perpendicular sections or parts—we proceed to give a summary explanation of the figures which, once so familiar, have become very enigmas to most persons in the present day, which constitute the *blazon* (Figs. 222 to 239).

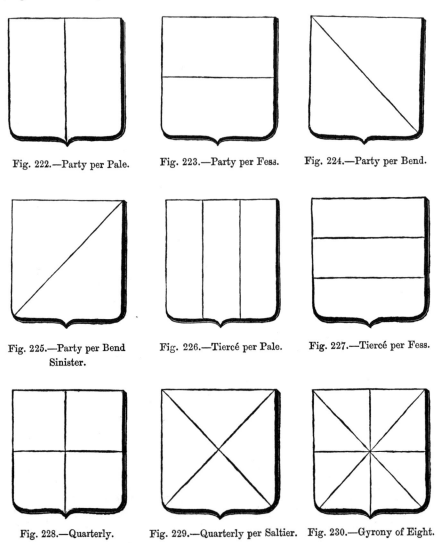

Fig. 222.—Party per Pale.   Fig. 223.—Party per Fess.   Fig. 224.—Party per Bend.

Fig. 225.—Party per Bend   Fig. 226.—Tiercé per Pale.   Fig. 227.—Tiercé per Fess.
Sinister.

Fig. 228.—Quarterly.   Fig. 229.—Quarterly per Saltier.   Fig. 230.—Gyrony of Eight.

Terms of Heraldry.   Partitions of the Shield.

To the *colours* and *metals* already mentioned, and which seem to have been selected solely in order that they might harmonize with the variegated costume of the chivalry of the Middle Ages, must be added the *plush*, or *fur*—that is to say, the *ermine* and the *vair*—the valuable furs used in France by the nobles of the ninth century; for we read in the "Life of St. Géraud," written at this period, that the grandees of the Carlovingian court trimmed their fur mantles

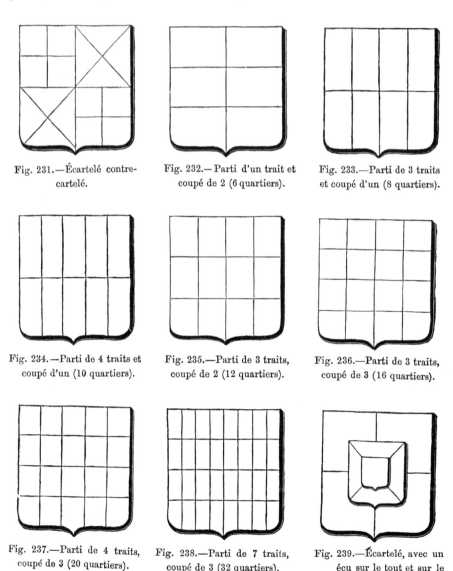

Fig. 231.—Écartelé contre-cartelé.

Fig. 232.— Parti d'un trait et coupé de 2 (6 quartiers).

Fig. 233.—Parti de 3 traits et coupé d'un (8 quartiers).

Fig. 234.—Parti de 4 traits et coupé d'un (10 quartiers).

Fig. 235.—Parti de 3 traits, coupé de 2 (12 quartiers).

Fig. 236.—Parti de 3 traits, coupé de 3 (16 quartiers).

Fig. 237.—Parti de 4 traits, coupé de 3 (20 quartiers).

Fig. 238.—Parti de 7 traits, coupé de 3 (32 quartiers).

Fig. 239.—Écartelé, avec un écu sur le tout et sur le tout du tout.

Terms of Heraldry. Partitions of the Shield.

with the fur of the ermine, or Armenian rat, and that they used lozenge-shaped strips of ermine or foumart to form the *vair* (variegated fur). The enamel, or *sable*, which represents black in the language of heraldry, was the fur of the sable, or fisher-weasel, as it is called by several poets of the twelfth and thirteenth centuries.

Amongst the panels in the coats-of-arms are to be found several other devices borrowed from the dress of the nobility of that period, such as the *labels*, or gold fringe of sashes; the *orles*, or trimmings of tunics; the *bands*, or *bars*, which represented scarfs; the *lambrequins* (mantles), or plumes made of silk or velvet, which were affixed to the extremity of the helmet; the *housseaux*, or top-boots with thick soles, which were only worn by men when they went out on foot in wet weather; the *pairle*, which, having the shape of the letter Y, resembled the bishop's pallium, and constituted, according to the heralds of the sixteenth century, the emblem of the great *devotions* of the chevalier: "His God, his Lady, and his King."

In addition to the hieroglyphics derived from the dress of the nobility, there were other heroic symbols: the *vals*, or marks of jurisdiction; the *frettiaux*, or *frettes*, the barriers which fenced in the lists; the *portcullis*, the *towers*, the *chains*, the *arrows*, and the *battering-rams*, emblems which carry their own explanation with them; and also the *keys*, which were a souvenir of the capitulation of a castle or of a city.

Fire, water, clouds, and even the stars (Figs. 240 to 244) also entered into the composition of the shield. The Chalus family has *azure* with three *crescents argent*, and that of Cernon *azure*, with six *comets or*, three in chief, and three in point, with the crescent *en abisme* (in the centre of the shield).

The whole of the human body is not so often used in the blazon as the separate parts of the body—head, hands, eyes, legs, &c.—which are sometimes represented, as also are animals, plants, and various objects, with their natural colour, called in heraldry *carnation*.

The animals, quadrupeds especially, which, as a general rule, imply allegorical ideas, are very common in the blazon, though they are always represented after a type more or less untrue to nature: the lion (generosity), the elephant (courtesy), the squirrel (foresight, because that animal is careful to close the apertures of his nest), and the lamb (gentleness). For instance, the Montalembert arms are *or*, with *three wolves' heads*, *sable;* the Portal arms, *azure*, with ox *or*, accompanied in chief by six *fleurs-de-lis*, the same; the Coignieux arms, *azure*, porcupine *passant sable*.

As a general rule, birds express change of residence, of nationality, and of

Fig. 240.—The Piccolominis, a Family belonging to Rome, and established at Sienna about the Eighth Century. —A Crescent, with the Motto, "Sine maculâ."

Fig. 241. — John II., King of France (1350—1364).—A radiating Star, with the Motto, "Monstrant regibus astra viam," in allusion to the star which guided the Magi to Bethlehem.

Fig. 242.—Richard Cœur-de-Lion, King of England (1189—1199).— A Star, probably that of Bethlehem, issuing from out of the Horns of the Crescent.

condition, irrespectively of the particular meaning applicable to each (Figs. 246

Fig. 243.—Martin, I., King of Arragon (1395—1410).—Faith triumphant, erect upon the Terrestrial Globe, with the Motto, "Non in tenebris."

Fig. 244.—Emanuel, King of Portugal (1495—1521).—The Terrestrial Globe, surrounded by the Ocean, across which are sailing several Portuguese Vessels. Motto, "Primus circumdedisti me."

and 247). Thus dominion is represented by the eagle; vigilance by the cock, the heron, or the stork; conjugal affection by the dove; eloquence by the parrot; long and laborious old age by the swan; and self-devotion by the pelican, which was believed by the ancients to nourish its young with the

Fig. 245.—Alfonso X., King of Castile (1252—1284).—A Pelican opening its side to nourish the Young. Motto, " Pro lege et grege."

flesh of its own breast, and which is represented (see Fig. 245) upon its nest, with extended wings, tearing its breast and brooding over its young. In the language of heraldry the drops of blood which the pelican draws from its

Fig. 246.—Robert of Anjou, King of Naples (1309—1343).—A Swallow bringing Food to its Young. Motto, " Concordia regni,"

Fig. 247.—William, Prince of Orange (1572—1584).—A Halcyon placing its Nest in the Sea, and above it the Monogram of Christ. Motto, " Sævis tranquillus in undis."

breast are called *piety*, when they are of a different *enamel* from the bird. Thus the house of Lecamus has *gules* (shield on a red ground), with pelican *argent*, vulning itself *gules*, in its eyrie; the chief seamed *azure*, charged with a

fleur-de-lis *or.* The ancient family of Vienne, which had given two admirals
and a marshal to France, has *gules*, with eagle *or.* The house of Savoy, in
Dauphiny, has *azure*, with three doves *or;* Montmorency, *or*, cross *gules*,
cantoned by sixteen spread-eagles, *azure.* These spread-eagles, which, as a
rule, represent eagles without beak or claws, and which indicate a victory
over some foreign foe (Fig. 248), have a special meaning in the arms of the
house of Lorraine. It is said that during a festival given in honour of King
Pepin, a quarrel having arisen between the Franks and the Lorrainers, the
Duke Begon, who held the post of seneschal, placed himself at the head of

Fig. 248.—Godfrey de Bouillon, Duke of Lorraine, King of Jerusalem (1099).—An Arrow trans-
fixing three Spread-Eagles. The Motto, taken from Virgil, is, " Dedebitne viam casusve
deusve?" The Spread Eagle still forms part of the Arms of the House of Hapsburg-Lorraine.

the kitchen servants, armed them with spoons, pokers, and fire-dogs, and,
seizing for himself a spit upon which several plovers were being roasted,
committed a frightful carnage amongst the Franks. It was in memory of
this exploit that the plovers, converted into *spread-eagles* to make it clear
that they were upon the spit, took their place in the arms of Lorraine, which
looked back with pride upon the fact of the Duke Begon having been one of
its early rulers.

Fish generally represent sea voyages and naval victories. One of the fish
oftenest used in the shield is the dolphin (Fig. 249), which even, by means

of heraldry, gave its name to Dauphiny, one of the greatest fiefs of the French crown.

Shell-fish, serpents, and insects also form part of the figures used in heraldry, but it is difficult to say what was the special signification attached to them. Lowan Geliot, however, in his "Armorial Index," published in 1650, states that the cricket represents all the domestic virtues, because this insect "only frequents the hearth of honest people."

According to the same author, whose imagination gets the better of him, as is the case with all the old heralds of arms, plants, flowers, and fruits had all a fixed symbolism: the oak, for instance, meant power; the *olive-tree*, peace; the *vine*, gladness; the *apple-tree*, love; the *cypress*, sadness; the

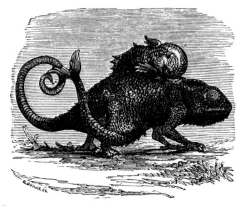

Fig. 249.—Pope Paul III. (1534—1549).—A Chameleon carrying a Dolphin.
Motto, "Mature."

pomegranate (Fig. 250), by an ingenious idea, was held to represent "the alliance of nations and men united under one religion." *Trifolium, columbine, tierce-feuilles, quatre-feuilles*, and *quinte-feuilles* represented hope, because their appearance in the spring presaged the summer and autumn crops; the *rose* naturally typified grace and beauty. The *fleur-de-lis* (which in France, at all events, may be called the queen of heraldic flowers) has a complex meaning, which justifies its selection by French kings to variegate the azure field of their banner bespangled with innumerable fleurs-de-lis *or*, before the heralds reduced the number of flowers to three (Fig. 276).

Various experts have argued that this so-called fleur-de-lis did not in reality belong to the vegetable kingdom. According to them the flower-shaped charges which Louis VI. first placed upon his seal, and which Philip of Valois, in the fourteenth century, reduced to three, were the iron tips of the three-headed javelins in use amongst the Merovingian Franks. Other dabblers in heraldry have described the shield of the early Kings of France as "*sable*, three toads *or*." The best contradiction to these ridiculous statements is to be found in the "Annals" of William of Nangis, and that ancient chronicler says, "The Kings of France had in their arms the fleur-de-lis painted in three leaves, as much as to say, 'Faith, wisdom, and chivalry are, by the grace of God, more abundant in our kingdom than anywhere else.' The two leaves of the fleur-de-lis which are bent signify wisdom and chivalry, which guard and protect the third leaf placed between them, and the

Fig. 250.—Catherine of Arragon, first Wife of Henry VIII. (1501).—A Pomegranate bearing a Red Rose and a White, in allusion to the White Rose of York and the Red Rose of Lancaster, uniting the Rights of the two Families to the English Crown.

greater length of which signifies faith, which must be governed by wisdom and protected by chivalry."

It is, therefore, beyond doubt, according to the evidence of this historian of the thirteenth century, that in the arms of the King of France the central petal of the fleur-de-lis represented religion, and that the wings or side-leaves represented the moral and material force which was intended to support it. Moreover, the fleur-de-lis was used in the arms of many noble families, both French and foreign, which were in no way connected with the kings of the third French race. It was only some of these families which had obtained the privilege of placing the fleur-de-lis upon their escutcheon, as a recompense for services rendered to the Crown. Thus Charles VII., when he ennobled the brothers of Joan of Arc, gave them not only the new name of Du Lys, which they assumed after their sister, but also an azure escutcheon, charged with a pointed sword, with two fleurs-de-lis *or*, dexter and sinister (Fig. 251).

After having made use of the principal emblems furnished by nature in the composition of armorial bearings, heraldic science borrowed from the work of human hands, or from the fanciful conceptions of the human mind. Thus certain families took for their escutcheon instruments of music, such as harps, guitars, or hunting-horns, and the ordinary utensils of domestic life, such as pots, drinking-glasses, knives, mill-stones, candlesticks, &c. Other

Fig. 251.—Family of Joan of Arc, *alias* Du Lys.—A Sword *argent* in pale, the point supporting a Crown *or*, and being flanked with two Fleurs-de-lis, with the Motto, "Consilio firmatei Dei." This Coat-of-arms was composed by Charles VII. himself, in 1429.

families, having more ambitious ideas, placed in their arms imaginary animals, such as the phœnix, the unicorn, harpies, and so forth.

It is worthy of remark that many arms were emblematic; that is to say, people *charged* them with certain common objects which happened to present an analogy with their family name (Fig. 252). For instance, the Bouesseaux had three *bushels* (boisseaux) *azure;* the Chabots, three *chabots* (a river-fish); the Maillys, three *maillets* (malets) *sinople;* the Du Palmiers, three *palms or;* the Rethels, three *râteaux* (ratres) *or;* the Créquys, a *créquier* (cherry-tree) *gules;* the Begassoux, three heads of the *bécasse* (woodcock) *or;* the Auchats, a *chat* (cat) startled, *argent;* the Héricés, three *hérissons* (hedgehogs) *sable;* the Gourdins, three *gourds,* or *calabashes, or;* the Guitons, a guitar *or.* Upon the same principle, the city of Rheims, then written *Rains,* took in its arms two *rainseaux,* or *rains,* intertwined branches, &c.

The close of the thirteenth and the whole of the fourteenth century were the most brilliant in the history of heraldry. It was a metaphorical language which at that time every one spoke and understood, from the highest to the lowest. Armorial bearings were placed everywhere, with the dead as with the living, for they were used to decorate tombs and epitaphs. They were to be seen sculptured, engraved, or in relief, designed or painted, in the great castles and in the modest manors, upon the lintels of doors, upon the locks, upon the weather-cocks, upon the brick pavements, upon the window-glass,

Fig. 252.—The Orsini (Roman) Family (Fourteenth Century).—A Bear crouched (the meaning of the name), holding a Sand-glass. Motto, " Tempus et hora."

upon the chimneys, upon the tapestry, and upon all the pieces of furniture (Fig. 253). They were even reproduced, in many different ways, upon the dress of the nobles and of their wives and families, as well as upon their servants' liveries, upon the trappings of their horses (Fig. 254), upon their dog-collars, and upon the hoods of their falcons and hawks.

Towards the fifteenth century the blazons were made more complex by the addition of the *helmet* or distinctive sign; that is to say, above the shield there was placed the *heaume* (chevalier's helmet), either full-face, three-parts face, or in profile; and according to its shape and the way in which it was made, it indicated exactly, and at a single glance, the condition and title

of the person.   Thus the kings had the helmet *or*, full-face, the visor completely open and without bars, to signify that a sovereign ought to know and

Fig. 253.—The Lords and Barons "make windows of their blazons;" that is to say, exhibit their
nobility by displaying their Banners and Coats-of-arms from the windows of the Heralds'
Lodge.—After a Miniature in the "Tournois du Roy René."—Manuscript of the Fifteenth
Century.—In the National Library, Paris.

to see everything.   The helmet of counts and viscounts was *argent* three-parts profile, the visor drawn down, and having nine bars *or*. That of a baron had only seven bars to the visor.   That of the gentry untitled was of polished steel, placed in profile, with five bars *argent*.   When the King conferred or sold a title, he invented as the crest of the blazon, for the person ennobled,

Fig. 254.—The Duc de Bourbon, armed cap-à-pie for the Tournament.—After a Miniature in the " Tournois du Roy René."—Manuscript of the Fifteenth Century.—In the National Library, Paris.

an iron helmet in profile, with the *vantaille* and nose piece half open.   The helmets further had pieces of cloth called *lambrequins*, which the wearers attached to the crests of their helmets, the size of which gradually attained enormous proportions.   These crests themselves became an essential ornament, and represented lions, horns, chimæras, and human arms bearing some weapon. Gradually, however, it became the custom to replace these accessories by plain coronets enriched with gems and pearls, the shape and number of which varied according to the rank of the wearer.

About the middle of the fifteenth century it became customary for families which had enrolled troops, and led them to join the *ost* (army) of the sovereign under their own banners, to place above the crests a *listel*, or *scroll*, bearing upon it their *battle-cry*. Gradually this right was claimed by every chevalier *banneret* who had the means of assembling under his *pennon*, or *gonfalon* (a standard with the arms or colours of a noble), four or five gentlemen and twelve or fifteen men-at-arms equipped at his expense.

Moreover, the battle-cry is of very much earlier date than the fifteenth century, for even the Barbarians were accustomed to nerve themselves for the fight by cries which were also used as signals. The usage of rallying the soldiers upon a field of battle by means of some shout uttered by the whole army in chorus is to be discovered in the Bible, for Gideon, when he was about to take the camp of the Midianites by surprise at night, ordered his own men to shout when they attacked the enemy whom the Lord had delivered into their hands, " For the Lord and for Gideon ! "

In the Middle Ages battle-cries were universal. Most of them were nothing more than the names of the different nobles and chevaliers, supplemented by some flattering epithet or pious invocation, such as *Mailly !—La Tremoille !—Bourbon, Bourbon, Notre Dame !—Coucy, à la Marveille !* The great barons used as a battle-cry the name of a province, of a lordship, or of an important town upon their domains, and these did not change even when the town or lordship changed owners. Under the Dukes of Burgundy the Hennuyers still cried, *Hainaut au noble duc !* The men of Gascony, Navarre, and Arragon shouted, *Bigorre ! Bigorre !* as under the Kings of Navarre and of Arragon. The men of Beauvais, when they went out to do battle, invoked *Beauvais la jolie !* while those of Louvain shouted, *Louvain au riche duc !*

The battle-cries of certain families contained allusions to the charges upon their coat-of-arms, and *Flandre au lion* was the cry of the Counts of Flanders, and *Au peigne d'or* (the golden comb) that of the lords of Callant. Another family used as its battle-cry a sort of exhortation to the valiant, or of menace to the vanquished, without any special or generic characteristic. The Counts of Champagne cried, *Passavant les meillors !* the Chevaliers of Bar, *Au feu !*

au feu! those of Brie, *Cans d'oiseaux!* The meaning of some battle-cries was evidently to implore the intercession of God, of the Virgin, and of the saints during the fight. The Dukes of Brittany exclaimed, *St. Yves! St. Malo!* the Dukes of Anjou, *St. Maurice!* the Montmorencys, *Dieu ayde au premier baron chrestien!* and the Chastel-Montforts, *St. Marie, aie!* (aid us!)

It is to this latter category of war-cries that assuredly belonged that of the Kings of France, *Montjoie St Denis!* the origin of which has given rise

Fig. 255.—Mary Tudor, Queen of England (1553—1558). A Double Rose intersected down the middle, with a Bundle of Arrows, surrounded with Rays, and surmounted by a royal Crown. The Double Rose is an allusion to the Houses of York and Lancaster, while the Arrows represent the House of Arragon.

to so many conflicting and misleading statements. One theory is that Clovis, giving battle in the valley of Conflans, drove back the enemy to the foot of a tower called Montjoie, and that he perpetuated the memory of his triumph by taking Montjoie as his battle-cry. Another theory is that Clovis, having invoked the aid of St. Denis at the battle of Tolbiac, called him, in French, *mon Jupiter, mon Job!* which was corrupted into *Montjoie.* But, as a matter of fact, *Montjoie St. Denis* merely means, "Follow the banner of St. Denis," for this banner during battle was hoisted upon a gilt chariot, as upon a

Fig. 256. — Device of Henry VII., King of England (1485 —1509).—A Haw- thorn-tree in flower, between the letters H. R. (" Henricus Rex ").

Fig. 257.—Device of Pope Leo X. (1513—1521).—A Yoke, with the Motto, " Suave."

Fig. 258. — Device of Charles IX., King of France (1560—1574). —Two Columns in- terlaced, the emblem of Piety and Justice (" Pietate et justi- cia ").

montjoie (an eminence or hillock), that it might be visible from afar while the

Fig. 259.—Device of Henry III., King of France (1574—1589).—Three Crowns, re- presenting those of France and Poland, and that which he hoped to obtain : " Manet ultima cœlo."

Fig. 260.—Device of the Emperor Charles V. —While yet King of Spain (1518) he adopted as his emblem a Sun rising above a Zodiac, and as his Motto, " Nondum in auge " (Not yet at its zenith).

combat was going on. The Kings of France were entitled to the banner of

St. Denis in their quality of *avoués* (lawyers) of the abbey of that name, and Counts of the Vexin. Louis VI. was the first to go and take the oriflamme, which was no other than this banner, in the basilica of St. Denis, upon the altar of the holy martyrs (which was called the *montjoie*), and his successors continued to come and ask for it from the monks of the royal abbey whenever they were about to start upon an expedition, "because," says Suger, "the blessed St. Denis was the special patron and protector of the kingdom." This same word was to be discovered in several other battle-cries, such as *Montjoie St. Andrieux! Montjoie Anjou!* and others.

War-cries ceased to be used during battle when Charles VII., having founded the ordinance companies, dispensed the bannerets from the duty of

Fig. 261.—Device of Catherine de' Medicis, Queen of France, during her Widowhood.

leading their vassals to the fight. It was then that these cries were inscribed upon the scroll placed above the crest, while underneath, upon another scroll, appeared, in letters of gold or of silver, the patrimonial motto of the house. There was, moreover, this difference between the battle-cry and the motto—that the latter was not always hereditary, for in some cases it changed at each generation even in the same family. For instance, the ordinary motto of the house of Sales, in Savoy, was originally, "Ni plus, ni moins," but several members of this family adopted other mottoes. That of Francis de Sales, Lord of Roisy, was, "En bonne foy;" that of John de Sales, "Adieu, biens mondains!" that of Galois de Sales, "In paucis quies;" that of St. Francis de Sales, "Numquam excedet," signifying, with the word *Charitas* understood, *Charity never dies out.*

In many cases mottoes, like the charges on the shield, are allusive, and reproduce the family name with a sort of play upon the words. Such are Achay, in the Franche-Comté, "Jamais las d'âcher;" Vaudray, "J'ai valu, vaux et vaudray;" Grandson, "A petite cloche, grand son;" Lauras, in Dauphiny, "Un jour l'auras;" Disemieux, "Il est nul qui dise mieux."

Several mottoes, also, contain allusions to the figures in the coats-of-arms. Thus the Simian family, whose arms are *or*, semé with fleurs-de-lis and turrets *azure*, has for motto, "Sustentant lilia turres" (The lilies support the turrets). There are mottoes, too, which evoke the recollection of a battle or of a proverb, or which enounce some indefinite and mys-

Fig. 262.—The Arms of Anne of Brittany, Queen of France.—An Ermine, pure and spotless, attached to the Order of the Cordelière, founded by the Queen for Ladies, with the Motto, "A ma vie." The royal Shield is supported by an Angel, with the Motto, "Rogo pro te Anna" (Anne, I pray for thee), and upon the other side a Lion rampant, with these words, in allusion to the ermine of Brittany : "Libera eam de ore leonis" (Deliver it from the jaws of the lion).—Miniature from the "Funérailles d'Anne de Bretagne."—Manuscript of the Sixteenth Century.—In the Library of M. Ambroise Firmin-Didot, Paris.

terious allusion. For instance, Antoine de Croy, "Souvenance;" Jean de la Trémoille, "Ne m'oubliez!" Johann Schenk, in Germany, "Plutôt rompre que fléchir;" Philip of Burgundy, after his marriage with Isabella of Portugal, "Autre n'auray," an alteration of the amorous motto, "Autre n'auray dame Isabeau, tant que vivray." The proud mottoes of the Rohans and the Coucys are very well known : "Roi ne puis, duc ne daigne, Rohan suis;" "Je ne suis roy, ne duc, ne comte aussi, je suis le sire de Coucy." Sometimes the mottoes were merely represented by mute emblems, such as the White Rose of the house of York, the Red Rose of Lancaster

Fig. 263.—Jean Le Feron, a learned French heraldic Scholar (1504—1570), presents one of his Works to King Henry II.—Miniature from the "Blason d'Armoiries," by Jehan Le Feron. —Manuscript of the Sixteenth Century, No. 795.—In the Arsenal Library, Paris.

(Fig. 255), the Thistle of Bourbon, and the Musket of Burgundy; and sometimes they comprised both emblems and inscriptions, as in Italy, where

Camillo Pallavicini, member of an ancient Milanese family, bore a flower, the
stem of which was being nibbled by a turtle, with the Italian inscription, "Ogni

Fig. 264. —Banner of the Calais Innkeepers.   Fig. 265.—Banner of the Amiens Butchers.

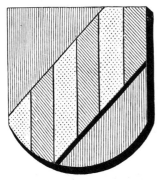

Fig. 266.—Banner of the Bethune Tailors.   Fig. 267.—Banner of the St. Omer Cobblers.

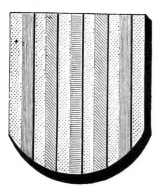

Fig. 268.—Banner of the St. Lô Dyers.   Fig. 269.—Banner of the Bordeaux Upholsterers.

belleza ha fine" (All beauty is perishable).   Another Italian, Paolo Sfortita, had painted at the side of his blazon an arrow strung upon the bow, and pointing heavenwards, with the words, " Sic itur ad astra " (Figs. 256 to 260).

Fig. 270.—Banner of the St. Lô Blacksmiths.

Fig. 271.—Banner of the Tours Slaters.

Fig. 272.—Banner of the Paris Founders.

Fig. 273.—Banner of the Lyons Tinmen.

Fig. 274.—Banner of the Douai Shoemakers.

Fig. 275.—Banner of the Pin and Needle Makers.

The mottoes forming riddles, more or less difficult to solve, came into fashion during the sixteenth century. The house of Medicis had in its arms a diamond and three ostrich feathers, with the motto forming a Latin pun, "Super adamas in pennis" (Above the diamond, in the wing feathers), and this strange device is only to be understood by translating it thus: *Always invincible in trouble.*

The art of devices—for it had become an art, as heraldry had become a science—was often used for the composition of enigmas which defied the sagacity of the solvers of riddles (Fig. 276). Pierre de Morvilliers, first President of the Paris Parliament, had as his device a portcullis connected with a Y, and his name was expressed by this figure (Mort Y liés), because the portcullis is the emblem of death, which makes all things equal.

Several hereditary devices perpetuated the memory of some historic event. Charles VIII., during the battle of Fornova (July 15th, 1495), when surrounded by a mass of the enemy, was saved by the Seigneur de Montoison, whose heroic valour soon changed the fate of the battle, and the King, after it was over, recompensed his deliverer by giving him as his motto the words which he had uttered in calling him to his assistance, "A la rescousse, Montoison!" Catherine de' Medicis, after the death of Henry II., who was killed by the thrust of a lance at a tournament (1559), changed her device and took a broken lance, with the motto, "Hinc dolor, hinc lacrimæ" (Hence my woe, hence my tears). Christopher Columbus, who discovered America, left to his descendants the noble Spanish motto—

> " Por Castille et por Leon
> Nuevo mundo hallo Colomb."
>
> (For Castile and Leon, Columbus discovers a new world.)

At about the time that devices of all kinds were becoming numerous, the custom was introduced of adding to coats-of-arms *supporters,* or *tenants* (Fig. 262). The first of these names was given to the animals which supported the shield; the second to the men of human form who held it up—the angels, chevaliers, heralds, moors, savages, &c. This was the most brilliant period of heraldry, but it was also the most confused and the most fatal to this ancient institution, which had done so much for the chivalry and the nobility, as the excessive exaggeration of heraldic signs was, as a matter of course, favourable to fraud and usurpation of armorial bearings (Fig. 263). This usurpation, which was generally a prelude to the usurpation of titles of nobility, did not involve any other punishment than a fine—a fact which is mentioned in an ordinance of Charles IX. addressed to the States of Orleans in 1560, and framed as follows:—"Those who shall falsely usurp the name and title of nobility, take or use crested arms, will be fined by our judges, and the most rigorous measures will be used to make them pay these fines." But, in spite of the numerous and severe decrees of the Crown against the assumption of titles, the evil increased, and by the end of the fifteenth century the merchants and the working mechanics, as well as the bourgeoisie, took for themselves arms and devices without any opposition upon the part of the

Fig. 276.—The Arms of France in the Fifteenth Century.—After a Miniature in the Missal of Charles VI.—In the Library of M. Ambroise Firmin-Didot, Paris.

judges of arms, who exercised an official supervision over all the matters relating to the nobility and their privileges. It may be supposed, therefore, that this assumption of armorial bearings by the middle classes was only tolerated in return for the payment of a tribute to the King as the supreme dispenser of all nobiliary privileges. The Crown had, moreover, recognised a sort of nobility of trade, by the grant of statutes to the workmen's corporations, which showed themselves as jealous as the nobility of their honorary distinctions, and of the arms which they had painted, engraved, or embroidered upon their insignia (see Figs. 264 to 275), at a time when Montaigne declared in his "Essays" that if "nobility is a good and reasonable institution, it is to be esteemed far below virtue," inasmuch as " it is a virtue, if it be one, of an artificial and visible kind, dependent upon time and fortune ; diverse in form, according to the country. . . ."   The ancient custom of solemnly interring the arms of an extinct family in the grave of its last representative had been abandoned for centuries.   Even if noble families became extinct, they were resuscitated with their armorial bearings, and formed new branches by substitution of name, by alliance, or by usurpation.   This was the cause of the different verifications and reforms of the nobility which took place in the fifteenth century, and which added a large sum in the way of fines and royalties to the King's treasury.

Heraldic science has, however, survived the noble institutions which first brought it into existence, and though it has lost a part of its primitive importance, it still remains almost intact as a picturesque monument of the past, and as a tradition of mediæval history.

PROVERBS.

HE popular sayings which compose what
has been called the "ancient wisdom of
nations" are of all times and of all lands,
for proverbs are to be found in the early
language of all nations ; but they belong
especially to the Middle Ages, which had
collected and preserved them as a precious
legacy of the early ages and peoples in the
world's history.

Every nation gives its own special
impress, so to speak, to its familiar proverbs.
The Italian proverb is witty and subtle ;
that of the Spaniards haughty and bold. The French proverb is incisive
and satirical : originating in the lower classes, it very often attacks the rich and
the powerful, and not unfrequently is expressed in language the liberty of which
has developed into license. In England, Germany, and in all Northern nations
the proverbs are severe, cold, formal, and pedantic. The proverb is used by
all classes of society to characterize an individual act, or some general or specific
occurrence, as occasion requires. It is never explained, but always understood.

Proverbs passed, as by a natural transition, from speech into writing, and
they are very abundant in the first works written in French, though the
worb *proverb* itself does not appear to be of earlier date than the thirteenth
century. Before this period, the word *proverbium*, though used by all authors

who wrote good Latin, had no better equivalent in French than *respit* or *reprovier.* In the oldest version of the Bible, in the twelfth century, the passage in the First Book of Kings (chap. xix.), "Unde et exivit proverbium," the word *proverbium* is translated *respit.*

The Bible was then The Book, which was read and learnt by heart before any other, and which served as a type for various literary compositions. It is only natural, therefore, that King Solomon, who may be said to have given the model for this kind of literature in his Book of Proverbs, should have been regarded as an oracle to be consulted with respect in the Middle Ages. Besides, the Jewish legend which represented Solomon as the King of Magic, and which made him supreme over the whole of nature, had become an article of faith with the Christians as well as with the Jews. According to this legend, the Queen of the Ants settled one day upon the hand of the King of Israel, and revealed to him the secrets of eternal truth. One of the first collections of French proverbs, published in the Middle Ages, was dedicated to Solomon, who is represented in it as the type of Divine wisdom, opposite to a man named *Marcol*, or *Marcoul*, who is the representative of human reason (Fig. 277). There is a dialogue in rhyme between the two. The Israelitish King utters some weighty saying, and Marcol answers him with an analogous axiom embodying the rough common sense of the people, and generally expressed in homely language. The "Dictz (sayings) de Salomon et Marcol," originally composed in Latin, were translated into all languages during the Middle Ages, and the French version probably dates from the twelfth century. One verse of it runs—

> " ' Qui sages hom sera
> Ici trop ne parlera.'
> *Ce dist Salomon.*
> ' Qui ja mot ne dira
> Grand noise (dispute) ne fera.'
> *Marcol lui respont.*"

The popularity of these rhymed proverbs, which were continually being revised, added to, and modified, is proved by the multitude of editions which appeared at the close of the fifteenth century. It is probable that the original Latin was written, in the tenth or eleventh century, by a student in the ecclesiastical schools of Paris, which undertook to vulgarise in this way the

Book of Proverbs and the Book of Wisdom, which latter was also attributed
to Solomon.

Fig. 277.—Solomon and Marcoul.—Fac-simile of a Wood Engraving in the "Dictz de Salomon
et Marcoul."—Edition of the Fifteenth Century.—In the National Library, Paris.

It is very probable, also, that this name of Marcol, or Marcoul, or Marcon,

given to the second person in the dialogue, was no other than Marcus, a celebrated philosopher of the Middle Ages, who was believed to be Marcus
Porcius Cato, called the Censor, or Marcus Cato, his son, who were considered
to be the joint authors of the "Moral Distiches" ("Disticha de Moribus")
which had since the seventh century been employed as works of education,
but which should rather be attributed to a monk named Valerius or Dionysius, and surnamed Cato. The celebrity of these distiches, which were read
and expounded in the schools, remained as great as ever all through the
Middle Ages. They were more than once translated, paraphrased, or imitated
in French verse during the twelfth and thirteenth centuries, and they were
frequently reprinted in verse during the fifteenth century under the title of
the "Grand Chaton," and again at the beginning of the sixteenth, by Peter
Grosnet, under the title of "Motz dorés du grand et saige Caton."

There was also in the twelfth century another collection of proverbs, or of
proverbial philosophy, which long had a great reputation in the schools, and
which was several times translated into French for the use of the upper as of
the lower classes, neither of which had much knowledge of Latin. This
collection, known as the "Philosophers' Proverbs," contained a selection of
sayings (sentences) in verse, most of which were apocryphal, attributed to the
most noted personages of ancient times, and in particular to various Greek
and Latin authors who were comprised in the category of philosophers. Thus
Virgil, Ovid, and Horace appeared in this compilation between Moses and
Solomon upon the one hand, and Homer and Æsop upon the other (Fig. 278).
Afterwards these moral sayings were translated into French with the title of
"Dits des Philosophes," but though they doubtless had some resemblance
to certain passages of the authors to whom they were attributed, they had
more in common, when moulded into verse, with the dialogue of Solomon and
Marcoul, as the following lines, which claim to be an imitation of Juvenal,
will show :—

> "Tant vaut amour comme argent dure :
> Quant argent fault (manque), amour est nule.
> Qui despent le sien follement,
> Si n'est amés (aimé) de nule gent."

In the fifteenth century, Guillaume de Tignonville, Provost of Paris, in
the reign of Charles VI. found time, amidst his other numerous occupations,

to make a fresh translation of the "Dits des Philosophes" in verse, with numerous additions, to which he appended biographical notices in prose of the philosophers, amongst whom he included not only warriors like Alexander the Great and Ptolemy, King of Egypt, but imaginary personages, such as Simicratis, Fonydes, Archasan, and Longinon. His book was a great success, for, in addition to the many manuscripts with miniatures, the printers of the fifteenth century published several editions of it.

These different collections of proverbs, attributed to such famous men as

Fig. 278.—The Wolf cheating the Donkey.—Fac-simile of a Wood Engraving from the "Dyalogue des Créatures" (Gouda, Gerart Leeu, 1482, in folio).—In the Library of M. Ambroise Firmin-Didot, Paris.

Solomon, Cato, and the ancient Greek and Latin philosophers, may be looked upon as the fruits of scholastic erudition and literary invention, while other collections, which had an equally great success at the same period, seem to emanate more directly from the homely good sense and native wit of the people, with all their facetious and picturesque qualities. It is not necessary to mention more than three or four of these collections, which, in spite of their immense popularity at the time, were not, with one exception, reproduced by the printers of the fifteenth and sixteenth centuries. They are, however, original proverbs, which owe nothing to the writers of Greece or of Rome, and which bear the Gallic stamp of our ancestors. The oldest of these collections is entitled, "Vulgar and Moral Proverbs." It is satisfactory to find that the six hundred proverbs which an unknown hand put together five or six centuries ago still display, notwithstanding the change which has taken place in manners, ideas, and even in language, a clear and plain text which, with the exception of a few differences in spelling, might be understood by the general body of modern readers. Some of these proverbs are : " Mieux vaut un tien que deux tu l'auras " (A bird in the hand is worth two in the bush) ; " Ki donne tost il donne deux fois " (Bis dat, qui cito dat) ; " Ki plus a plus convoite " (The more one has the more one wants) ; " Qui petit a petit perd " (He who possesses little can lose little) ; " Il fait mal esveiller le chien qui dort " (It is well to let a sleeping dog lie) ; " On oblie plus tost le mal que le bien " (An evil action is remembered longer than a good one).

The second selection, which must have been contemporary with the above, seems to have contained more homely proverbs, expressed in blunter terms. This piece, entitled " Proverbes aux Vilains," is divided into unequal stanzas of six, eight, or nine lines of rhyme, and some stanzas comprise several proverbs, others only one. This collection forms a pell-mell of old saws which the people were very fond of repeating, and which enlivened them amidst their sorrows and labours. In order fully to understand the meaning of these proverbs, the tone of which is a mixture of grave and gay, it is necessary first to understand the proper meaning of the word *villein*, which was, as a rule, taken in bad part, as synonymous with coward, poltroon, full of envy, do-nothing, &c. The *villein* was the man of the people in the worst acceptation of the term, as the subjoined proverb will show :—

> " Oignez villain, il vous poindra.
> Poignez villain, il vous oindra . . .
> Villain affamé demy enragé . . .
> Villain enrichy ne connoist pas d'amis."

The third collection does not date so far back as the two previous ones, though it consists of ancient proverbs in prose, with the title, " Common Proverbs," of which there are about seven hundred and fifty, arranged in alphabetical order by J. de la Véprie, prior of Clairvaux. The name of the compiler is a guarantee for the decency of these proverbs, and this perhaps was one of the causes of the success of this little collection, of which several Gothic editions appeared at the close of the fifteenth century.

Fig. 279.—A Court Jester.—Miniature from a French Bible.—Manuscript of the Fifteenth Century.—In the Library of M. Ambroise Firmin-Didot, Paris.

The "Dit de l'Apostoile," which must be mentioned, though it is in reality a collection of popular sayings rather than of proverbs, is of much less ancient date, belonging as it probably does to the thirteenth century. The

"Apostoile" (apostle) is the name vulgarly given to the Pope, and it is
the Pope who, in this piece of verse, decides as to the titles and epithets

Fig. 280.—Device of Louis XII., King of
France (1498—1515). A Porcupine;
with the Motto, "Cominus et eminus "
(From far and near). This was the device of his grandfather, who, in 1397,
instituted the Order of the Porcupine.

Fig. 281.—François I., King of France (1515—
1547).—A Salamander amidst the Flames,
with the Motto, "Nutrisco et extinguo" (I
feed on it and extinguish it). It was the
popular belief that this salamander lived in
the fire, and could extinguish it.

which are suitable to the principal towns of France and the different
countries of Europe. These epithets accord with the origin, the customs,

Fig. 282.—Device of the Flemish Gueux (1566).—A Wallet held by two Hands clasped,
with the Motto, " Jusques à porter la besace."

the physical position, the moral state, and the special characteristics of
the town or country. The veritable physiognomy of persons and things is

expressed by proverbial sayings, and this feudal society is faithfully represented in this simple enumeration: "Concile d'Apostoile," "Parliaments of the King," "Assembly of Chevaliers," "Company of Clerks," "Beuverie de Bourgeois," "Crowd of Villeins," &c. We see that at that time proverbs were couched in a very few words, but those few expressing a great deal.

The transition from these plain proverbs, which express some moral truth or ordinary idea, to the historical proverb (Figs. 280 and 281), which mentions some remarkable event to celebrate the name of any remarkable person, or contains an allusion to the special characteristics of a country, a province, or a town, is a very natural one. One might imagine that the people were bent upon writing in this concrete and striking shape the history of the facts which seemed worth remembering.

The ancient proverbs relating to France are numerous, for there is not a town or a village which has not one referring to it. In the "Dit de l'Apostoile" are to be found six concerning the Flemish (Fig. 282), five about the Gascons, eighteen about the Normans, twelve about Orleans, thirty about Paris, and so forth. Each of these proverbs would afford matter for an interesting dissertation from the double point of view of history and philosophy.

We have already (see chapter on the *Science of Heraldry*) spoken of the heraldic devices and mottoes, but there are also a certain number of popular sayings which relate to the nobility of the ancient provinces of France. For Burgundy :—

> " Riche de Chalons,
> Noble de Vienne,
> Preux de Vergy,
> Fin de Neuchatel,
> Et la maison de Beaufremont
> D'où sont sortis les bons barons."

For Brittany :—

> " Antiquité de Penhoet,
> Vaillance de Chastel,
> Richesse de Kerman,
> Chevalerie de Kergournadec."

These are allusions to the qualities of the different places and families mentioned.

The proverbs relating to the names of men of ancient or modern times have, as a rule, some satirical meaning:—"Old as Herod;" "Homer sometimes nods;" "Hippocrates says yes, and Galen says no."

But a better idea can be formed of the tendency of the French proverbs which were current in the Middle Ages, and which held their own almost intact until the middle of the sixteenth century, by quoting a few of them which, with slight alterations in spelling, are still in use:—

" A beau parleur closes oreilles.
    A chacun oiseau son nid lui est beau.
    A dur ane dur aguillon.
    Aide-toi, Dieu te aidera (God helps those who help themselves).
    Amis valent mieux que argent.
    A Dieu, à père et à maître, nul ne peut rendre equivalent.
    Au besoin voit-on l'ami (A friend in need is a friend indeed).
    Besoin fait vieille trotter.
    Bon cœur ne peut mentir.
    Bienfaict n'est jamais perdu.
    Bonne vie embellit.
    Borgne est roy entre aveugles (Amongst the blind the one-eyed man is king).
    Gain de cordonnier entre par l'huis et ist (sort) par le fumier.
    Ce n'est pas or tout ce qui luit (All is not gold that glitters).
    Celuy sçait assez qui vit bien.
    De brebis comptées mange bien le loup.
    De nouveau tout est beau.
    Diligence passe science.
    La faim chasse le loup hors bois.
    La nuit porte conseil.
    La plus méchante roue du char crie toujours.
    Les petits sont sujets aux lois, les grands en font à leur guise.
    L'eau dormant vault pis que l'eau courant (Still waters run deep).
    Tout vray n'est pas bon à dire (The truth is not always welcome).
    Trop parler nuit, trop grater cuit.
    Vin vieux, ami vieux et or vieux sont aimés en tous lieux (Old wine, old friends, and old gold are always appreciated)."

There can be no doubt that proverbs were at one time much used in common parlance, and this must have lent an originality and a piquancy to conversation. The proverb, which represented, so to speak, general opinion, was perpetually recurring in conversation, which was animated by being thus impregnated with the personal thought of the speaker. Most of the proverbs originated with the people, but they were used by the nobles and the bourgeois, and they soon passed from conversation into writing, and were quoted by the greatest authors.

Thus in the thirteenth century many sermons and many pieces of poetry began with a proverb, or even by several proverbs. The Trouvère, Chrestien de Troyes, commences his description of the Quest of the Holy Grail, in the romance entitled "Perceval," with the following proverbs :—

> " Qui petit seme petit cuelt,
> Et qui onques recoillir voelt,
> En tel lieu sa semance espande
> Que fruit à cent dobles li rande :
> Car en terre qui rien ne vault,
> Bonne semance i sèche et fault."

The same author also commences his romance of " Erie et Enide " with the proverb—

> " Li villains dist, en son respit,
> Que tel chose a l'en en despit,
> Qui mult valt mielx que l'on ne cuide."

The example of the celebrated Chrestien de Troyes was naturally followed by his contemporaries, and the author of the well-known romance, " Baudoin de Sebourc, third King of Jerusalem," terminates each stanza of his long poem with a proverb. He in his turn was imitated by several writers, and there are many pieces of poetry, dating from the fourteenth and fifteenth centuries, in which the proverb recurs at the end of each stanza ; amongst others, in the " Complainte " of twenty-two couplets, which the Paris students composed, in 1381, against Hugh Aubriot, Provost of Paris, out of spite for his severity towards them, and also in the ballad against the English, which was written in verse by Alain Chartier (1449), after the capture of Fougères.

Another proof of the large place given to proverbs in the very best books is to be found in the old " Chronique de Rains," the author of which is not known to us, though of all the historic writings of the thirteenth century his are at once the most remarkable for their veracity and dramatic style. The author could not have witnessed the events in the reign of Philip Augustus and of St. Louis which he describes, yet he reproduces the true character- istics of the period when he typifies the principal occurrences by means of plain proverbs. After pointing out the imprudence of the King of Spain, who attacked the doughty Richard Cœur-de-Lion, King of England, he comes to the conclusion that " tant grate chièvre, que mal gist ;" and in another part, when he represents Philip Augustus as having set out with a small escort, thinking that Richard had not yet disembarked in France, he borrows from the "Dit des Villains" a proverb afterwards put in the mouth of Sancho Panza : "En un muis de quidance, n'a pas plein pot de sapience."

Proverbs were applied to history (see Figs. 283 and 284), and they also had a large place in the comic theatre of the fifteenth century. The farce of *Maître Pathelin*, attributed alternately to Pierre Blanchet and to François Villon, abounds in vulgar proverbs, which add great zest to the dialogue. The lawyer Pathelin goes off with a piece of cloth, which the shopkeeper

Fig. 283.—Device of Louis, Duke of Orleans (1406).—A knotted Stick, with the Motto, "Je l'envy," a term used in the game of dice, signifying, "I utter defiance." This was meant as a defiance to Jean sans Peur.

Fig. 284.—Device of Jean sans Peur, Duke of Burgundy (1406).—A Plane, with the Motto, in Flemish, "Hic houd" (I have him), which was a reply to the challenge of the Duke of Orleans.

Guillaume is induced, by his specious talk, to sell him on credit; but though he succeeds in satisfying even the judge that he had not cheated the shopkeeper, he is in turn made the dupe of a humble shepherd, whom he had taught how to hoodwink the judge, and obtain an acquittal for a robbery even more impudent than his own. The moral of the comedy is comprised in the proverb—

> "Or n'es'-il si fort entendeur
> Qui ne trouve plus fort vendeur."

It may be said of this farce, which was in great favour when first written, that each line is redolent of Gallic proverbs, and that for more than three centuries the people of Paris adopted the proverbial sayings which it contains. Moreover, most of the farces played by the Pont-Alais troupe, by the clerks of the Basoche, by the brotherhood of the Mère Sotte, and by other strolling bands, were full of common and vulgar proverbs which excited the hearty laughter of the audience.

The proverb also prevailed in all kinds of poetry, and especially in that which addressed itself to the people. François Villon, himself a true Parisian, bore this in mind when he inserted in his two "Testaments" a number of popular sayings and adages which had become, or were fitted to become, proverbs. Indeed, his ballads are, in reality, an ingenious paraphrase of the rhymed proverb which forms the refrain, as in the ballad "Dames du temps jadis," which contains the oft-quoted line—

> " Mais où sont les neiges d'antan ? "
> (Where are last year's snows ?)

It is not surprising that Pierre Gringoire, who had long been at the head of the dramatic association of the Mère Sotte, before becoming herald of arms at the court of Lorraine, gave a large place to proverbs in all his works. Many of his poetical compositions are merely collections of rhymed proverbs ; amongst others, the "Menus Propos," the "Abus du Monde," and especially the "Fantaisies de Mère Sotte." This last collection, the best known of all terminates thus :—

> " Femme est l'ennemy de l'amy,
> Femme est péché inévitable,
> Femme est familier ennemy,
> Femme déçoit plus que le diable. . . .
> Femme est tempeste de maison. . . .
> Femme est le serpent des serpens." . . .

Prince Charles of Orleans, who was a court poet, and who composed nothing but ballads and roundelays for the young nobles and young dames of France and England, did not think it undignified to embody in them several popular proverbs, which were pearls picked up from the dungheap. Amongst others, he quoted the proverb—

"Jeu qui trop dure ne vaut rien . . .
 Il convient que trop parler nuise. . . .
Chose qui plaist est à moitié vendue." . . .

When in the fifteenth century French literature began to abound with tales, stories, *joyeux devis*, *menus propos*, *paradoxes*, and other works known under the general title of *facéties*, proverbs naturally took their place in the list as being quite in harmony with the genius and tendencies of the people : so much so, that skilful prose-writers became rather too fond of embodying proverbs in their works, and many of these adages are enshrined in Antoine de la Sale's novel, " Jehan de Saintré," and in the " Cent Nouvelles nouvelles,"

Fig. 285.—Shoemaker fitting a Shoe.—Copied after one of the Stalls called *Miséricordes* in the Choir of Rouen Cathedral (Fifteenth Century).

by King Louis XI. In the taste for proverbs the sixteenth century was not behind its predecessors, and poets such as Clément Marot and Antoine de Baïf, narrators such as Rabelais and Noël Dufail, polemical writers such as Henry Estienne, and satirists like the author of the " Satyre Ménippée," were very well versed in this science. The proverb, in fact, may be termed the passport of all true ideas, which, expressed as a proverb, assumed, as it was thought, a more striking and vivid shape, and became better impressed upon the memory.

Looking to what took place in other parts of Europe, we find that proverbial literature was alike fruitful, though in each case the produce was of
native growth, Spain and Italy being the countries whose proverbs have the
greatest similarity to those of France. England had not so many proverbs,
but those of English origin are specially remarkable for that Britannic
humour which is not to be met with elsewhere, and which lends great originality to her proverbs. Such are: "If one knew what prices were going
to rise, one would not need to be in trade more than a year;" "Exchange
is no robbery;" "God sent us meat, and the devil sent the cooks;" "The
devil makes his Christmas pudding with attorneys' fingers and lawyers'
tongues."

Fig. 286.—The Shoemaker and his Customer.—Copied after one of the Stalls called *Miséricordes*
in the Choir of Rouen Cathedral (Fifteenth Century).

In painting, sculpture (Figs. 285 and 286), and in nearly all other
branches of art were reproduced the figurative expressions implied by proverbs. Pictures, drawings, engravings, and tapestry were all employed in the
interpretation of these proverbs, which were also to be found engraved upon
the blades of swords and of daggers, and upon the helmets and breast-plates.
Medals and counters were coined with proverbs on them, and they were also
worn in the shape of embroidered sashes and scarfs by persons of both

sexes. They were inserted, also, in the stained-glass windows, and upon the carved furniture (Fig. 287), as also upon drinking-glasses and other articles of daily use. One of the rooms in Agnès Sorel's Château de Beauté was paved with squares of painted delf, upon which were inscribed witty proverbs. Many shopkeepers' sign-boards displayed proverbs suitable to their trade, and it was the custom of booksellers and printers to add a proverb to the tokens which

Fig. 287.—A Comb, made of Carved Wood, of the Fifteenth Century. Upon one side are the words "Prenes en gié," and upon the other, "Ce petit doun."—In the Collection of M. Achille Jubinal.—In the centre of the inscription is a puzzle, representing a flower, a flaming heart, and an arm holding a dart, with the two letters M. P. It was colloquially said of a passionate man that he would kill a mercer for a comb.

they placed upon the title-page of their books (Figs. 288, 289, and 293). Some of these proverbs were facetious, but most of them were of a graver kind

There are to be found in several public libraries various collections of pro-

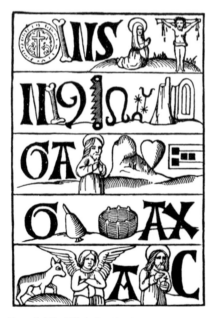

Beneath this riddle is the following explanation :—

"Let us salute Mary praying for Jesus on the cross;
Let us hope for his peace in our hearts.
I have given my heart to God.
I hope to gain Paradise,
Praise be to God."

Fig. 288.—Riddle taken from the "Heures de Nostredame," printed by Guillaume Godart, Bookseller at Paris, in 1513.

verbs, represented by miniatures or drawings executed with the pen, and doing great honour to the talents of their unknown authors; but we will only mention out of all these a curious collection of water-colour drawings

Fig. 289.—Token of Jehan de Brie, in the "Heures à l'usaige de Paris," printed by Jehan Bignon in 1512.—This strange riddle is to be translated, "In vico sancti Jacobi, à la Limace. Cy me vend et achète."

Fig. 290.—Drawings of Proverbs, Adages, &c.—Manuscript of the Fifteenth Century (No. 4,316,
Fonds La Vallière, 44).—In the National Library, Paris.

executed by the Constable de Bourbon, at the beginning of Francis I.'s
reign, and now preserved in the Paris National Library (Fonds La Vallière,
Department of Manuscripts). This handsome book contains sixty-one

" Dieu veult souventesfois permettre   Quoy qu'il en peut advenir, mettre
L'homme périr, qui dist : Je veulx,   La charette devant les bœufs."

Fig. 291.—Drawings of Proverbs, Adages, &c.—Manuscript of the Fifteenth Century (No. 4,316,
Fonds La Vallière, 44).—In the National Library, Paris.

proverbs illustrated with great ingenuity. He whom the artist has surnamed "Margaritas ante porcos" (a proverb taken from the Old Testament), is
represented by a herd of pigs upsetting a basket of flowers (Fig. 290), with
the French distich—

"Belles rai-ons qui sont mal entendues
Ressemblent fleurs à pourceaux estendues."

"Je suis Fauveau qui désire à tou'e heure
Estre estrillé et devant et darrière.
De m'estriller qui ne scet la manière
A coup pert temps et trop en vain labeure."

Fig. 292.—Drawings of Proverbs, Adages, &c.—Manuscript of the Fifteenth Century (No. 4,316,
Fonds La Vallière, 44).—In the National Library, Paris.

Amongst the other striking compositions in this collection are those which relate to the following proverbs (Fig. 291) :—"Tant va le pot à l'eau, qu'il brise" (The pitcher may go to the well once too often); "Mal sur mal n'est pas santé" (Two wrongs do not make a right); "En forgeant on devient forgeron;" "A petit mercier petit panier." Each proverb in this collection has a rhymed quatrain explaining the drawing. The inscription in verse which is placed at the foot of Constable Bourbon's portrait informs us that this collection, commenced during his lifetime, was not completed until after his death, so that it is a sort of monument raised by the poet and the artist to his memory.

Fig. 293.—Token of Michel Fezandat, Printer at Paris (1552), with a Proverbial Device attributed to Rabelais.

LANGUAGES.

O soon as a language has reached the stage of making the task of understanding it a difficult one, the dissolution of the social elements is not far off. . . . . Babel is symbolic of the destiny of languages." We take this remark from the work of M. Francis Wey on the "Variations of the French Language," in which he points out that idioms, like everything else mortal, have their periods of rise and fall, and that a time arrives when they are rendered diffuse by neologism, or decomposed by the influence of equivocation.

The history of the confusion of tongues, as described by Moses in the Book of Genesis, might be looked upon as typical of what happened in Europe when the Roman people endeavoured to establish their dominion over all the lands which they had conquered by means of their language, which was to be the social cement of the whole nationality. "And the whole earth was of one language and of one speech. . . . . And the Lord came down to see the city and the tower, which the children of men builded. And the Lord said, Behold, the people is one, and they have all one language; and this they begin to do: and now nothing will be restrained from them, which they have imagined to do. Go to, let us go down, and there confound their language, that they may not understand one another's speech. So the Lord scattered them abroad from thence upon the face of all the earth : and they left off to build the city. Therefore is the name of it called Babel; because the Lord did there confound the language of all the earth " (Fig. 294).

In the beginning of the fifth century the empire of the Cæsars had become, like Babel, a vast ruin ; the Latin tongue, which since the Roman conquest and occupation had been the legal, religious, civil, and administrative language of nearly all Europe, was invaded by the barbarian tongues, as the soil was by the savage hordes which, from the heart of Asia, the extremities of Germany, and the unknown regions of the North, poured in upon the Roman world. From this epoch dates the origin of the languages of modern Europe (Fig. 295), which were formed out of a mixture of the idiom of the invader with the Latin tongue, which latter had become too deeply rooted in the usages of ordinary life to be extirpated altogether. It is true that the classic language of Livy, Cicero, and Sallust was only spoken and understood by the upper classes of society, but the other classes used a rustic language which varied with the district and population, but which was derived from the true Latin tongue. This rustic language (*lingua Romana*) consisted of an infinity of dialects proceeding from one and another, and differing, some more, some less, from the mother tongue.

The Celtic language also comprised a certain number of dialects, which existed amongst the Gauls at the epoch of the expeditions of Cæsar, and which were, as he says in his "Commentaries," merely variations of the same language. Strabo also says that the Gauls everywhere used a single native language, merely modified by differences of dialect. Moreover, the Celtic language simply underwent certain modifications, under the influence of the Latin language, when the latter became exclusively the political or official language of the Roman colony. The Emperors established in the principal cities of Gaul, notably at Lyons, Autun, and Besançon, schools in which the Latin language was taught, and the most earnest efforts were made to propagate it not only in the aristocratic classes, but amongst the people, who were more stubborn in the retention of their national idiom. This policy of the Romans was very successful. Not only did the Gallo-Romans rush into servitude, as Tacitus expresses it, but they took willingly to the language of their conquerors, with the exception of a few unavoidable errors of pronunciation and the introduction of a few Celtic words into the Latin vocabulary. In short, when the Barbarians established themselves in Gaul, all the inhabitants, except a few country-people, had for centuries used a bastard *lingua Romana*. These Barbarians imported new idiomatic elements into this hybrid language, as modified by the Gauls, but they could not destroy it, and Latin remained the foundation or root of French.

Moreover, the Gauls had no written history or literature, with the exception of a few war songs and religious hymns, which stood then in room of national archives, and which were preserved in the memory of the Druids and the heads of families. The Celtic language, not having received the consecration of literary works which would have insured its perpetuation, tended inevitably to dissolution and disuse. This law of dissolution had

Fig. 294.—Construction of the Tower of Babel, in the Valley of Senaar, by the Descendants of Noah.—Miniature from a Manuscript of the Fifteenth Century.—National Library, Paris.

probably taken effect by the time that the Franks, after their repeated invasions of Gaul, had at length established themselves in the territory which they had conquered. The men of letters, the ecclesiastics, and the patricians still spoke Latin, but of a very mongrel and sometimes unintelligible kind. Only those who had studied in the academies of Lyons, Vienne, Narbonne, and Aquitaine were familiar with the principles of the language, and were able to write it without making any gross faults of grammar (Fig. 296).

Fig. 295.—The Institution of Languages.—Fac-simile of a Wood Engraving of the " Margarita Philosophica Nova," Argentoratum, J. Gruninger, 1512, in quarto.—In the Arsenal Library, Paris.

But the general language used was the *lingua Romana,* and in this vulgar tongue were written works of prose—probably works of poetry as well—which have not survived to our day.

The Franks had such a great respect for the Roman institutions that, far from attempting to destroy them, they generally left undisturbed the political and administrative organization of the Gauls. This is why the Latin tongue continued to be under Frankish dominion the general language of the people

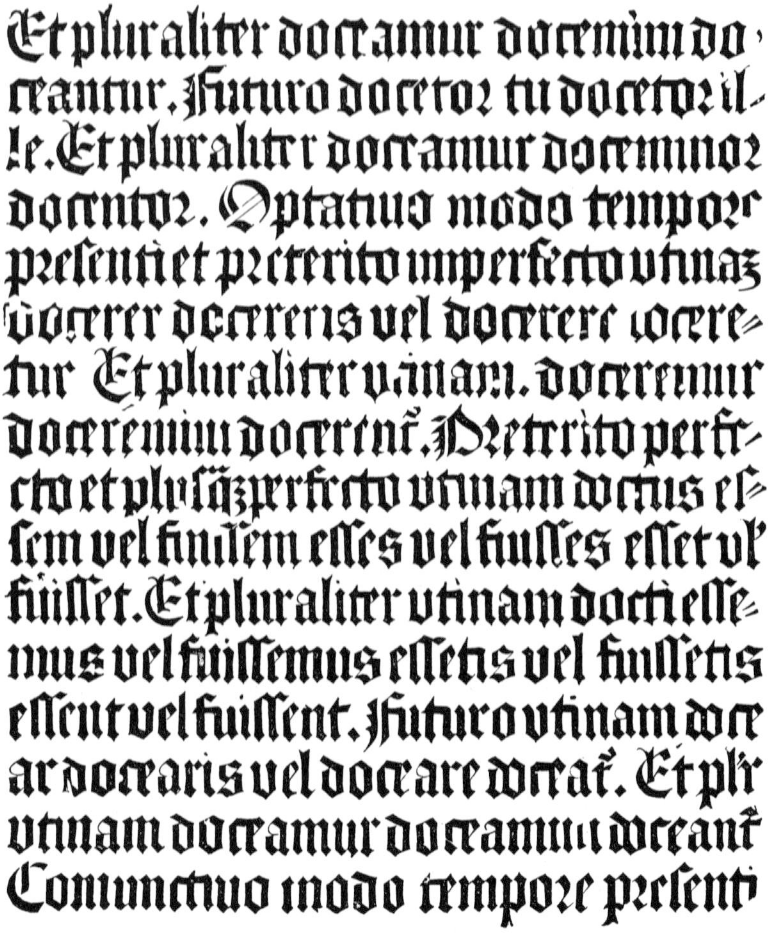
Et pluraliter doceamur doceminini do-
ceantur. Futuro docetor tu docetor il-
le. Et pluraliter doceamur doceminor
docentor. Optatiuo modo tempore
presenti et preterito imperfecto utinam
docerer docereris vel docerere docere-
tur Et pluraliter utinam doceremur
doceremini docerent. Preterito perfe-
cto et plusquamperfecto utinam doctus es-
sem vel fuissem esses vel fuisses esset vel
fuisset. Et pluraliter utinam docti esse-
mus vel fuissemus essetis vel fuissetis
essent vel fuissent. Futuro utinam doce-
ar docearis vel doceare doceat. Et plr
utinam doceamur doceamini doceant
Coniunctiuo modo tempore presenti

Fig. 296.—Specimen of a page of the "Grammaire Latine," by Ælius Donatus, a grammarian of the Fourth Century.—Fac-simile of a Wood Engraving for the Xylographical Edition, published at Mayence, by Gutenberg.—This Wood Engraving was preserved in the Library of the Duc de la Vallière.

(Fig. 296), and it was a more refined and learned language as spoken by the public officials, the clergy, and the magistracy. The Franks used the Teutonic language amongst themselves until they were converted to Christianity after the example of their king (Clovis). Thenceforward their regular intercourse with the ecclesiastics who instructed them in their new religion led to their learning the Latin language, and speaking it more or less correctly. Being endowed with a lively intelligence and ready wit, they were not long in acquiring a knowledge of a new language which recommended itself to them as having about it the halo of Roman greatness.

In fine, the French language is composed of three perfectly distinct elements—Celtic, Germanic, and Latin; the last, however, being by far the most predominant. There are not more than a thousand words of Germanic origin in the French language, and far fewer of Celtic origin. Nearly all the rest are Latin, and it has been said with perfect truth that "French is merely a patois of Latin."

From the time of Clovis the progress made by Latin was very rapid. The laws of the Franks, as of the other barbarian people who invaded the Roman empire, were written in Latin; not, it is true, in scholarly Latin, but in what was called the *sermo quotidianus*, or every-day language, so termed because everybody understood and spoke it. It is true that the Teutonic language continued to be spoken by the Frankish tribes which occupied the banks of the Rhine and the provinces of Germania; but the Franks under Clovis and the other kings or chiefs who had established themselves at Orleans, Paris, and Soissons, soon adopted the vulgar Latin as their language.

The *leudes*, or great vassals, either out of indolence or pride, adhered for a longer period to their national language, and it was probably in use amongst the upper classes as late as Charlemagne's reign. The kings of the first race, in order to gain the sympathies of the Gallo-Roman population, nevertheless assumed to feel an interest in the progress of the Latin vulgar tongue. Thus two centuries earlier, the Gauls, who still spoke Celtic, endeavoured, according to the expression of Sidonius Apollinaris, "to rid themselves of the rust of this ancient language, in order to make themselves familiar with the graces of the beautiful Latin language." Chilperic I., King of Soissons, in the middle of the sixth century, plumed himself upon imitating in his speeches the rhetoric of the most learned Romans. He endeavoured to develop the study of the Latin tongue in his dominions, and as his subjects could not manage to reproduce the sounds of the Teutonic idiom with the letters of the Roman alphabet, he suggested the use of certain Greek and Hebrew letters which lent themselves better to the intonations of the Frankish tongue. Contemporary with him, Caribert, King of Paris, set up the pretension of being learned in jurisprudence, and of expressing himself in the language of Cicero with the eloquence of a true Roman. Bishop Fortunatus addressed him some Latin verses complimenting him on speaking Latin as if he had been a Roman born, instead of being of Sicambric origin. The poet added, "What must be your eloquence when you speak your mother tongue, you who are more eloquent than we ourselves in ours!"

But, for all these fulsome eulogies, there was scarcely, perhaps, a single person capable of writing and speaking classical Latin correctly in the Gallo-Roman provinces of which the Franks were masters, though the Teutonic language had been almost universally succeeded by the rustic or vulgar tongue.

Gregory of Tours, whose "History of the Franks" throws so much light upon this remote epoch, confesses in one of his works ("De Gloriâ Confessorum") that he was almost completely ignorant of the rules of Latin, and he admits to having frequently confused genders and cases, used the feminine for the masculine or neuter, and the ablative for the accusative, and neglected the rules as to prepositions. The text of his valuable chronicle, written between the years 573 and 593, is, as a matter of fact, full of inaccuracies, though the early copyists corrected some of the most glaring blunders out of respect for the memory of the illustrious Bishop of Tours.

From the time of Chilperic to that of Charlemagne the true Latin language gradually degenerated amongst the Franks, notwithstanding the praiseworthy efforts of the monks to preserve it, as if it were a sacred ark, in their monasteries. Upon the other hand, the vulgar tongue, consisting of mongrel Latin and Latinised Teutonic, continued to spread amongst the population. Charlemagne, who spoke this language before he learned grammatical Latin, was much vexed at this decadence. What pained him the most was to find that bishops and other dignitaries of the Church were incapable of reading the Bible in the Vulgate. He accordingly instituted the Palatine School, under the direction of Alcuin, with the view of purifying ecclesiastical Latin. His peers and his barons, his leudes and his military officers, retained their Teutonic language, but his personal influence was none the less favourable to the preservation of the Latin tongue, which became the language of the Church, and which profited by the written works of sacred literature.

In addition to the literary Latin which was not used in conversation, but in books and public documents, there were only two general languages throughout the whole of Charlemagne's vast empire—Romance and Teutonic. The most ancient monument which we possess in the middle of the ninth century is the double oath which Charles the Bald, King of France, and Louis the German, leagued against their brother, the Emperor Lothair, took in presence of their armies upon the 14th of February, 842. It will be sufficient for present purposes to cite the oath taken by Louis the German in Romance, in order to be heard and understood by the army of Charles, which was composed of Franks and Gallo-Romans from Neustria, Aquitaine, and other Southern regions:—" Pro Deo amur et pro Christian poblo, et nostro commun salvament, d'ist di en avant, in quant Deus savir et podir me dunat, si salvarai eo cist meon fradre Carle, et in adjudha, et in cadhuna nosa, si cum om per dreit son fradre salvar dist, in o quid il mi altresi fazet. Et ab Ludher nul plaid numquam prindrai, qui, meon vol, cist meon fradre Karle in damno sit."

This was the vulgar tongue as spoken in the greater part of France at this period, and it is worthy of remark that nearly all the words in the above document are taken, disfigured in pronunciation or spelling, from the Latin. Thus the common language was rustic Latin ; the Romance formed from a fusion of Celtic, German, and Latin. This was the language of France, and the Germans called France " Latin " (*Francia Latina*), because this language, which was only a hybrid product of the Latin tongue, was spoken there. According to Luitprand, an historian of the tenth century, Gaul was always named *Francia Romana*, and a later writer says that this denomination was not given to France on account of Rome, but because of the Romance language spoken there (" sic dicta, non a Româ, sed a linguâ Romanâ "). And this is how the Franks of Gaul came to be called *Francs Latin* (Latin Franks).

Still the *Gallic nobles*, as the great lords of the soil called themselves, protested against this general invasion of the Latin vulgar tongue. The Emperor Lothair, son of Louis the Mild, had steadfastly refused to learn Latin, even the vulgar tongue, and his father had endeavoured to preserve the use of the Teutonic language in his states by means of a decree to the effect that the Bible should be translated into this language, which had few representatives out of Germany itself. At the Council of Tours (813) the bishops furthered the intentions of Charlemagne's successor by expressing

their desire that the homilies of the Church should be translated simultaneously both into Teutonic and Romance (Fig. 297).

The Teutonic language none the less disappeared at the end of the tenth
century, for Duke Hugh Capet, before he became the first king of the third
race, during an interview with the Emperor Otho II., who spoke in pure
Latin so as to make himself understood by the bishops, could only reply to
him in Romance ; and the historian Richer, who was present at the interview,
relates that Arnulf, Bishop of Orleans, was obliged to translate what Otho

Fig. 297.—King Robert, Son of Hugh Capet, composing Sequences and Responses in Latin.—
Miniature from the " Chroniques de France."—Manuscript of the Fourteenth Century, No. 3.
—In the Burgundy Library, Brussels.

said into the vulgar tongue in order that Duke Hugh might understand it.
A little later, however, when Duke Hugh was upon the throne, the Bishop of
Verdun was appointed to speak at the Synod of Mouzon because he knew
Teutonic. The Romance or vulgar tongue had none the less continued to
make its way throughout the western provinces which formed the kingdom
of France, and it was the language both of the nobles and of the people.

William the Conqueror, Duke of Normandy, introduced it into England, just as Robert Guiscard, his contemporary, did into Sicily and Naples. William decreed that the laws of England should be written in French—that is to say, in Norman, which was merely a dialect of the Romance language—and that French should be taught in the schools before Latin. At Naples, according to an historian of the time, whoever was ignorant of French was held in very poor esteem at this essentially French court. One of the articles (No. 38) in the Laws of William the Conqueror shows what progress had been made by the Romance language at the end of the eleventh century to arrive at being transformed into the *Langue d'Oil:* "Si home enpuisuned altre, seit occis, u permanablement essillé. Jo jettai vos choses por cause de mort, et de ço ne me poez emplaider: car leist à faire damage à altres par poür de mort, quant par el ne pot eschaper."

The Romance, otherwise the Neo-Latin, languages are French, Provençal, Italian, Spanish, Portuguese, and Roumanic. They were formed at the same time, but under different influences with regard to pronunciation, and they are, in truth, all of them Latin issuing from different throats and looked at in different lights. It was poetry which, when emerging from the cradle of chivalry, inaugurated the creation of modern languages, for grammarians and rhetoricians do not make languages; all they can do is to superintend the best use of its wealth when a language has been enriched by the efforts of its poets and writers who employ it. Moreover, the two currents which carried the national idiom, without resistance and without admixture, into its two principal beds, the *Oc language* and the *Oil language*, had long been manifest. The one was the language of the poets, the other that of the troubadours and the trouvères, and the two languages, or rather the two dialects, both acquired simultaneously their relative perfection. The first literary records of the Provençal language are the poem of Boethius, "The Mystery of the Wise and of the Foolish Virgins," and several other poems anterior to William IX., Duke of Aquitaine (1071—1127), who has often been cited as the earliest of the troubadours. The first memorials of the French language, after the oath of 842 quoted above, are the Cantilena of St. Eulalie, the two poems in the library of Clermont dedicated to St. Leger and to the Passion, and the "Life of St. Alexis," which was composed about 1050. Next come the warlike epodes, called *chansons de geste* or *romans de chevalerie,* and it was in this way that the Homeric epode was one of the first inspirations of the Greek language.

In these vigorous pictures of heroic life the qualities of invention, imagination, and national genius are most conspicuous, and there are signs of brilliant and sparkling style before the regular formation of the language.

It is in the famous "Chanson de Roland" that is to be found the oldest type of the language, which, as M. Francis Wey has remarked, was still in its infancy. But this beautiful poem, attributed without sufficient proof to a trouvère named Turold, none the less contains many passages worthy to be compared with the Iliad. The following is the description which he gives of the death of Oliver, one of Charlemagne's twelve peers, in the Pass of Roncevaux, where Roland and his companions sustained the attack of the Saracen army :—

> "Oliviers sent que la mort mult l'anguisset:
> Ambdui li oil en la teste li turnent,
> L'oie pert e la veüe tute;
> Descent à pied, à la tere se culchet,
> Forment en halt si recleimet sa culpe,
> Cuntre le ciel ambesdous ses mains juintes,
> Si preiet Dieu que paréis li dunget,
> E beneiet Carlun e France dulce,
> Sun cumpagnun Rollant desur tuz humes.
> Falt li le coer, li helmes li embrunchet;
> Trestut le cors à la tere li justet.
> Morz est li quens que plus ne se demuret.
> Rollanz li ber le pluret, si l'duluset.
> Jamais en tere n'orrez plus dolent hume." * . . .

Henceforward the French language is an accomplished fact. It is the *Oil language.* It still clings close to Latin, from which it borrows some of its most ingenious and narrowly defined rules; amongst others, the declension of words and adjectives, represented in French by the adjunction or suppression of the final *s.* This rule was not, however, generally adopted by French writers, but it is easy to see that it was pointed out and followed by some of

---

* The literal translation of these lines is, " Oliver feels the agony of death creep over him. His eyes turn in his head. He loses hearing and sight. Dismounts and throws himself upon the ground. Recites his *mea culpa* aloud. Joins his two hands and raises them heavenward. Prays God to let him enter Paradise. Blesses Charlemagne and gentle France, and, above all, his companion Roland. His heart fails him, his head droops. He falls at full length upon the ground. 'Tis done, the Count is dead; and Baron Roland bewails him and weeps for him. Never on earth will you see a man more afflicted."

them. It must, however, be said that as yet there was no such a thing as grammar; every one spoke and wrote at his fancy, according to his instinct or tendencies, and the language was clear or obscure, heavy or light, according to the person that employed it. Even the spelling of words varied almost *ad infinitum*, and it did not occur to anybody to establish a regular system of orthography.

The great romances of chivalry imported to the Oil language a sort of nobility, grandeur, and force very suitable to the epic style. But other trouvères, of humble origin no doubt, and, as such, more satiric and facetious than the poets who wrote the *chansons de geste*, invented the *Fabliau*, the *Conte*,

Fig. 298.—Conflagration of the Bel-Accueil Prison.   Fig. 299.—Narcissus at the Fountain.

Miniatures from the "Romance of the Rose."—Manuscript of the Fourteenth Century.
In the Library of M. Ambroise Firmin-Didot, Paris.

and the *Dit*, which abounded in comedy and sarcasm. The vices, the defects, the passions, and the foibles of society, from the villein to the king, were hit off in popular poetry, much to the amusement of the persons portrayed. The language must have become richer and more supple for it to have been made the medium of such satire as this, which was couched in the familiar and even trite expressions in use amongst the common people both of town and country. As time went on it became more vivid, more pointed, more incisive, and more sprightly. Its best types are the various fabliaux, and also the "Romance of the Rose" (Figs. 298 and 299), begun by William de Lorris about 1220, and completed fifty years later by Jean de Meung, surnamed Clopinel.

The "Romance of the Rose" was beyond all doubt a reminiscence of Provençal poetry, which for two centuries had charmed the populations of the South by the soft and gracious imagery with which it expressed the sentiments of the heart. The Romance language of the South, the Oc language purified, perfected, and developed, might have become, from the twelfth century, the rival of the Latin, Italian, and Spanish languages; but the troubadours, who were dreamy and pensive poets, were too addicted to singing of love, of women, of flowers, and the enervating pleasures of earthly life. Their *chansons*, their *tensons*, their *plancts*, &c., which were recited to the accompaniment of some stringed instrument, were imitated by the Northern trouvères, but with less monotony and more force. William de Lorris and his successor added to the complimentary allegories and subtleties of the "Romance of the Rose" the satirical and sarcastic element, which was, perhaps, the outcome of the Gallic spirit. In short, the French language may be said, in this work of the thirteenth century, to have already acquired all its original qualities. The following description of spring may be quoted as a proof thereof :—

> " En mai estoie, ce songoie,
> El tems amoreus plain de joie,
> El tems où tote riens s'esgaie,
> Que l'en ne voit boisson ne haie
> Qui en mai parer ne se voille
> Et covrir de novele foille.
> Li bois recovrent lor verdure,
> Qui sunt sec tant com yver dure ;
> La terre meismes s'orgoille
> Par la rosée qui la moille
> Et oblie la poverté
> Où elle a tot l'yver esté.
> Lors devient la terre si gobe
> Qu'el volt avoir novele robe," &c.

William de Lorris belonged rather to the troubadour school, while Jean de Meung had more in common with the trouvères of the Artois, Picardy, and Champagne provinces, though the style of both, correct and full of elegance, was thoroughly representative of the Oil language, which at that time was almost in as much favour as Latin, though the latter still survived as a spoken language in the Universities. The Oil language had become so famous throughout Europe that Brunetto Latini, who was the tutor of Dante, wrote in French the encyclopædia published by him under the title of "The Treasure." Dante Alighieri, to whom Brunetto Latini had taught the Oil language, came to Paris in order to complete his linguistic and scholastic studies (Fig. 300).

Poetry had served to stimulate the progress of French, as it had done of all other languages, but, from the beginning of the thirteenth century, good

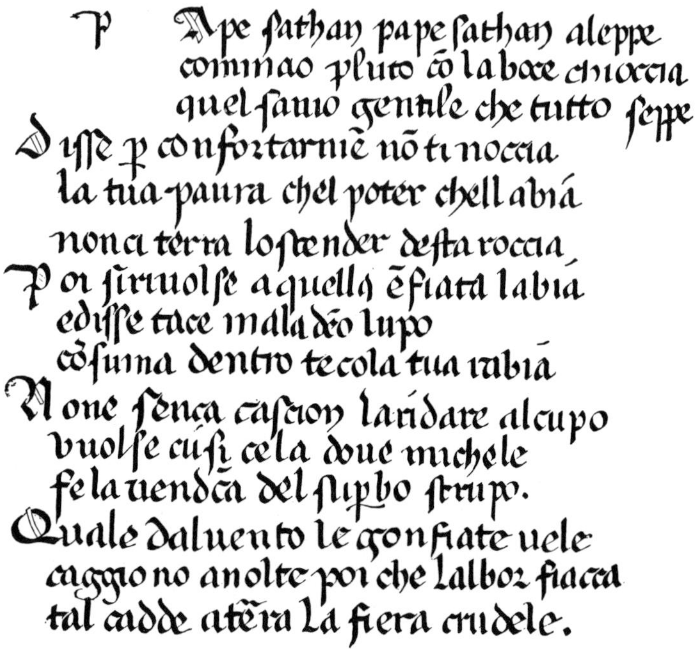
P
Ape sathan pape sathan aleppe
cominciao pluto cō la boce chiocia
quel sauio gentile che tutto seppe
Disse p confortarmē nō ti noccia
la tua paura chel poter chell abiá
non ci terra lo scender desta roccia
Poi si riuolse aquella ēfiata labia
edisse tace maladecto lupo
cōsuma dentro te cola tua rabiá
None sença casciō landare alcupo
vuolse cusi cela doue michele
fe la uendeca del supbo strupo.
Quale dal uento le gonfiate uele
caggiono auolte poi che lalbor fiacca
tal cadde aterra la fiera crudele.

Fig. 300.—Fragment of Dante's "Divina Commedia."—Manuscript of the Fourteenth Century. In the National Library, Paris.

prose made its appearance in France, with Geoffroi de Villehardouin's book on the Conquest of Constantinople. This writer, a man of little education, who wrote with great facility and precision, and who used the true historic language, was a noble and a warrior, and he was the first to bring out the real qualities of the French language in his description of what took place during the Crusade of 1202, at which he was present. This crusader, a native of Champagne, attained perfection almost at a bound; and the Sire de Joinville, who half a century later narrated the Crusades of St. Louis, did not, perhaps, equal him, though he could command the use of a vocabulary much richer and more supple. The reign of Louis saw the formation of a polite society, in which the language, while becoming more variegated, more incisive, and more abundant, preserved its early simplicity and grace. The Sire de Join-ville's sly good-humour makes him the pleasantest and most attractive tale-teller of the Middle Ages.

The French language, which was spoken all over Europe, and even in the East, during the thirteenth century, but which was more especially the

Fig. 301.—The Three Virtues (Reason, Uprightness, and Justice) urge Christina de Pisan to write a Book of Ethics for the Instruction of Ladies.—Miniature from the "Livre des Vertus," unpublished Manuscript, dating from 1405.—In the Library of M. Ambroise Firmin-Didot, Paris.

privileged language of the courts, could not avoid declining in the following century, even though that century possessed such a distinguished writer as Jean Froissart. This chronicler, in the opinion of M. Francis Wey, who is, perhaps, a little severe upon him, was endowed with the instinct of his art, was clever without elevation of thought and without discernment, seeking for effect rather than to excite emotion, narrating trifles with tedious prolixity, and not imposing any check upon his style, which is often heavy and diffuse. The tendency of the language was to become turgid and monotonous.

The usurpation of the Flemish writers into all branches of French literature was not favourable to the latter, which, becoming affected and involved, finally lapsed into pedantic and fallacious verbosity. Christina de Pisan (Fig. 301), the historiographer of Charles V., set the example of this fictitious pathos, but she was very soon outdone by the historians of the court of Burgundy, George Chastelain, Olivier de la Marche, and Molinet. Jean d'Auton, the chronicler of Louis XII., appears to have been more than any other writer responsible for the involved style which formed the Gordian knot of the French language.

Antoine de la Sale, a pleasant chronicler of the court of Burgundy, did not in any way contribute to tighten this knot, though he did not cut it; and his romance, "Petit Jehan de Saintré," must have been a welcome change to the reader after he had perused so many compilations written in a style at once pretentious and involved. Antoine de la Sale wrote French, and this remark applies with even greater truth to the authors of the "Cent Nouvelles nouvelles," who seemed to descend in a direct line from the ancient trouvères who had set to rhyme so many joyous fabliaux. The French language, spoilt by too much erudition, once more recovered its original force, when put in the mouth of the people at large by a poet who drew from his own inspiration, without the aid of Latin words or of declamation, eloquence of a simple and natural kind. This was François Villon, who writes the language of the "Romance of the Rose," only with greater force and boldness. While he was restoring to its place of honour the language of Paris, a statesman and a courtier, Philippe de Comines, was preparing Memoirs which are a perfect model of the grave, sustained, and philosophical language of history. As M. Francis Wey remarks, "The Seigneur of Argenton writes in a style which is flexible, precise, ample, and nervous; his language seems entirely modern, and, excepting a few differences in spelling and a few obsolete words, separated by only a few years from the reign of Henry IV." Yet there was nearly a century between Philippe de Comines and the King of Navarre.

During the reign of François I. there was a tendency to imitate the Italian, and for a hundred years this tendency prevailed, but at the same time the language was fortified by its continuous contact with Greek and Latin. Rabelais satirizes in "Pantagruel" this abuse of Latinism, which Geoffroy

Tory had previously condemned by his denunciation of the "skimmers of Latin" in the preface to "Champfleury," which contains an "exhortation to set the French language in good order, so as to speak with elegance in good and wholesome French" (Fig. 302). Rabelais, while very justly ridiculing the jargon of the French students, was not himself sufficiently on his guard against erudition of style, but he none the less raised to the highest degree of perfection the language of the sixteenth century. Clément Marot and like poets of his school, Bonaventure des Périers and others, sought their models, as François Villon had done, in the authors of the thirteenth century, and they were the custodians of the real French language, clear and transparent, precise and correct, elegant and witty. Calvin and several Protestant writers belong to this school, but their style was harder, colder, and somewhat colourless.

The sixteenth century teems with chefs-d'œuvre of every kind, but the finest productions of French genius are tainted with Neologism, Hellenism, and Latinism, and the *courtier-like and Italianised language*, as Henri Estienne termed it in his treatise upon this subject, permeated from the court of the Valois into the spoken rather than into the written language. For the most part it was the poets—and the best of them into the bargain—who, owing to their affection for Greek, Latin, and Italian, became the demolishers and ravagers of the French language. Ronsard and the Pléiade were the main promoters of this deplorable change. (See below, chapter on *National Poetry*.) The prose-writers, on the other hand, set themselves against this sacrilege, and resolutely remained French. Historians such as Blaise de Montluc, humanists like Amyot, polemists like Henri Estienne, narrators like Bonaventure des Périers and Noël du Fail, and moralists like Montaigne, show that the French language was still known in France.

But the worst enemies of the French language were the reformers of grammar and spelling, Jacques Pelletier, Louis Meigret, and Pierre Ramus. These extravagant philosophers, who wanted to change the whole system of language, were far more absurd than the Limoges student of Geoffroy Tory and of Rabelais, and the good sense of the general public prevented them from making many proselytes. What little success they did obtain was neutralised soon afterwards by Montaigne and Malherbe. Of the former M. Francis Wey says, "His was a wit at once unrestrained, undulating, and various; his genius was supple, disdained imperious doctrines, and was profoundly imbued with Roman thought, a subtle and tempered savour of which pervaded his style. His erudition as a philosopher invigorated his genius and his style; his independence, unfettered and yet flexible in its course of action, preserved him from imitative servility; a painter of the human mind, he knew no model but nature, and could only speak the language which corresponded with his thoughts. He expressed that language without translating it." Montaigne is, in fact, the writer who, before Pascal's time, made the best and most remarkable use of the French language.

Malherbe seems to have made it his task to free the language from the servitude of Italianism and Hellenism. He did his work with unbending sternness, and he restored to poetry its national characteristics, while maintaining it in the regions of the most majestic *lyrism*. To him we owe French verse which possessed the primordial features of the French language—purity, clearness, and truth. But Henry IV. did more than any one else to renovate the old French language and French wit; for that king, who hated affectation and despised Greek and Latin pathos, was the personification of common sense. He thought like a philosopher, spoke like a soldier, and wrote at once like Brantôme and Amyot. The French language, which tended to become Italian under the Valois, was being made Spanish during the League; but it once more became essentially French under Henry IV.

Fig. 302.—The Broken Jar.—Token of Geoffroy Tory, Bookseller, at Paris, in the first Edition of his "Champfleury," 1529, small folio.

ROMANCES.

OVELS and romances, or works of imagination
of a similar character, were in great demand
in Greece and Rome, especially among those
who had no business occupation, and who
read for amusement rather than for instruction. The name *romance* (which meant a
work written in the Romance tongue) was
not used until the eleventh or twelfth century, and with a very different meaning
from that which now attaches to it.

The ancient Latin and Greek romances
were merely recitals of imaginary occurrences. The "Satire" of Petronius and
the "Golden Ass" of Apuleius were doubtless imitated very frequently in the
Roman literature of the time of the Cæsars, but it is in the literature of Greece
that we must look for the progress of a literary school which long held its sway
at Constantinople, and throughout the empire of the East. Achilles Tatius
of Alexandria set up the model for this kind of book when he composed the
"Loves of Clitophon and Leucippe" in the third century, and he was succeeded by Heliodorus, Bishop of Tricca, in Thessaly, who wrote the "Loves of
Theagenes and of Chariclea," and Longus, who wrote the "Loves of Daphnis
and Chloe." The last named was unequalled for its simplicity and grace, and

stood far above the love romances published by Theodore Prodromos, Nicetas Eugenianus, and a number of other writers in the twelfth century.

The Middle Ages, however, cared little for stories of profane love and works of pagan origin, but in the eighth century St. John Damascenus composed in Greek a sort of romance of mystic love concerning the legend of St. Barlaam and Josaphat, King of India, and this fabulous story was so warmly welcome that it was translated into every language. We must then come down to the twelfth century to find any fabulous stories written in Latin which can be connected with the literature of romance; as, for instance, the "Romance of the Seven Sages" (*Septem Sapientes*), translated or imitated from the Hebrew by a monk of the Abbey of Haute-Selve, and the celebrated compilation entitled "Gesta Romanorum." When these two works appeared, the name of *romance* was already given to the *chansons de geste* and other stories of chivalry, of wonderland, or of religion, which were written in "Romance" verse or in "Romance" prose.

For nearly half a century the most gifted scholars of France, Germany, and Belgium have been endeavouring to trace the origin of the old French romances, and M. Paulin Paris, more especially, has elucidated this question better than any one else by being the first to publish the early text of some of these romances. His system, which appears to us the most logical and the most satisfactory, has been discussed and opposed by such men as Michelet, Edgar Quinet, and Léon Gautier; yet the last named, great as is his experience on such a subject, could only retard the solution of the literary and historic problem which his predecessor, M. Paulin Paris, had all but solved. We propose, therefore, to sum up the opinions given by so many learned disputants, and to endeavour to draw from them some logical conclusion.

According to M. Gautier's system, which is based upon great erudition, the *chansons de geste* and the romances of chivalry, invented and set to verse by the jugglers in the twelfth century, had their origin in the popular songs and Teutonic *cantilenæ*. But M. Gautier could not discover these cantilenæ, or original songs, in the Germanic language. He cites only one, which he calls the Cantilena of Hildebrand, and which has nothing in common with the *chansons de geste*, inasmuch as it makes mention of Odoacer, King of the Heruli, at the end of the fifth century. He also mentions a popular song of the seventh century, which the Bishop of Meaux, Hildegaire, has collated and translated into Latin in his "Life of St. Faron," and which is supposed to have been composed in Romance to celebrate the victory of Clotaire II. over the Saxons. Finally, he mentions a very beautiful Teutonic song about the battle which Louis III., son of Louis the Stammerer, fought against the Normans at Saucourt in 881. But M. Gautier is obliged to confess that these Teutonic cantilenæ, which were believed to be the germ of the *chansons de geste* of the twelfth century, are no longer in existence, confining himself to the supposition that they did at one time exist, because Eginhard relates in his Chronicles that Charlemagne gave strict orders that the old songs (*antiquissima carmina*), in which were celebrated the mighty deeds and wars of ancient times, should be collected and transcribed.

The existence of these old popular songs is beyond all question, but those which Charlemagne had collected were only preserved in the memory of the inhabitants of Gaul by being translated into the rustic or Romance tongue. Thus the Anglo-Norman poet, Robert Wace, in his " Roman du Rou," recalls in the following lines the primitive *chansons de geste* which were sung, previously to the battle of Hastings, in the presence of the army of William the Conqueror :—

> " Taillefer qui mult bien cantoit
> Sur un cheval qui tost aloit
> Devant eus s'en alloit cantant
> De Callemaine et de Rollant
> Et d'Olivier et des vassaux
> Qui morurent à Rainschevaux."

Here was the veritable origin of the " Chanson de Roland," which is rightly regarded as the oldest of the *chansons de geste* which were composed into Romance. That it is formed of an aggregation of various popular songs which had already been *romanced*—that is to say, written in the vulgar or Romance tongue—is very probable; but it is impossible to believe that the *chansons de geste* relating to the reign of Charlemagne and his successors, excepting, perhaps, the famous "Garin le Loherain," were composed by French jugglers after Teutonic cantilenæ. It was undoubtedly the popular songs in the Romance language which were the preludes of the *chansons de geste* and the great romances of chivalry. But, as M. Paulin Paris has proved to demonstration, these popular songs had first given birth to histories and chronicles written in Latin, which were the principal source of the rhymed romances.

It may be affirmed, for instance, that the Latin Chronicle of Nennius, the

" History of the Bretons," and the " Life of Merlin," written in Latin by
Geoffrey of Monmouth, were the materials used by Wace in his romances of
the " Rou " and of the " Brut," as also by Robert de Borron in his romance,
" Joseph of Arimathea," and by the anonymous author of the " St. Graal."
Then, too, there is the Latin Chronicle attributed to Archbishop Turpin of
Rheims. This spurious Chronicle is in two parts : the first, consisting of five
chapters, was written by a monk of Compostello in the middle of the eleventh
century ; the second, beginning at Chapter VI., is the work of a monk of
St. Andrew of Vienna, who wrote between the years 1109 and 1119. Such, at

Fig. 303.—Joshua, King David, and Judas Maccabæus.—From a Series of Ancient Engravings,
representing the Nine Heroes of Sacred, Ancient, and Modern History, who figure in the
Romance, " Le Triomphe des Neuf Preux." These Coloured Drawings, apparently of the
Fifteenth Century, form the Frontispiece of a Manuscript in the Colbert Room, National
Library, Paris.

least, are the conclusions arrived at by M. Gaston Paris. This Chronicle at
once acquired such celebrity that five or six prose translations were made,
and this was the source from which the jugglers obtained much of their lore.

Chrestien de Troyes, the beginning of whose romances is here appended,
intimates that he has merely put into verse a rose romance :—

" Chrestiens qui entent et paine
A rimoier le meillor conte
Par le commandement le Comte

Qu'il soit contez en cort royal :
Ce est li contes de Graal
Dont li quens li bailla le livre," &c.

Claude Fauchet, in his "Recueil de l'Origine de la Langue et Poésie françoise," from which these lines are taken, adds, "This shows that some of the
romances were written in prose before being rhymed." M. Gautier, therefore, is in error when he asserts that the romances in prose date only from the
fifteenth century; on the contrary, it is certain that the prose versions were
contemporary with those in rhyme. Claude Fauchet was of opinion that the

Fig. 304.—Imaginary Election of St. Peter as Pope. " St. Pol kissed the body of St. Peter in the
prison at Antioch, and, at the request of the two Apostles, Our Lord restored to life the son of
a King who had been dead more than fifteen years; and henceforward St. Peter was seated
in the chair as Pope and true Lieutenant of God upon earth, and held the seat as Pope for
the term of eight years holily." In the division to the left is seen St. Peter being tonsured
by the " tirans," and this is erroneously said to be the origin of the ecclesiastical tonsure.—
Miniature of the " Sainte Escripture."—Manuscript of the Fifteenth Century.—In the
Burgundy Library, Brussels.

printed romances of his day, such as "Lancelot du Lac," "Tristan," and others,
were rewritten after the old prose and verse editions. We know that the
romances in rhyme were sung, or rather recited, to the sounds of some instru-

ment, while the prose romances were merely read or narrated without a musical accompaniment of any kind, and rhyme must naturally have been better adapted than prose to the *chansons de geste* during the most flourishing period of romances; that is to say, in the twelfth and thirteenth centuries.

M. Paulin Paris has set forth very clearly the reasons why the name of *romance (roman)* was given in France to the narratives of chivalry before it became the special name for a whole branch of literature. For some time it had been the custom throughout France to *talk Romance,* but it was not until the close of the eleventh century that any attempt was made to write in Romance: whatever was thus written in the vulgar tongue was Romance. M. Paulin Paris adds, "In this way the same generic name was retained for all these writings. There were romances of the Bible (Fig. 303), romances of the Crusades, romances of King Arthur, romances of the Virgin, romances of the Saints (Fig. 304), of the Passion, of the Image of the World, of Sallust," &c. They were for the most part narratives of warlike and wonderful adventures, which the French trouveurs and jugglers had told during the Crusades to all the foreigners who composed the armies from beyond the seas, and these foreigners in course of time gave the unique name of *romance* to all works of imagination written in prose. Dante, who could write and speak French, has himself fixed the meaning of the word at the end of the thirteenth century in the line—

"Versi d'amore, prose di romanzi."

Thus the romances in prose were as numerous as those in verse when Dante came to Paris to study the language of Oil.

The jugglers had, from the thirteenth century, divided romances into three categories, which proceeded from three distinct sources: the romances of Charlemagne, the romances of the Round Table, and the romances of Greek and Roman antiquity. These three categories of romances are thus designated in the "Song of the Saxons:"—

"Ne sont que trois materes à tout home entendant :
De France, de Bretagne et de Rome la Grant,
Et de ces trois materes n'i a nule semblant.
Li conte de Bretagne sont et vain et plaisant,
Cil de Rome sont sage et de sens apparent,
Cil de France sont voir (*vrais*)." . . .

But each of these matters comprised a number of different subjects, which corresponded with one another by a succession of homogeneous and analogous facts. They were so many cycles forming one vast whole, in which were grouped personages of the same race and of the same character. The three principal cycles of the Geste in France, for instance, were those which had

Fig. 305.—A Compiler.—Miniature from a Manuscript of the Fifteenth Century. In the Burgundy Library, Brussels.

for their central figures Charlemagne, William of Orange, and Renaud de Montauban, as is indicated by the following line from the romance of " Girars de Viane : "—" N'ot que trois Gestes en France la garnie." A geste

may be compared to a tree of ancient growth, the branches of which spread
out in all directions from the mother trunk; and each of these branches,
grafted thereupon, gave birth to new branches.

M. Gautier has classed in systematic order all the romances in rhyme still
extant which belong to the three great cycles of France, and the mere
mention of them shows how rich French literature is in works of this kind.
The "Geste du Roi," or of "Charlemagne," is divided into six parts:—1st,
Berte aux Grans Piés, Enfances Charlemagne, Enfances Roland. 2nd, Aspre-
mont, Fierabras, Otinel, Gui de Bourgogne, Entry into Spain, the Capture of
Pampelona, la Chanson de Roland, Gaidon, Anseïs de Carthage. 3rd, Acquin,
or the Conquest of Little Brittany; Jehan de Lanson; Simon de Pouille;
Galien; Voyage to Jerusalem. 4th, Song of the Saxons. 5th, Macaire,
Huon de Bordeaux. 6th, Charlemagne, by Girart of Amiens. The "Geste of
Garin de Montglane," or of "William of Orange," comprises no less than
twenty-three or twenty-four romances, which, chronologically arranged, are as
follows:—Les Enfances Garin de Montglane, Garin de Montglane, Girars
de Viane, Hernaut de Beaulande, Renier de Gennes, Aimeri de Narbonne,
les Enfances Guillaume, le Département des Enfans Aimeri, le Siége de
Narbonne, le Couronnement Looys, le Charroi de Nismes, la Prise d'Orange,
le Siége de Barbastre (Beuves de Comarchis, as revised), Guibert d'Andrenas,
Mort d'Aimeri de Narbonne, Enfances Vivien, Chevalerie Vivien, Aliscanps,
Rainoart, Moniage Guillaume, Bataille Loquifer, Moniage Rainoart, Renier,
la Prise de Cordres, Foulques de Candie. There are but ten or eleven
romances in the "Geste of Renaud de Montauban," or "Doon de Mayence,"
viz.:—Doon de Mayence, Gaufrey, les Enfances Ogier, la Chevalerie Ogier, Aye
d'Avignon, Gui de Nanteuil, Tristan de Nanteuil, Parise la Duchesse, Maugis
d'Aigremont, Vivien l'Amachour de Monbranc, and les Quatre Fils Aimon,
or Renaut de Montauban. The other cycles are composed of the following
elements:—Cycle of the Crusade: Hélias, les Enfances Godefroi, les Chétifs,
Antioch, Jerusalem, Baudouin de Sebourc, and le Bastart de Bouillon. The
"Geste des Lorrains:"—Hervis de Metz; Carin de Loherain; Girbert de Metz;
Anseis, son of Gierbert; and Yon. The "Geste du Nord:"—Raoul de Cambrai,
Gormond and Isembart. "Burgundian Geste:"—Girart de Roussillon and
Aubri le Bourgoing. "Petite Geste de Blaives:"—Amis et Amiles, and
Jourdain de Blaives. "Petite Geste de St. Gilles:"—Aiol and Elie de
St. Gilles. "English Geste:"—Horn and Beuves d'Hanstonne. Various

Gestes:—Siperis de Vignevaux, Floovant, Charles the Bald, Hugh Capet, Doon de la Roche, Lion de Bourges, Florent and Octavian, &c.

Fig. 306.—The St. Mark Library, Venice, founded in the Fifteenth Century by Cardinal Bessarion.

A perusal of the titles of these *chansons de geste* and romances, some of which have not yet been published, and most of which contain from six to eight thousand lines, will give an idea of the extent to which the romance literature flourished from the twelfth to the thirteenth century. There are, in addition to the above, some twenty romances which belong to the Brittany cycle, and four or five very long ones which should be included in the cycle of Rome or of antiquity: amongst others, the "Romance of the Seven Sages" and the well-known "Romance of Alexander," begun in the twelfth century by Lambert "li Tors," and continued by Alexandre de Bernay. Most of the romances which are given above are in ten-syllable verse, arranged in couplets, or *laisses*, with assonances, which were not replaced by rhymes until the second age of romances. Many others, less ancient, are in lines of twelve syllables, called Alexandrines, because the first attempt to write lines with this metre was made in the "Romance of Alexander." There are a few in lines of eight syllables, rhymed in couplets, and this system of versification seems to have been applied, in the first instance, to romances of a more homely kind, which, like the well-known "Roman de Renard," have the vivacity and sprightliness of the fabliau, and appeal more to the wit than to the imagination of the readers, or, it should rather be said, of the listeners.

The jugglers were very loath to part with the manuscripts of their *chansons de geste* and romances, and it was not for some time that these manuscripts were to be found in the libraries of monasteries and castles. Many of these manuscripts, as one can see, have been copied from the original at the cost of some wealthy noble. The jugglers themselves were always eager to procure good romances, which they learnt by heart and sang in public, to the accompaniment of the violin or the *rote*. Those who had the best repertory were certain of meeting with the most numerous audiences during their peregrinations through the country. These jugglers, although in the Middle Ages they formed one vast association, had many points of difference the one with the other, and preserved the distinctions of rank, which were dependent in the main upon their talent and fortune. Some of them would not sing other than national songs, and only condescended to appear in the houses of the great nobles. They travelled about on horseback, accompanied by their servants, received a warm welcome at the castles and abbeys which they visited, and were handsomely paid. Others, again, excited suspicion by their mean and hungry appearance, and were often ordered away from the door of the houses before which they halted to sing for their supper. It may be taken for granted, too, that their stock of songs was limited, and that they were as little versed in the art of music as of tale-tellers.

Amongst the jugglers were a great many *assembleurs* and *trouveurs.* The

Fig. 307.—Coronation of Charlemagne in the City of Jerusalem.—Miniatures from the " Chroniques de Charlemagne," taken from Manuscript No. 9,066, in the Burgundy Library, Brussels (Fifteenth Century).

latter composed romances in prose and in rhyme. The *assembleurs* (Fig. 305), though capable of writing in prose or in verse, more generally confined themselves to compiling the various episodes of a romance or of several romances, so as to vary the impressions produced on the audience. These assembleurs, like the Greek rhapsodists of Homer's time, modified the text which they intended to narrate or to sing, and they in many instances corrected and transformed the ancient romances when the language in which they were couched had become obsolete, and especially when the popular taste of the day called for the addition of some new ornaments. This is how it came to pass that the primitive text of many romances underwent changes of dialect, the existence of which it would otherwise be difficult to understand. Sometimes an assembleur who desired to transpose the original into another dialect, or even into another language, simply changed the termination of the words, and so composed a sort of grammatical balderdash utterly incomprehensible. There still exist certain romances written in the Oïl language which have been thus travestied by the jugglers into the Limousin and Provençal dialects, and even into Italian. The public library of St. Mark, Venice (Fig. 306), contains some curious manuscripts of these Italianised French romances, which are, while preserving the precise original form, neither more nor less than gibberish.

Most of the romances belonged, as we have said, not only to the ancient popular songs in Celtic, Teutonic, or Romance, but also to the early legends written in Latin under the name of *Gesta*. These two distinct but not incongruous sources are often to be traced in the romances of the first epoch, in which the author, in order to distinguish the two different origins, repeats either *cum dit la Geste*, or *si cum dit la Chanson*. The Geste soon acquired more influence than the Chanson, and nearly all the trouveurs felt no scruple in declaring that they had obtained their stories from some of the old monasteries, notably from the Abbey of St. Denis. This is the case with several romances relating to the history of France. In the "Enfances Guillaume," a *gentil moine* (a good-natured monk) is said by the author to have supplied him with the materials for his work, "Si m'a les vers enseignés et monstrés."

The author of "Berte aux Grans Piés" states even more explicitly that it was a courteous monk (*moine cortois*) of St. Denis, named Savari, who

" Le livre as histoires me monstra."

Moreover, the monks of St. Denis themselves composed fables which they declared to be original texts, and which the romance-writers, naturally inclined to credulity, accepted blindfold when they had occasion to quote them. Thus, exclusively of the spurious Chronicle of Turpin, which was at that time accepted as authentic, there were two or three old Latin poems upon the supposed conquests of Charlemagne in Spain and the East. One of

Fig. 308.—The Battle of Roncevaux and the Death of Roland.—Fragment of a Stained-glass Window in Chartres Cathedral (Thirteenth Century).

these legends, which was composed during the eleventh century within the walls of the Abbey of St. Denis, contained the narrative of a Crusade which the great Emperor was supposed to have led himself to Jerusalem in order to reseat the Patriarch of the Holy City upon his archiepiscopal throne. This work, as well as the Chronicle of Turpin, served as a theme for several romances, which made the princes and lords who took part in later Crusades feel quite certain that Charlemagne had undertaken the journey to Palestine (Fig. 307).

In any event, the authors of many of the early romances remain unknown, and it was not until the second epoch of this period of literature that the trouveurs appended their names either at the beginning or at the end of their works. Moreover, there is good ground for believing that the jugglers, who recited or sang the romances, were very chary of giving the author's name, as they very often claimed the authorship for themselves. The first romances preceded by only a very few years the period of the Crusades, and must have almost coincided with the inauguration of the feudal epoch, according to Claude Fauchet, who says, "It was at this time, I believe, that romances began to be written, and that the jugglers, trouveurs, and singers frequented the courts of these princes (grand feudatories of the crown of France), to recite and sing their narratives without rhyme, their songs, and other poetic inventions, using the rustic Romance language as well as that which was understood by more people." Thus we see that Claude Fauchet appears convinced that the romances in prose were anterior to the romances in rhyme. He even says in so many words, "If any of you believe that the romance was written only in rhyme, I will tell him that there were also romances not rhymed and in prose. For in the "Life of Charles the Great" (Chronicle of Turpin), put into French before the year 1200 at the request of Yoland, Comtesse de St. Paul, sister of Baudoin, Comte de Hainau, surnamed the Bastisseur, in the fourth book the author says, "Baudoin, Comte de Hainau, discovered at Sens in Burgundy the 'Life of Charlemagne,' and, when on his death-bed, gave it to his sister Yoland, Comtesse de Sainct Paul, who asked me to publish it in a prose romance, because many people who would not read it in Latin would read it as a romance."

The rhymed romance of Charlemagne, which the translator of Turpin declared to be spurious, was apparently the famous "Chanson de Roland," which is attributed to a trouveur named Turolde, and which, according to M. Léon Gautier, was composed after popular songs of Teutonic origin and tendencies, while M. Paulin Paris and other learned critics believe that it belongs to the Romance or rustic language. The "Chanson de Roland" is a true French Iliad, full of lofty, generous, and patriotic ideas, and it may be termed the highest and most touching specimen of early French poetry. The predominant feature in it is attachment to the Catholic faith and to gentle France. When Roland is expiring from the effect of his wounds in the defile of Ronceraux (Fig. 308), his last look and his last thought are for France. Assuredly there is nothing German or Teutonic in this the oldest of the French romances, second in order to which was, we may fairly suppose, the original version of "Aliscans." These romances of the first epoch often began abruptly; as, for instance, the "Chanson de Roland," the first two lines of which run—

> "Carles li reis, nostre emperere magne,
> Set anz tuz pleins ad ested en Espaigne."

This is a very characteristic opening for a popular song, in which it was necessary to explain the subject matter in a very few words. It is the poet, not the juggler, who has to make a direct appeal to the public whom he addresses, that speaks in these two lines.

But nothing can give so good an idea of the early *chansons de geste* as a few quotations, and appended is the narrative of the death of Roland at Ronceraux (Fig. 308), where the nephew of Charlemagne was slain by the Saracens:—

> "Roland sent que la mort lui est proche:
> Sa cervelle s'en va par les oreilles.
> Le voilà qui prie pour ses pairs d'abord, afin que Dieu les appelle;
> Puis, il se recommande à l'ange Gabriel.
> Il prend l'olifant d'une main, pour n'en pas avoir de reproche,
> Et de l'autre saisit Durendal, son épée.
> Il s'avance plus loin qu'une portée d'arbalète,
> Fait quelques pas sur la terre d'Espagne, entre en un champ de blé,
> Monte sur un tertre. Sous deux beaux arbres,
> Il y a là quatre perrons de marbre.
> Roland tombe à l'envers sur l'herbe verte
> Et se pâme: car la mort lui est proche. . . .
>
> A trois reprises, Roland frappe sur le rocher pour briser son épée:
> Plus en abat que je ne saurais dire.
> L'acier grince: il ne rompt pas:
> L'épée remonte en amont vers le ciel.
> Quand le comte s'aperçoit qu'il ne la peut briser,
> Tout doucement il la plaint en lui-même:
> 'Ma Durendal, comme tu es belle et sainte!

Dans ta garde dorée il y a bien des reliques :
Une dent de saint Pierre, du sang de saint Basile,
Des cheveux de monseigneur saint Denis,
Du vêtement de la Vierge Marie.
Non, non, ce n'est pas droit que païens te possèdent.
Ta place est seulement entre des mains chrétiennes.
Plaise à Dieu que tu ne tombes pas entre celles d'un lâche !
Combien de terres j'aurai par toi conquises,
Que tient Charles à la barbe fleurie,
Et qui sont aujourd'hui la richesse de l'Empereur !
. . . Et maintenant j'ai grande douleur, à cause de cette épée.
Plutôt mourir que de la laisser aux Païens :
Que Dieu n'inflige pas cette honte à la France.'

Roland sent que la mort l'entreprend
Et qu'elle lui descend de la tête sur le cœur.
Il court se jeter sous un pin,
Sur l'herbe verte se couche face contre terre,
Met sous lui son olifant et son épée,
Et se tourne la tête du côté des païens.
Et pourquoi le fait-il ?   Ah ! c'est qu'il veut
Faire dire à Charlemagne et à toute l'armée des Francs,
Le noble comte, qu'il est mort en conquérant.
Il bat sa coulpe, il répète son *mea culpa*.
Pour ses péchés, au ciel il tend son gant.

Roland sent que son temps est fini.
Il est là au sommet d'un pic qui regarde l'Espagne ;
D'une main il frappe sa poitrine :
' *Mea culpa*, mon Dieu, et pardon au nom de ta puissance,
Pour mes péchés, pour les petits et pour les grands,
Pour tous ceux que j'ai faits depuis l'heure de ma naissance
Jusqu'à ce jour où je suis parvenu.'
Il tend à Dieu le gant de sa main droite,
Et voici que les Anges du ciel s'abattent près de lui.

Il est là gisant sous un pin, le comte Roland ;
Il a voulu se tourner du côté de l'Espagne.
Il se prit alors à se souvenir de plusieurs choses :
De tous les royaumes qu'il a conquis,
Et de douce France, et des gens de sa famille,
Et de Charlemagne, son seigneur, qui l'a nourri ;
Il ne peut s'empêcher d'en pleurer et de soupirer.
Mais il ne veut pas se mettre lui-même en oubli,
Et, de nouveau, réclame le pardon de Dieu :
' O notre vrai Père,' dit-il, 'qui jamais ne mentis,
Qui ressuscitas saint Lazare d'entre les morts
Et défendis Daniel contre les lions,

Sauve, sauve mon âme et défends-la contre tous périls,
A cause des péchés que j'ai faits en ma vie.'
Il a tendu à Dieu le gant de sa main droite :
Saint Gabriel l'a reçu.
Alors sa tête s'est inclinée sur son bras,
Et il est allé, mains jointes, à sa fin.
Dieu lui envoie un de ses anges chérubins
Et saint Michel du Péril.
Saint Gabriel est venu avec eux :
Ils emportent l'âme du comte au Paradis." * . .

"Roland" and the first romances were, as we see, essentially French creations, in which the trouveurs had embodied in a literary and dramatic form the scattered and uncertain traditions which were embedded in the memory of the nobility, and vaguely retained by means of the popular songs in the recollection of the lower classes. There can be no doubt that their object was to stimulate the warlike and patriotic feeling of the lords and barons of France who listened to them with such unfeigned satisfaction. It is thus easy to infer, by comparison of dates, that they must have come into existence at about the time of the first Crusade in 1095, and that they were imported into the East during the great Crusade led by Godfrey de Bouillon, Duke of Lorraine, and his brothers, Baudoin, Count of Flanders, and Eustace, Count of Boulogne; by Hugh the Great, Count of Vermandois, son of King Henry I.; by Raymond, Count of Toulouse; by Robert, Duke of Normandy; and by other chiefs of the French race. The heroic songs of the jugglers were well calculated to lessen the dreariness of the long and perilous voyage undertaken by the chevaliers, who remained absent for five or six years, and did not consider their task accomplished until after they had captured Jerusalem (1099). It was then that Godfrey de Bouillon, proclaimed King by his companions in arms, converted Palestine into a Christian kingdom, introducing into it the laws, the language, and the customs of France. It may be said that from this period the *chansons de geste* and national romances obtained a foothold in this new France of the East, the residents in which were ever gazing westward.

The romances, originating in France, returned thither with the crusaders, and spread at the same time throughout Europe, where their popularity increased from year to year. They became the fashion, and romances,

---

* Translation of M. Léon Gautier.

trouveurs, and jugglers made their appearance in all countries. The twelfth century was the great epoch of romance and of jugglery. There were several changes, however, in the style and fashion of the ancient romances, in proportion as the vulgar tongue underwent its successive modifications, and it would be difficult to recognise in the present day the ancient text when comparing it with the new. It would be not less difficult to assign a fixed date to the beginning of each cycle, all of which started from the primitive cycle of Charlemagne. There was an incessant competition between the jugglers, whose audiences were always clamouring for some new thing; and it was to satisfy this demand that the trouveurs of the Oïl language put into rhyme and prose the old Breton lays, and increased the already large domain of French romance. This was the commencement of the long series of Breton romances, otherwise called of the "Round Table," and which must not be confounded with the *chansons de geste*.

M. Paulin Paris, whose opinions on these matters may generally be relied upon, holds that the chevaliers of Flanders and the Franche-Comté had previously to this gathered from the conversation of Breton jugglers, or from Latin books written upon the authority of ancient narratives, the traditions of the Celts and of the fabled kings of Armorican Brittany. There were, for instance, the stories of Tristan, son of a King of Leon, in Little Brittany, who was in love with his uncle's wife; of King Mark, under the fatal influence of a philter against which all remedies were powerless; of King Arthur, the Celtic Hercules, the husband of Queen Guinivere, the most beautiful and the most inconstant of women, and surrounded by a court of heroes such as Launcelot, Gauvain, Perceval, Lionel, Agravain, &c. For some time already the sham combats in which the young nobles learnt the rude art of war were called *tournaments* (*tournoys*), because the champions turned about in a sort of circular arena, while endeavouring to hit a certain mark, a movable figure, or a quintain, with their lance or their sword. The authors of the Breton romances represented King Arthur as the founder of chivalry and the creator of tournaments, and said that this valorous king assembled at his Round Table the twenty-four bravest chevaliers of his kingdom, who thus formed his Supreme Court of Chivalry. These old Breton romances, in which the fair sex was assigned a more dignified and attractive part than in the Carlovingian romances, were, so to speak, the school in which were formed the manners of chivalry, and which favoured the development of refined politeness. The sort of worship paid to women at this distant epoch, and the delicate attentions lavished upon them by the opposite sex, contrasted very strongly with the roughness and brutality of a state of society in which all misunderstandings between people of noble birth were washed out in blood.

A succinct analysis of "Tristan" will give the reader a better idea of the characteristics of the Breton romance, which, according to certain critics, dates from an earlier period than the romances of the Charlemagne cycle.

Fig. 309.—Tristan at the Chase.—After a Miniature from the "Romance of Tristan."—Manuscript of the Fifteenth Century, No. 7,174.—In the National Library, Paris.

The principal action of the romance, which is the first in order of chronology as of merit, unfolds itself clearly, and in a way to enthral the reader's attention, around three personages, whose physiognomy stands out in distinct relief. Mark, King of Cornwall, is a good prince and a man of great worth, the beautiful Ysolt being his wife, and the valiant and poetic Tristan

(Fig. 309) his nephew. A draught which the two latter have taken without meaning any harm deprives them of the power of obeying the voice of honour and of reason ; they fall violently in love, and the irresistible force of the enchantment which is upon them serves to excuse their fault. King Mark passes his whole time in watching them, in detecting them, and in forgiving them. One day, however, his anger and jealousy are too much for him when he discovers Tristan in the Queen's chamber playing the harp to her. He strikes him from behind with a poisoned dart (Fig. 310), given him by the fairy Morgana, but he is suddenly seized with terror, and retreats in silence. Tristan, though wounded, displays great courage in bidding good-bye to Ysolt, mounts his horse, and takes refuge with his friend Dinas, who receives him in a dying state. The poison has made rapid progress, and Tristan, notwithstanding the care with which he is tended, has become almost a corpse. His friends shed tears over his sad state day and night. The only signs of life in his motionless body are the piercing cries which he utters. The good King Mark has repented him of his cowardly act of vengeance, and regrets having surprised his nephew and wounded him. Moreover, the unhappy Ysolt does not attempt to conceal her sorrow ; and when she learns that her dear Tristan is dying, she openly declares that she will not survive him.

Tristan feels that his last hour is at hand. He sends for his uncle, to say that he should like to see him, and that he bears him no ill-will for causing his death. King Mark, when he receives this message, exclaims, with the tears running down his cheeks, "Alas, alas! Woe to me for having stabbed my nephew, the best chevalier in the whole world!" He then repairs to Dinas's castle, where Tristan, whose voice was very faint, said, "This is my last fête; the one you have so eagerly desired to see." Tristan weeps, and the King sheds even more abundant tears, but consents to send for Queen Ysolt at his nephew's request. Her presence, however, fails to revive his failing forces, and she exclaims, "Alas, dear friend! is it thus you are to die?" Whereupon he says, "Yes, my lady! Tristan must die. . . . . Look at my arms; they are no longer those of Tristan, but of a corpse. . . . ." And Ysolt sobs by his side, praying that she too may die.

The next day Tristan half opens his eyes, and, like a good chevalier, has his sword drawn from its sheath that he may see it for the last time. "Alas, good sword!" he says, "what will become of you henceforward, without your trusty lord? I now take leave of chivalry, which I have honoured and loved; but I have no longer anything in common with it. Alas, my friends! to-day Tristan is vanquished." His tears begin to flow afresh, and he kisses his sword, which he bequeaths to his dearest companion in arms. He then turns to the Queen, who, since the previous day, had been weeping incessantly, and says to her, "My very dear lady, what will you do when I die? Will you not die with me?" To which she replies, "Gentle friend,

Fig. 310.—King Mark stabbing Tristan in the presence of Ysolt.—After a Miniature in Manuscript of the Fifteenth Century, No. 7,675.—In the National Library, Paris.

I call God to witness that nothing would afford me so much joy as to bear you company this day. Assuredly, if ever woman could die of anguish or sorrow, I should have died several times since I have been by your side." "And you would like, then, to die with me?" rejoined Tristan. "God knows that never did I desire anything so sincerely." "Approach me, then, for I feel death coming upon me, and I should like to breathe my last in your arms." Ysolt leans over Tristan, who takes her into his wasted arms, and presses her so tightly that her heart bursts, and he expires with her, thus mingling their last sigh.

The description of the beautiful Ysolt, as Luce du Gault, author of the prose version of the fourteenth century, makes Tristan himself trace it, will complete this touching story, and show what was the ideal of female beauty at this period :—"Her beautiful hair shines like golden threads; her forehead is whiter than the lily; her eyebrows are arched like small crossbows; and a narrow line, milk-white, dimples her nostrils. Her eyelids are brighter than emeralds, shining in her forehead like two stars. Her face has the beauty of morning, for it is both white and vermilion, each colour having its due proportion. Her lips are a trifle thick, and ardent with bright colour; her teeth, whiter than pearls, are regular and of good size. No spices can be compared to the sweet breath of her mouth. The chin is smoother than marble. From her stately shoulders sweep two thin arms, and long hands, the flesh of which is tender and soft. The fingers are long and straight, and her nails are beautiful. Her waist is so narrow that it can be spanned with the two hands." There is nothing, perhaps, in the old French language so graceful and picturesque as these two prose romances of " Tristan " and " Launcelot of the Lake."

The romance of " Launcelot " appears to be a fresh embodiment of the Armorican legends relating to Tristan. Launcelot, the son of the King of Benoïc (Bourges), and nephew of the King of Gannes, falls in love with Queen Guinivere (Fig. 311), wife of King Arthur, and he deceives the latter in as great good faith as Tristan had deceived King Mark. M. Paulin Paris points out that there is a mixture in these two romances of the souvenirs of ancient Greek and of Celtic traditions. Thus King Mark has many points of resemblance with King Midas, and Tristan, in his expedition against the Morhouet of Ireland, is no other than Theseus, who slew the Minotaur of Crete; while, when he dies reconciled with King Mark, the black veil attached to the vessel is also a reminiscence of the death of Theseus's father. In the romance of " Launcelot " the giant who asks young Launcelot riddles which he must solve under penalty of death is an imitation of the Sphinx which Œdipus faced upon Mount Cithæron. Launcelot at the court of the Lady of the Lake is Achilles at the court of the King of Scyros, and Guinivere, the wife of King Arthur, is Dejanira, who proved fatal to

Hercules.   There is something very singular in this invasion of the ancient
Greek fables into the books of the Round Table.

Fig. 311.—Launcelot and Guinivere.—After a Miniature in Manuscript of the Eleventh Century,
No. 6,964.—In the National Library, Paris.

The "Book of Merlin" and the "Book of the Grail," though contemporary with " Tristan " and " Launcelot," do not come from the same source, and are not inspired by the same ideas. In " Merlin " the marvellous forms by far the largest element, and the author seems to have had always in view

Fig. 312.—The Enchanter Merlin, transformed into a Student, meets in the Forest of Broceliande the Fairy Viviana.—Fragment of the Binding of a Book in Enamelled Metal-work of Limoges. —In the Museum of Antiquities at the Louvre.

the imitation of the Bible. The book, which none the less preserves the purest traditions of the Gallo-Breton legends, opens, like the Book of Job, with a council-meeting held in the infernal regions by the spirits of darkness. Satan declares that he cannot hope to counterbalance upon earth the influence of Christ, unless he can cause to be born of an immaculate virgin a man-demon. This man-demon is Merlin, who takes under his protection King Arthur, and who, after having rendered him great services, is buried alive in

Fig. 313.—Death of Joseph of Arimathea.—After a Miniature from the "History of Saint Grail."—Manuscript of the Fifteenth Century.—In the National Library, Paris.

a stone tomb by the Lady of the Lake, who has inherited some of his super-natural power (Fig. 312).

The "Book of the Grail" is an evocation of the old religious legends of Brittany. According to a pretended gospel, attributed to St. Joseph of Arimathea, the latter was said to have been the original possessor of the "grail" (Fig. 313), a sacred vessel in which the blood of Jesus, when He died upon the cross, was received by the angels. This vessel, after having passed into the possession of Joseph's son and of his descendants, remained concealed for several centuries, when King Arthur and his chevaliers set out in quest of it, and the honour of its discovery fell upon Perceval, the Gaul, who found it at the court of the King Pécheur. The author of this curious romance, composed in the beginning of the thirteenth century, was the trouveur, Robert de Borron, who, in the opinion of several critics, was assisted by Gautier Map, chaplain to King Henry II. of England.

The complement to the romances of the Round Table was the book which is known as the "Death of Arthur," as "Bret," and as the "Quest of the Holy Grail," and it is the least felicitous of them all. It was written by several authors, whose one object was to bring into it all the knights of the Round Table—Perceval, Lionel, Hector, Palamede, Gauvain, Bliomberis, Mordrain, and others, and to represent them as engaged in unceasing battle with wild beasts, giants, and enchanters. It was not till the fifteenth century that the romance-writers lengthened the stories contained in the books of the Round Table by describing the adventures and deeds of daring of Little Tristan, of Meliadus, of Perceforest, of Constant, of Little Arthur, of Isaiah the Doleful, &c.

The fourteenth century ushered in the decadence of the romances of chivalry. At the end of the previous century an effort had been made to revive the popularity of these romances, which had been more than once revised and altered from their original composition, the cycle of Charlemagne and even that of the Round Table being no longer in vogue. Still less success attended the provincial cycles, as the Gestes relating thereto were only of interest to the inhabitants of the province in which the events described took place. Thus the graphic "Geste des Lorrains," comprising "Hervis de Metz," "Garin le Loherain," and "Girbert et Anseis;" the "Burgundian Geste," consisting of the two romances, "Girart de Roussillon" and "Aubri le Bourgoing;" and other equally ancient Gestes, such as "Amis et Amiles," "Jourdain de Blaives," "Aiol et Mirabel," "Raoul de Cambrai," &c., no longer excited the enthusiasm of the hearers, who were out of patience with the jugglers, and did not care to receive them into their houses on account of their bad reputation. This bad reputation was in a great measure due to the misconduct of their confrères, the singers and the story-tellers, and though most of the jugglers themselves led respectable lives, their contact with the latter, who were nearly all thieves and drunkards, told very much against them. This, beyond all doubt, was one of the causes which brought about the decadence of romance as a branch of literature.

The last features of importance in this branch of literature were the cycle of the Crusades and a few romances which appealed more especially to the pride of certain noble families which had been made famous by the wars

Fig. 314—The Arming of a Knight after the Ceremonial instituted by King Arthur.—Fac-simile of a Miniature from Manuscript of the Fifteenth Century.—In the Burgundy Library, Brussels.

beyond the seas. These romances, " Hélias," the " Enfances Godefroi," the " Chétifs," and " Antioch and Jerusalem" (the latter two being merely extracts from the same poem), were recited in all the châteaux of France; and the jugglers, proud of having won a fresh popularity, thought they could dispense with a musical accompaniment, and got rid of their instrument-players. The result was that the romances, being no longer sung to the accompaniment of the harp or the violin, but recited in a monotonous tone, became submerged in a mass of marvellous and improbable stories, and were drawn out to a wearisome length. Not only were new compositions with thirty or forty thousand Alexandrine lines brought out, but the ancient romances written in ten-syllable verse were recast, and the lines lengthened. The primitive work, thus disfigured, lost all its original qualities. The trouveurs who were writing for the jugglers succeeded, however, in opening a fresh cycle, which belongs at once to the history of Charlemagne's successors and to that of the Crusades. The romances of "Charles the Bald" and of "Hugues Capet" were not more voluminous than the ancient romances, but "Baudouin de Sebourc" had more than thirty thousand lines, and "Tristan de Nanteuil" twenty-four thousand. The "Lion de Bourges," which consists of forty thousand tame and prolix lines, is a riot of the imagination in which there is no trace of the traditions relating to Charlemagne's epoch, which the writer professed to portray for the last time.

This was the death-blow to the jugglers, for they could not find any one to listen to the recital of these interminable romances. Nevertheless, as many of them turned copyists in order to gain a livelihood, the manuscripts went on increasing, and the longest and dullest of romances still found readers. But though the reading of romances increased rather than diminished amongst the wealthy and noble classes, with whom the taste for tournaments, jousts, and other games and institutions appertaining to chivalry (Fig. 314) grew very rapidly, only prose romances found any favour. The rhymed romances were condemned as a nuisance, and the consequence was a rapid transformation of them into prose. There was no lack of scribes in the palaces of the kings, as in the castles of the nobility, to undertake this work, and the anonymous author of the translation of "Aimeri de Beaulande" gives as his reason for having undertaken the work that it suits the popular taste. In the preface to the prose version of "Anseis de Carthage" the *acteur*, as he was called, openly states that he felt great hesitation and mistrust of his own person in transposing from rhyme into prose, "according to the tastes of the day," the achievements of ancient chivalry.

The old romances in verse disappeared and fell into oblivion, but the prose versions, arranged according to the tastes of the day, tricked out with sentimental and pedantic digressions, and lengthened with a mass of descriptions

and dialogues, were twice as prolix, but were received with great favour.
Many copies of them were brought out, and some of these copies, written in
large letters upon costly vellum (Fig. 315), were ornamented with capitals in
gold and colours, and with artistically painted miniatures. The libraries of the
great houses were made up of these manuscripts, most of them in folio, bound

Fig. 315.—Copyist writing upon a Sheet of Vellum.—Miniature from Manuscript of the Fifteenth
Century.—In the Royal Library, Brussels.

in wood, with a covering of leather or some rich material. These enormous
volumes, which could only be read from a desk, were much used by the ladies
of the family, who, undismayed by the length to which these stories of love
and chivalry extended, read from them every day. This was a very favourable period for the romances; nor was it the last, for, when printing was
discovered, fresh editions of nearly all the romances made their appearance

(Fig. 317). The text was much abridged in these later editions, and certain compilers, such as Pierre Desrey de Troyes, obtained for themselves a great reputation for this work, which exacted patience rather than genius. The romances thus revised had a great many new readers, especially among the middle classes, who had not before been able to see them. Chivalry, during the reigns of Charles VIII., of Louis XII., and of François I., seemed to shine with renewed brightness previously to its final extinction, and the romances which had heralded its triumph seemed, so to speak, to reflect its last rays.

During the reign of Charles VII., and more especially at the court of Burgundy, writers of real merit and discernment endeavoured to create a new kind of romantic literature, appealing to persons of more refined and elevated tastes (Fig. 316). They wrote love-stories or satires which were not less remarkable for the grace and interest of the narrative than for the realism of the passions and sentiments depicted. These romances, put together in a very plain but ingenious manner, were in as great favour as the more ambitious compilations relating to chivalry which it took two or three months to read. Antoine de la Sale furnished the model for works of this kind with his " Histoire et Chronique du Petit Jehan de Saintré," which was followed by the histories of " Parise et Vianne sa mie," of the " Chevaleureux Comte d'Artois," of " Ferrant de Flandres," of " Baudoin d'Avesnes," of " Pierre de Provence," of " Jean de Calais," and of " Jean de Paris." It began to be understood that the romance, discarding the marvellous and fantastic elements, might possess the most varied characteristics and become didactic, like the book of the " Sept Sages " and the " Cité des Dames; " sententious and instructive, like the " Jouvencel," by Admiral Jean de Bueil; or satirical, like King René's " Abusé en Cour." Romance became satirical and philosophical with Rabelais, who at first, when he wrote " Gargantua," intended to satirize the romances of chivalry, and who continued in " Pantagruel " to criticize the customs of his own time. Nevertheless, the romances of chivalry continued to be in vogue until the middle of the sixteenth century; but after that the modern romance, which is now only represented by a few insipid works, such as the " Histoire de l'Escuyer Gyrard et de Damoiselle Alyson," the " Amant ressuscité de la Mort d'Amour," the " Amours de la belle Luce," &c., transformed itself into the *Conte*, or tale, after the fashion of the " Cent Nouvelles nouvelles." The " Heptaméron " of the Queen of Navarre gave

birth to the " Recréations et Joyeux Devis " of Bonaventure des Périers ; to
the " Discours d'Eutrapel ; " to the " Matinées " and to the " Après-dînées " of
Cholières ; and, lastly, to the " Soirées," by Guillaume Bouchet.

In the meanwhile the ancient romances of chivalry, all originating in

Fig. 316.—" How the Actor lost his way, and arrived in front of the Palace of Love, into which
Desire bid him enter, while Remembrance held him back."—Miniature from the " Chevalier
Délibéré," by Olivier de la Marche.—Manuscript of the Fifteenth Century, No. 173.—In the
Arsenal Library, Paris.

France and bearing upon them the impress of that origin, had been translated or adapted into every language since the thirteenth century.   Not only
in Germany, Holland, and England, but in Sweden, Denmark, and even in

Iceland. These translations and imitations, which preserved the generic name of *romance*, were, however, fashioned to suit the taste of the nation for which they were intended, though they still retained the characteristics of their place of birth. In Italy there was composed only one prose romance after the manner of the French romances of the twelfth and thirteenth centuries; but from this crude compilation, which was called " Reali di Francia," there issued a great number of long poems on chivalry—" Rinaldo," " Morgante," " Orlando," " Guarino," &c.—upon which the Italian genius lavished all the wealth of its poetry to disguise the extravagant and affected sentiments which it attributed somewhat too freely to the rude paladins of Charlemagne, and to the Christian warriors who took part in the Crusades. Spain, whose heroic traditions were carefully preserved in the romances of the Campeador Cid, showed little liking for the peers of Charlemagne; but she took more kindly to the Breton romances about the Knights of the Round Table, and from them derived her inspirations for the composition of a romance similar in characteristics, which soon obtained a reputation equal to, if not greater than, that of the French works. This romance, "Amadis de Gaule," which Portugal has always claimed the possession of from Spain, was composed, or at all events begun, in the first years of the sixteenth century by an anonymous author, who wrote only the first four books of it. The writers who took up the work where he left it, and whose names are also unknown, added to these four books the stories of Esplandian, of Florisande, of Catane, and of the Knight of the Burning Sword. The success of " Amadis " was even greater in France and Italy than it was in Spain, and the French translation of Nicholas de Herberay, Sieur des Essars, shone like a beacon light above all the romantic compositions of the sixteenth century, during which the Spaniards published many romances of chivalry—"Primaleon of Greece," " Gerileon of England," &c.—all of which were cast into the shade by the masterpiece of Cervantes. The English and the Dutch continued to read the translations of the old French romances, but they did not attempt to imitate them, and the first national romance in England was Sidney's " Arcadia," published in 1591, and continued by his sister, the Countess of Pembroke. The Germanic nations, which had also translated a great number of the old French romances, were even less successful than the English in this branch of literature, and the few national and historical romances which they published in the sixteenth century only served to manifest their inferiority. Their tendency was rather towards the invention of stories at once supernatural and facetious, such as " Fortunatus," " Ulespiegel," and " Faust," or satirical allegories, such as the famous romance of " Renard," to which France gave letters of naturalisation, borrowing from Germany the data of this fanciful and allegorical story.

Fig. 317.—Token of Antoine Verard (1498), Printer, Wood Engraver, and Bookseller, at Paris, who published most of the Romances of Chivalry in Prose during the reigns of Louis XII. and François I.

POPULAR SONGS.

Definition and Classification of Popular Song.—Songs of the Germans, the Gauls, the Goths, and the Franks.—They are collected by Order of Charlemagne.—Vestiges of the most Ancient Songs.—The Historical Songs of France down to the Sixteenth Century.—Romanesque Songs. —Religious Songs.—The Christmas Carols and the Canticles.—Legendary Songs.—Domestic Songs.—The Music of the Popular Songs.—Provincial Songs.—The Songs of Germany.—The Minnesingers and the Meistersingers.—The Songs of England, of Scotland, and of Northern Countries.—The Songs of Greece, of Italy, and of Spain.

 Y the words Popular Song we mean a sort of poetry born spontaneously amongst the people, and therefore anonymous, and which, instead of being ascribed to such and such a poet, is, on the contrary, the work of certain unknown authors. We may also look upon it as the collective and successive work of whole generations, which, by the adoption of this poetry set to music in which is reflected the feeling of the mass, have preserved it more or less intact as a traditional souvenir of early ages. Montaigne characterized, with striking truth, this kind of popular poetry, which is contemporary with the origin of nations and of languages, when he said, " Poetry which is popular and wholly natural possesses charms of simplicity and grace which are worthy to be compared with the highest of artificial beauties, as may be seen by the pastoral poetry (*villanelles*) of Gascony and the songs coming to us from foreign parts."

M. Eugène Fermin, the commentator of the " Burgundy Christmas Carols" of La Monnoye, says, " Every nation possesses its popular songs; and as with all of them these songs must have had their origin in analogous causes, it follows that these songs must possess a certain analogy with each other. They were always inspired either by public occurrences, or by religious feeling, or by domestic joys and sorrows, whence we have the three distinct and marked categories which comprise the historic songs, the religious songs, and the domestic songs."

Fig. 318.—Poetry and Music.—The Nine Muses inspiring Arion, Orpheus, and Pythagoras, under the auspices of the Personified Air, source of all Harmony.—Miniature from the " Liber Pontificalis."—Manuscript of the Thirteenth Century.—In the Public Library, Rheims.

All nations have had their singers, and the national songs, composed of rhymed words with which corresponded a musical melody that had not the same

principles of duration, were the primitive expression of the passions, the
beliefs, and the ideas of each great human family (Fig. 318). It is easy to
understand how most of these popular songs were lost as time rolled on, and
why only a few faint echoes of them are now preserved, for the very essence
of a popular song is that it receives no written publicity, but passes from
mouth to mouth, leaving no other trace than verbal reminiscences.   The
early peoples were not in the habit of writing.   "The Germans," says

Allegro.

Da ik mab gwenn Drouiz, o - re;   Da - ik pe - tra fell d'id-de? pe - tra ga-ninn-

me d'id - de? — Kan d'in euz a - eur rann,   Ken a ouf-enn   bre - man.

— Heb   rann ar Red   heb-ken : An - Kou, tad ann   an - ken ; Ne-

tra kent ne   tra ken. — Da - ik mab gwenn Drouiz, o - re ;   Da - ik pe-tra

fell d'id - de?   pe - tra ga-ninn - me d'id - de? — Kan d'in euz a   zaou rann,

Ken a ouf-enn   bre - man.

Fig. 319.—A Song of the Druidic Epoch, Words and Music.   Translated by Fétis in his
"General History of Music."

Tacitus, "possessed some very ancient poems, in which were celebrated the
warlike actions and noble deeds of their ancestors, and which were transmitted
from father to son as the only annals of their race."   Among the Gauls the
Druids preserved as a sacred deposit the religious poems which dated from
the very earliest times, and which contained the mysteries of their religion
(Fig. 319), and these religious poems were in no case committed to writing.

At a later period, according to the testimony of Jornandès, the great Germanic nation of the Goths possessed no other history than the ancient songs which had been preserved as a venerable tradition in the well-stored memory of the people (" quemadmodum et in priscis eorum carminibus pene historico ritu in commune recolitur "). Thus Boulainvilliers remarks with truth, in his " Essay upon the Nobility," " The history of the French is stored up in their historical songs."

Unfortunately there does not now exist a single one of these songs, which the Gallic bards, according to Diodorus Siculus and Ammianus Marcellinus, were set to compose in Celtic, in order to perpetuate the memory of heroic deeds, and which they sang themselves at their assemblies to the accompaniment of the harp or the lyre. (See the volume on " The Arts," chapter *Music*.) We possess nothing of an earlier date than the Latin translation of the first verses of a popular song composed in 622, after the victory won by King Clotaire II. over the Saxons. This song went from mouth to mouth, because it was in the rustic language (*juxta rusticitatem*), and it was repeated by the women, who sang it while dancing and clapping their hands. The popular historical songs became very numerous in Gaul and in Germany, but many of them had disappeared when Charlemagne, who held this ancient literature of the people in high esteem, had them carefully collected in all the countries under his dominion, and it is much to be regretted that this valuable compilation, which testified to Charlemagne's esteem for this kind of vulgar poetry, should have been lost. Eginhard mentions in this connection that Charlemagne often sought relief from the cares of state in the songs of some Breton bard or some Scandinavian scald. Upon one occasion he allowed a Lombard juggler (*joculator*) to execute before him and his court a *cantiuncula* which that *minstrel* had composed. There existed, no doubt, some very popular and famous songs of the kind in honour of Charlemagne, for in the tenth century the words were still sung in the German language to the old tune, which is described in a manuscript at Wolfenbuttel as *Modus carelmanninc* (Charlemagne's tune).

From the ninth to the twelfth century we can only cite eight or ten popular songs, most of which were written in Latin, and which were, therefore, the work of clerks or men of letters, viz. a lament on the death of Charlemagne (" Planctus Caroli "); a very beautiful song upon the battle of Fontanet, in 841, by Angilbert the Frank; a song upon the death of Eric,

Duke of Frioul, in 799, by Paulin, Patriarch of Alexandria; a song to
celebrate the victory of the Emperor Otho III. over the Hungarians; a song
upon the death of Abbot Hug, the natural son of Charlemagne. But it is
doubtful how far these songs were really popular, and the "Ludwigslied" is
the only song of that period which we know to have been unmistakably
so. This song is in German, and celebrates the great victory won by
Louis III. in 881 over the Normans, and it was sung in the North of France
as late as the twelfth century.

The songs in the Romance rustic language were the only ones generally

Fig. 320.—Song of the Crusaders, dating from the First Crusade (1096), and set to Modern Music
by Fétis in his "General History of Music."

current among the people at a time when the German language was only
used at the court of the Carlovingian kings and emperors, and when the
clerks used the Latin language almost exclusively in the monasteries and in
the schools. A great number of these songs were devoted to the marvellous
and historical incidents in the legend of Charlemagne, and they served for
the composition of the early *chansons de geste* and romances of chivalry, in
which they were gradually absorbed and lost (Fig. 320). It is, therefore,
impossible to advance any direct and certain proof as to the existence of these
primitive songs. (See above, chapter on *Romances*.)

There are no traces of historical songs in the vulgar tongue of France

earlier than the thirteenth century, but there may be instanced a very singular
Latin song relating to the story of Abelard, and composed by his pupil Hilaire

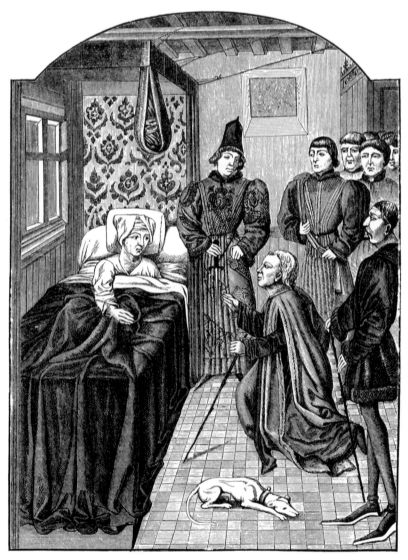

Fig. 321.—Duke Philip the Good, being sick, intrusts the education of his son Charles, Comte de
Charolois, to Georges Chastelain, the Poet and Chronicler.—Miniature from the "Instruction
d'un jeune Prince."—Manuscript of the Fifteenth Century, executed by the Painters of the
Court of Burgundy.—In the Arsenal Library, Paris.

about 1122, when his illustrious master, condemned by the Council of Soissons for his bold views on philosophy, finally gave up tuition. This song is divided into rhymed verses of four lines each, with the following refrain in French :—

> "Tort a vers nos li mestre."

Seventy-seven years later, at the death of Richard Cœur de Lion, who was killed while besieging the Castle of Chalus, in the province of Limousin, the French jugglers remembered that the valiant King of England had been delivered from prison by the aid of his minstrel, Blondel of Nesles, who made himself known by singing an air which Richard had composed himself. A popular song, in the style of the *chansons de geste,* was therefore composed about the death of Richard, and soon became popular throughout France, and doubtless in England as well. Amongst other lines were the following :—

> "Et ço dont dei tos jors pleindre en plorant,
> M'avient à dire en chantant et retraire
> Que cil qui est de valur chief et paire
> Li très-valens Richarz, rois des Engleis, est morz. . . .
> Morz est li rois, et sunt passé mil ans
> Que tant prodom ne fust ne n'est de son semblant."

The historical songs from the thirteenth to the sixteenth century recall such events as the Crusades, the wars of the French and the English, the death of the Constable Bertrand Duguesclin, and other popular heroes. Le Roux de Lincy has published an interesting collection of historical and popular French songs from the twelfth to the eighteenth century, and a second, comprising those of the time of Charles VII. and Louis XI., and in these two collections are to be found all that remains of these songs, most of which have lapsed into oblivion. It is very strange that none of the numerous ballads which the miraculous mission of Joan of Arc evoked at the time should have been treasured up, while there is still extant in the neighbourhood of Tournay a long ballad upon the death of Philip, the good Duke of Burgundy (Fig. 321). Although this ballad dates from 1467, it does not differ much from the language of the present day, as may be gathered from the extract appended :—

> "Le bon duc, avant son trespas,
> Et sentant la mort près de luy,
> Tout bellement et par compas,
> Fist ses regrès en grant annuy :

> ' Las ! ' dit-il, ' je laisse aujourd'hui
> Ma chiere espouse encor vivant.
> Adieu, ma dame à qui je suy !
> Priés pour moy, je voys morant.' "

The importance of a popular song was not, moreover, always to be judged by that of the event which gave it birth. It often happened that great political and national questions inspired only a few insignificant rhymes, which lapsed into oblivion without evoking the sympathies of the masses, while a tournament, a plenary court, a public ceremony, or a fête at some feudal castle sufficed to evoke the muse of the people. The inspirations of this fanciful muse were often in striking contrast to the circumstances which had given them birth, for while some tragic occurrence would serve as a theme for sarcastic or flippant songs, a matter which seemed to be a cause of universal rejoicing would form the subject for some doleful ballad. The divisions in popular opinion often found expression in their songs, and thus, when Jacques Clément assassinated King Henry III., who had been driven from Paris by the League, at St. Cloud, some fanatical people sang the murderer's praises in the following lines :—

> " O le sainct religieux,
> Jacques Clément bienheureux,
> Des Jacobins l'excellence,
> Qui, par sa bénévolence,
> Et de par le Sainct-Esprit,
> A mérité asseurance
> Là haut au Ciel où il vist."

The Politicians, or Royalists, rejoined with the following lines :—

> " Il fut tué par un meschant mutin
> Jacques Clément qui estoit jacobin.
> Jacques Clément, si tu estois à naistre,
> Las ! nous aurions nostre Roy, nostre maistre ! "

It would sometimes happen that after a certain interval a song of noble and solemn melancholy would be converted into a burlesque parody without any apparent cause or reason. Thus the battle of Pavia (1525), at which the flower of the French nobility perished around François I., who was made prisoner, was a most appropriate subject for a popular song, and amongst other touching incidents was the death of Jacques de Chabannes, Lord of La Palice, who was killed at the feet of his sovereign.   The ballad, composed in his honour, began—

> " Monsieur de La Palice est mort.
> Est mort devant Pavie." . . .

But within a century this national song had been travestied in such a way that it had become impossible to recognise it, and some one made it ridiculous by adding as a joke to the above two lines—

> " Hélas ! s'il n'estoit pas mort,
> Il seroit encore en vie."

Sometimes, too, there would reappear in a new shape some old song which was scarcely remembered by the older generation, but which seemed to acquire fresh youth when, with an altered name, it was applied to some other subject.   Thus, after the battle of Malplaquet in 1709, the rumour of the death of the English commander, the Duke of Marlborough, having spread through the ranks of the French army, which had suffered so much at his hands, the soldiers began to sing, out of revenge, a sort of comic ballad, which was only the imitation of a popular song entitled the " Convoi du Duc de Guise," which all the Huguenot soldiers knew by heart after the assassination of François de Lorraine, called Le Balafré (covered with scars), beneath the walls of Orleans (1563).   Appended are some of the couplets of this old song which most resemble the " Chanson de Malbrough," and which was revived two centuries later by the court of Louis XVI., when Madame Poitrine, the nurse of the Dauphin, taught it to Marie Antoinette :—

> " Qui veut ouïr chanson ?
> C'est du grand duc de Guise,
> Doub, dan, don, dan, dou, don,
> Dou, dou, dou,
> Qu'est mort et enterré.

> Qu'est mort et enterré.
> Aux quatre coins de sa tombe,
> Doub, dan, don, &c.
> Quatr'gentilhomm's y avoit.

Quatr'gentilhomm's y avoit,
Dont l'un portoit son casque
Doub, dan, don, &c.
L'autre ses pistolets.

L'autre ses pistolets,
Et l'autre son épée,
Doub, dan, don, &c.
Qui tant d'Hugu'nots a tués

. . . . , .
La cérémonie faite,
Doub, dan, don, etc.
Chacun s'allit coucher.

Chacun s'allit coucher,
Les uns avec leurs femme ,
Doub, dan, don, &c.
Et les autres tous seuls."

Several critics, Génin amongst others, have attributed a still more ancient origin to the "Chanson de Malbrough," or at least to part of this song, in which may be recognised the naïve and sentimental cast of the popular songs of the thirteenth century. There are many instances which might be cited of songs coming down from century to century, gradually losing all the souvenirs which connected them with the distant period during which they gushed forth from the heart of the people. The children in the villages of Poitou still sing as an anthem the following verse, half Latin, half French, which doubtless refers to the captivity of King John, who was taken prisoner at the battle of Poitiers (September 17th, 1356) :—

" *Christiana Francia*
De laquelle le chef est pris,
Splendens regni gloria
Aux armes de la fleur de lys."

By the side of the historical songs, and in the same category with them, must be cited the romantic songs. As has been remarked by one of those who have studied the most deeply this poetry of the people, " the narrative in them is abrupt and digressive, leaving secondary details in the shade, and treating only of the salient points. The same forms of language are repeated several times, and the dialogues are reproduced word for word as in Homer. The refrain is sometimes entirely unconnected with the subject of the narrative." Perhaps the most beautiful of these short poems is the following, which has taken different forms in different provinces of France, and which is known as the " Complainte de Renaud." The poem forms a complete drama :—

" Quand Renaud de la guerre vint,
. . . .
Sa mère, à la fenêtre en haut,
Dit : ' Voici venir mon fils Renaud.'

La Mère. Renaud, Renaud, réjouis-toi,
Ta femme est accouchée d'un roi.
Renaud. Ni de ma femme, ni de mon fils,
Mon cœur ne peut se réjoui ;

Qu'on me fasse vite un lit blanc
Pour que je m'y couche dedans.
Et quand il fut mis dans son lit,
Pauvre Renaud rendit l'esprit.
(*Les cloches sonnent le trépassement.*)

La Reine. Or, dites-moi, mère m'amie,
Qu'est-ce que j'entends sonner ici ?
La Mère. Ma fille, ce sont les processions
Qui sortent pour les Rogations.
(*On cloue le cercueil.*)

La Reine. Or, dites-moi, mère m'amie,
Qu'est-ce que j'entends cogner ici ?
La Mère. Ma fille, c' sont les charpentiers
Qui raccommodent nos greniers.
(*Les prêtres enlèvent le corps.*)

La Reine. Or, dites-moi, mère m'amie,
Qu'est-ce que j'entends chanter ici ?
La Mère. Ma fille, c' sont les processions
Qu'on fait autour de nos maisons.

La Reine. Or dites-moi, mère m'amie,
Quelle robe prendrai-je aujourd'hui ?
La Mère. Quittez le rose, quittez le gris.
Prenez le noir, pour mieux choisi.

La Reine. Or, dites-moi, mère m'amie,
Qu'ai-je donc à pleurer ici ?
La Mère. Ma fille, je n' puis plus vous le cacher :
Renaud est mort et enterré.

La Reine. Terre, ouvre-toi ! terre, fends-toi !
　　　　　Que j' rejoigne Renaud, mon roi.
　　　　　Terre s'ouvrit, terre fendit,
　　　　　Et la belle fut engloutie.''

Religious songs, which must not be confused with the liturgical songs,

Fig. 322.—The Shepherds celebrating the Birth of the Messiah with Hymns and Dancing (End of the Fifteenth Century).—Fac-simile of a Wood Engraving from a " Livre d'Heures" printed by Antoine Verard.

had a much more extensive sphere than the historical songs, for they comprised prayers, legends, the lives of the saints, miracles, canticles, and the songs pertaining to the ceremonies of religion and the festivals of the Church. Of the three distinct categories referred to above, that of religious song is the most fruitful in ingenuous works which bear the impress of the faith and piety of our forefathers, for in France the people have always been sincerely attached to religion. It is true that popular religious songs were sometimes of a slightly facetious and bantering tone, but this was merely a natural emanation of the Gallic character and temperament. The Church very properly opposed the introduction of profane songs into the sanctuary, though, as we saw in the chapter on *Popular Beliefs*, the " Prose of the Ass " long held its own against the condemnations of councils and synods. We may believe, therefore, that in many dioceses during the Middle Ages the religious songs in the vulgar tongue, known under the generic title of Noëls

Fig. 323.—A Carol in Burgundy Patois, with the Music annotated.—After the " Noël Borguignon de Gui Barôzai," published by Bernard de La Monnoye.

(Christmas Carols), were sometimes mixed up with the sacred hymns which celebrated the birth of Jesus in the stall at Bethlehem. These songs in the vulgar tongue were sung during the solemn procession which was formed during the night of Christmas, to the sound of instruments, and in the dress of shepherds, around the crib of the infant Jesus (Fig. 323). The persons who represented the shepherds are said to have sung, as early as the thirteenth century, a carol which began—

" Seignors, or entendez à nous.
De loin sommes venus à vous
Pour querre Noël."

Another carol of the same period, which was entirely rewritten in the sixteenth century, described the joy of the animals at the news of the birth of the Holy Child, and gave an opening for musical effects, as the singers imitated the crowing of the cock, the lowing of the ox, the bleating of the goat, the braying of the ass, and the bellowing of a calf. It ran as follows :—

> " Comme les bestes autrefois
>   Parloient mieux latin que françois,
>   Le coq, de loin voyant le faict,
>   S'écria : *Christus natus est* (le Christ est né) ;
>   Le bœuf, d'un air tout ébaubi,
>   Demande : *Ubi, ubi, ubi ?* (Où, où, où ?)
>   La chèvre, se tordant le groin,
>   Respond que c'est à *Bethléem.*
>   Maistre baudet, *curiosus* (curieux)
>   De l'aller voir, dit : *Eamus !* (Allons !)
>   Et droit sur ses pattes, le veau
>   Beugle deux fois : *Volo ! volo !* (je veux ! je veux !) "

This was only an exception, for, as a general rule, the carol was so distinguished above all other religious songs for its pious and touching simplicity that it might almost have passed for a canticle. The most picturesque and emotional carols were those of Brittany, though all over France, in town as well as in country, the carols preserved their former characteristics as long as religion remained supreme in men's hearts. The whole song was devoted to glorifying the Divine Messiah, and at most it contained a final couplet praying God to pardon miserable sinners. But gradually human thoughts displaced divine and religious thoughts in this popular song, and the carols, while still retaining their original form and pretensions, became changed into personal appeals addressed to Jesus and the Holy Virgin in the interests of those who sang them.

In the Beauce district, for instance, it is still the custom to sing—

> " Honneur à la compagnie
>   De cette maison.
>   A l'entour de votre table,
>   Nous vous saluons.
>   Nous sommes v'nus de païs étrange
>   Dedans ces lieux :
>   C'est pour vous faire la demande
>   De la part à Dieu."

There is also a very long carol which was composed and sung during the

League, and this carol, doubly remarkable with regard to the sentiments it contains and the way in which they are expressed, is in reality a popular song at once political and religious, and in which staunch Catholics deplore the evil of their time. The three couplets subjoined will give the reader an idea of the general tone of this pathetic lay :—

> " Nous te requérons, à mains jointes,
> Vouloir ouïr nos griefves plaintes,
> 　　Nous, pauvres pastoureaux ;
> De toutes parts on nous saccage,
> On nous détruit, on nous ravage,
> 　　Et brebis et agneaux.

> Le soldat, tous les jours, sans cesse,
> En nos casettes nous oppresse,
> 　　Pille et emporte tout :
> Il nous compresse, il nous rançonne ;
> A son départ, souvent nous donne
> 　　Encore un meschant coup.

> Que si bientost tu n'y prends garde,
> Nous mettant sous ta sauvegarde,
> 　　Hélas ! c'est fait de nous.
> Oste-nous donc de ces misères,
> Fais cesser nos civiles guerres,
> 　　Te prions à genoux ! "

The Christmas carol soon assumed a different shape, and, ceasing to be even a religious song, was made to contain allusions to the current events of the day, allusions replete with epigrams and sarcasms. It became in some cases impertinent, indelicate, and blasphemous, though more generally it was but the arch expression of popular good-humour. The appended couplet gives a fair idea of the carol of the sixteenth century :—

> " Messire Jean Guillot,
> Curé de Saint-Denis,
> Apporte plein un pot
> Du vin of son logis.
> Prestres et escolliers,
> Toute icelle nuictée,
> Se sont mis à sauter,
> 　　Chanter
> Ut, ré, mi, fa, sol, la,
> 　　la la,
> A gorge desployée."

The religious canticles and ballads preserved their characteristics of single-minded devotion much longer than the carols, and, unlike the works manu-factured by a professional poet, they resemble rather the prayers and orisons set to church music. The pilgrims, the relic showers, and the vendors of consecrated medals chanted in slow and monotonous tones the interminable stories of saints, male and female—" Geneviève de Brabant," " St. Roch," " St. Antoine," and many other masterpieces of simple faith, which have

Fig. 324.—A Ballad Singer accompanying himself upon the Violin.—Miniature from Manuscript of the Thirteenth century, No. 6,819.—In the National Library, Paris.

come down to us in modern form, and which will, perhaps, survive centuries after much of the modern and printed poetry has been forgotten (Fig. 320). The following modernised song dates, beyond all doubt, from a very ancient epoch :—

> " C'est sainte Catherine,
> La fille d'un grand roi :
> Son père était païen,
> Sa mère ne l'était pas.
> *Ave Maria, Sancta Catharina,*
> *Dei mater, alleluia.*

> Un jour à sa prière
> Son père la trouva :
> 'Catherine, ô ma fille,
> Catherine, que fais-tu là ?'
> *Ave Maria,* &c.

> 'J'adore, j'adore, mon père,
> Le bon Dieu que voilà.
> C'est le Dieu de ma mère :
> Votre Dieu n'est pas là.'
> *Ave Maria,* &c."

The legends relating to the Virgin form a class apart, and are many of them endowed with special charms. Several narratives of the Middle Ages were devoted to celebrating her mercy and the influence which she possessed, because of her motherhood, over God himself. There is a Périgord song brought to light by Count de Mellet, which in modern French runs—

> "Une âme est morte cette nuit :
> Elle est morte sans confession.
> Personne ne la va voir,
> Excepté la Sainte Vierge.
> Le Démon est à l'entour :
> 'Tenez, tenez, mon fils Jésus,
> Accordez-moi le pardon de cette pauvre âme.'
> 'Comment voulez-vous que je lui pardonne ?
> Jamais elle ne m'a demandé de pardon.'
> 'Mais si bien à moi, mon fils Jésus ;
> Elle m'a bien demandé pardon.'
> 'Eh bien ! ma mère, vous le voulez ?
> Dans le moment même je lui pardonne.'"

The popular domestic songs are infinite both in regard to numbers and variety, and they appealed the most directly to the heart of the people. Conjugal and maternal love inspired most of these songs, in which are depicted with singular fidelity the joys and sorrows of home, and in which the business of life is shown in its varying shades. These songs are a mixture of epigram and elegy, of the open expression of the tenderest feelings of the human heart and of the wildest fancies, and they depict the different gradations of the social scale. These domestic songs may be subdivided into many categories : the songs of the soldier and of the sailor, of the shepherd and of the labourer, of the fisherman and of the hunter ; the songs of indoor workmen, such as the weavers, the shoemakers, the spinners, the smiths, and the carpenters; the songs of the *compagnonnages* (trades unions); the songs relating to the culture of the soil, such as seed-time, harvest, and vintage; satirical songs; songs bearing upon the various phases of family life, such as christening, confirmation, marriage, death, widowhood, &c.; convivial and playful songs; roundelays and songs of childhood; and so forth. Types of all these songs are to be found in M. Ampère's excellent treatise called the "Instructions du Comité de la Langue, de l'Histoire et des Arts de la France."

Fig. 325.—The Personification of Music.—Fac-simile of a Wood Engraving in the "Margarita Philosophica" (Bale Edition, 4to, 1508).

All these songs, be it remembered, which had no known authors, or which were adopted by the great anonymous and collective poet called the People, are in reality popular songs, and must not be confounded with the individual productions of written poetry, many of them very indifferent in quality,

which Montaigne contemptuously designated as being " void of honour and
of value." Some of these popular songs, for all their errors of grammar and
their incompleteness, are very remarkable works. The metre often seems
wrong, the rhyme is replaced by a mere assonance, and the meaning is badly
expressed ; but these trifling compositions have a charm all their own, and
present the true type of popular poetry. The professional poets, even the
greatest of them, did not think it beneath their dignity to borrow from this
popular poetry, which, in attempting to improve, they often spoilt. A charming couplet is that which Georges de Lalaing, a gentleman of the court of
Burgundy, who happened to remember having heard it somewhere in Brabant,
wrote in the album of Hélène de Mérode :—

> " Elle s'en va aux champs, la petite bergièie,
>   Sa quenouille filant ; son troupeau suyt derrière.
>   Tant il la fait bon veoir, la petite bergière,
>   Tant il la fait bon veoir."

In the same album is preserved a village roundelay which was sung in the
Hainault :—

> " Nous estions trois sœurs tout d'une volonté,
>   Nous allîmes au fond du joly bois jouer. . . .
>   Vray Dieu ! Qu'il est heureux, qui se garde d'aimer ! "

Most of these songs were set to popular airs which were familiar to
everybody, and the unknown origin of which in many cases went back for
centuries. Sometimes, however, the music had been composed at the same
time as the words, and also belonged to the music of the people, which has
always been remarkable for its exquisite grace and simplicity (Fig. 325).

Every province and town—one might almost add every village—had its
particular songs, which were preserved in the memory of the inhabitants as
safely as if they were deposited in the local archives. These songs represented the ideas, the beliefs, the manners, and, above all, the idiom of the
district, and this idiom limited the preservation of them to the region in
which they were composed. Hence we have a mass of popular songs which
have become embedded in the various patois, and which date from every
period in history. The patois may be Flemish, Picard, Norman, Poitou,
Burgundian, Provençal, Auvergnat, or Languedoc, but in all alike one
hears the voice of the people. How ancient some of these songs are, not-

withstanding the modern dialect in which they are expressed, may be readily understood when one hears the Berry peasants driving their oxen to an unintelligible air interspersed with Latin words, such as *I bos* and *Sta bos;* and so, again, in several popular songs in the Chartrain and Auvergne districts there occurs the refrain *la guilloné* and *la guillona,* which is no other than the song of Gallic origin terminating with the words *Gui l'an neu,* and which long survived the Druidic ceremonies.

The various races of men settled in Europe, and the various countries which make up that continent, formerly possessed their own popular songs, and they were anxious to preserve them as records of their nationality, for

Fig. 326.—Minnesingers.—Poésies des Minnesingers.—Manuscript of the Fourteenth Century. In the National Library, Paris.

these popular songs were, in fact, the native expression of the character of the nation which produced them. An effort is now being made to collect them, for they are the rarest and most interesting documents of the history of peoples.

In Germany, whose national songs had already been collected by Charlemagne, there appeared in the twelfth century a series of long poems, derived from them, which made up the splendid epode known as "Niebelungen." The German poets then created a new branch of songs, which were destined by their very characteristics to become popular, but which must not, with a few exceptions, be looked upon as works emanating from the people themselves. The Minnesingers (or singers of love-songs), who composed a great many of these lyric songs, differed but little from the troubadours of Southern France (Fig. 326), while the Meistersingers (master singers) had more in common with the jugglers of the tongue of Oil. The work of the Minnesingers did not reach, from the twelfth to the fourteenth century, beyond the courts of the princes and the castles of the nobles, who themselves aspired to sing love-songs, and who waged unceasing war against the ancient popular songs of Germany. The work of the Meistersingers, upon the contrary, was intended for the middle and the lower classes (Fig. 327). These poets and musicians, who devoted their efforts to a branch of literature more in conformity with the German character, had quite eclipsed the Minnesingers by the fifteenth century, and popularised a new branch of poetry which contained within itself the germs of dramatic art. (See below, chapter on *National Poetry*.)

The popular songs of Germany are especially worth studying when they take the eminently poetic form of ballads, for there is in the German ballad, to use the felicitous expression of M. Fertiault, something soft and pensive, which can be felt better than it can be described—something at once vague and touching. It embodies, as a rule, a slight drama, in which are united and fused lyric, dramatic, and familiar elements. Pensive and mystic, it hints at more than it actually says, and it exhales as it were a refined perfume of the soul which kindles the deepest emotions. Germany, like France, has her popular songs, both historical, religious, and domestic, and they are in a more complete state of preservation.

England, too, is rich in ancient ballads equal to those of Germany. The English ballads are, as a rule, somewhat epic in their tendencies, and many of them are of such a length that they assume the proportions of a poem in several cantos. But, whatever may be their length or manner of composition, they are replete with tender and refined sentiments culled from the marvellous fables of ancient Britain. Scotland has also a number of national ballads reflecting the poetic majesty of her wild scenery, of her mist-enveloped lakes, and of her pine-covered mountains. Sir Walter Scott, in his "Songs of the Scotch," remarks that traditional tales and songs, accompanied by the flute and the harp of the minstrel, were probably the sole sources of amusement possessed by the Highlanders during their short intervals of peace. In them we may trace the source whence Macpherson drew the fanciful utterances which he puts in the mouth of his Ossian. Ireland is not less proud of her national ballads, and Thomas Moore, who published them for the first time, preferred them to the Scotch ballads.

In Denmark, Sweden, and Norway the popular songs were for centuries the only history transmitted from generation to generation: all these countries had their national poets, named *Scalds*, who sang upon the battle-fields in order to inspirit the combatants (Fig. 328). These poets, themselves warriors, improvised to the sound of the harp rhymed songs in which they related, after a fashion at once simple and striking, the great military achievements of their heroes, whom they associated with the sombre deities

Fig. 327.—German Musicians playing the Lute and the Guitar.—Engraved by J. Amman
(Sixteenth Century).

of the Odin mythology. The people drank deeply and incessantly from the springs of this wild and warlike, yet pensive poetry, and these anonymous, and in the true sense popular, works formed a collection known by the name of "Kemperiser." M. Marmier points out the resemblance of the popular songs of Sweden to those of Scotland, Germany, Holland, and Denmark. The Danes, as he remarks, were long enough in direct communication with England to interchange the legends of heroism, religion, and love.

Russia and Poland have popular songs which, though dissimilar from one another, date from the same epoch of the Middle Ages. In Poland the popular songs are mainly historical and warlike, or touch upon chivalry, while in Russia they are rather religious and domestic, and are used by the peasants to portray their joys and sorrows. Servia and the Danubian provinces are equally rich in popular songs, which have been collated in a work called "Danitza," many of them being of very ancient date. They consist, for the most part, of love and war songs, and are remarkable for their exquisite refinement. Modern Greece has, like Servia, formed a collection of her ancient popular songs, many of which, in the shape of a legendary ballad

Fig. 328.—Song of the Sword. Original Melody of the "Krakumal," an ancient record of the Scandinavian Scalds, published by Fétis in his "History of Music," after the version of it by M. Legis. Each of the couplets of this melody commences with a line meaning, "We have fought with the sword."

of the Middle Ages, retain a perfume of antiquity. Some of these songs are contemporaneous with the conquest of Constantinople by the French crusaders in the twelfth century, and with the occupation of the Morea, which then became a French principality.

Italy cannot well claim as popular songs the *canzoni* composed by her poets, who styled themselves *reciters in rhyme* and *love swains*, after the fashion of the troubadours of Provence and Languedoc. These pieces of poetry, full of concetti, metaphors, and mystic exaggerations, were doubtless considered,

by the gallants and ladies of the court, to confer great honour upon Guido
Cavalcanti, Cino de Pistoia, Guido Orlandi, and the rest of the composers;
but they took no root amongst the people, who either did not understand
them or turned them into jest. Rhythm and song were in a measure instinctive requirements in a land where the love of poetry and music is innate. As
late as the last century the gondoliers of Venice were in the habit of singing
verses from Tasso while plying the oar (Fig. 329). But these were not

Fig. 329.—Venetian Gondola.—From the " Grand Procession of the Doge of Venice," attributed
to Jost Amman, published at Frankfort in 1597.

popular songs, to find which we must search the numerous patois, which were,
many of them, equal, if not superior, to the correct Italian language. There
was not a town or village which had not its local literature, and which could
not boast of the clever and poetical works of some one or more of its sons.

In Spain, more than in any other country of Europe, popular song had a
very marked and special physiognomy, and assumed the form, not of ballad,

dreamy and pensive, or light and airy, but of the heroic songs, such as the *chansons de geste* written in Romanic. Nothing, too, answers more closely to the best definition which has been given of popular song. M. Damas-Hinard, the translator of the "Cid," says, "Romances are not only the true history of the Middle Ages in Spain, they are also its poetry. The Spanish people, the poets of the Romances, composed with enthusiasm these songs, of which they themselves are the subject and the heroes. For many centuries, and in each generation, the greatest writers set themselves to improve and to embellish them." The most important part of the Spanish *Romancero* consists of the romances of the "Cid," which date, according to the critics, from the eleventh or the thirteenth century, but long before this Spain possessed popular songs which must date from the reign of King Roderick in the eighth century. A collection of the Spanish popular songs, from the conquest of Granada, by Gonzalvo of Cordova, in 1492, to the end of the sixteenth century, would be a very onerous task, but if not undertaken the world will ultimately lose the beautiful historical romances which the muleteers of Andalusia used to sing to the accompaniment of the mandolin.

Fig. 330.—French Trouveur.—After a Drawing from the Poems of Guillaume de Machaut. Manuscript of the Fourteenth Century.—In the National Library, Paris.

NATIONAL POETRY.

NCE the Barbarians established themselves upon the ruins of the Roman empire in the West," says M. Charles Nisard, in his graphic history of poetry amongst the different peoples of Europe, "the downfall of eloquence and of poetry occurred with startling rapidity. Boethius wrote in his prison the treatise on the 'Consolation of Philosophy,' and was put to death shortly afterwards (524). This treatise, which combines the highest of ancient morality with the tenderest feelings of Christian resignation, is the last protest of an expiring art ; it is the voice of the swan exhaling its last melody beneath the knife which is about to immolate it."

Boethius was, in fact, one of the last Romans who wrote Latin verses with the true classic ring in them. Since the reign of Theodosius the Great, Latin poetry had been gradually declining, and the Church had ceased to use it except for her sacred hymns. This is why most of the poets from the fifth to the seventh century—St. Paulinus, Sedulius, St. Prosper, Sidonius Apollinaris, Juvencus, Venantius Fortunatus, &c.—wrote only upon pious or moral subjects. The singing of hymns was calculated, in the opinion of the

Church, to put an end to certain heretical or blasphemous songs which the Barbarians or the Romans of the decadence were in the habit of repeating; and the hopes of the Church were eventually fulfilled.

The Romanic language, which in various forms was current throughout Europe from the sixth to the tenth century, produced no other poetical works than the popular songs which were transmitted from generation to generation, and which, not having been collected, as the Teutonic songs were by order of Charlemagne, soon became effaced from the memory of the people. (See previous chapter, *Popular Songs*.) The written poetry, which was cultivated by a few men of letters and clerks, continued to be in Latin (Fig. 331), but it was disfigured by words of new creation. It is not until the tenth century

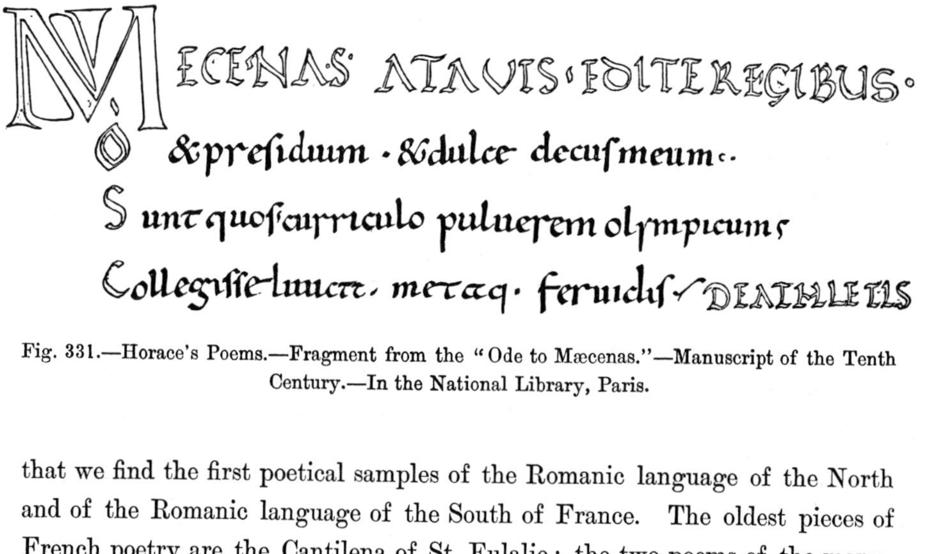
MECENAS ATAVIS EDITE REGIBUS
O & presidium & dulce decus meum.
Sunt quos curriculo puluerem olympicum
Collegisse iuuat, metaq. feruidis DE ATHLETIS

Fig. 331.—Horace's Poems.—Fragment from the "Ode to Mæcenas."—Manuscript of the Tenth Century.—In the National Library, Paris.

that we find the first poetical samples of the Romanic language of the North and of the Romanic language of the South of France. The oldest pieces of French poetry are the Cantilena of St. Eulalie; the two poems of the manuscript of Clermont-Ferrand, devoted to St. Leger and to the Passion of Jesus Christ; and, in the eleventh century, the "Chanson de St. Alexis." In the Provençal language we have the "Mystery of the Wise and of the Foolish Virgins," previously to which came the "Poem of Boethius." The latter is a piece in verse, of about two hundred and fifty lines, upon the captivity of Boëthius, and these lines, of ten syllables each, are divided into stanzas of unequal length, each stanza terminating with the same masculine rhyme. This kind of poem is unquestionably anterior to the tenth century. Such are the origins of the language of French poetry.

From this period vulgar poetry was founded, like Latin rhymed poetry, upon the accent and the assonance. It may further be affirmed that this vulgar poetry was sung, and that the jugglers, who repeated verses after a musical mood while playing the violin, had at that time come into existence. It is therefore certain that the first trouveurs and troubadours were contemporary with the formation of this Romanic language, which was expressed in accented, syllabic, and consonant verse. The trouveur in the North and the troubadour in the South were alike the poets who knew how to *find* (*trobar*)— that is to say, invent—and who clothed their thoughts in literary shape. We do not know of any troubadours before the eleventh century, and the first to open the brilliant era of this new poetry was William IX., Count of Poitiers, born in 1070, who, at the death of his father, became Duke of Aquitaine and Gascony. Several pieces of his which have been published show that the Romanic language was already in a flourishing state. After this there was a general development of poetry, and it is necessary to subdivide the troubadours into several schools. The first, and perhaps the most important, is the Limousin school, of which Bertrand de Born, Gaucelm Faydit, and Bernard de Ventadour were the chiefs. To the Gascony school belong Geoffroy Rudel, Arnauld de Marveilh, and twenty others. The school of Auvergne can claim the sturdy satirist, Pierre Cardinal, and Pons de Capdeuil (Fig. 332). Raymond Vidal is the hero of the Toulouse school, Guillaume Riquier of that of Narbonne, and Raymond Gaucelm of that of Béziers. Lastly comes the Provençal school, to which belong Raimbaud of Vaqueiras and Folquet of Marseilles, and a hundred other writers scarcely less famous.

These troubadours were men of lively imagination and ready wit, possessed of abundant humour, which was by turn gay, spiteful, and caustic. Their poetry, which is a dim reflection of the works of the early Roman writers, is essentially southern, being devoted in most cases to the multiform expression of the most refined gallantry; it abounds in tender reveries and in descriptions of beautiful scenery. This poetry was highly appreciated by the society of that age, and every one, from the princes and nobles to the tradesmen and the artisans, held it a high honour to be a poet. We know of more than two hundred troubadours who, during three centuries, wrote with success in every branch of Romanic poetry, and who have left behind them an immense collection of charming and polished works. These works, most of which are still unpublished, had reached as far as Italy, inasmuch as we know that they were highly appreciated by Dante; and the poetry of the troubadours was specially notable for its gracefulness of invention, science of rhythm, infinite variety of form, abundant imagery, and richness of colour. Most of it consisted of love-songs and pastorals, but there were some religious and satirical pieces, many of the latter being very severe, known by the name of *sirventes*.

When certain strolling jugglers of the South imported the poems of the troubadours into the central and northern provinces of France in the beginning

Fig. 332.—Song of the Troubadour, Pons de Capdeuil, with the Music.—Published by Fétis, after Manuscript in National Library, Paris.

of the thirteenth century, these provinces had long possessed a native poetry in the vulgar tongue, and they also possessed poets who called themselves trouveurs (Fig. 333), to distinguish them from the jugglers who had been in the habit, for three or four centuries past, of singing popular songs while playing upon different stringed instruments. As soon as the Romanic language of Northern France had made sufficient progress to become a written language, poetry was its spontaneous expression. It was to indicate the line of demarcation which separated the Tongue of Oil and the Romanic language of the South that the latter took the name of the Tongue of Oc. But it must be expressly mentioned that the trouveurs, notwithstanding certain local imitations of the poetry of the troubadours, have nothing in common with the latter in respect to literary invention and poetical genius. It was the trouveurs who had the honour of creating in the eleventh century, or even earlier, the *chansons de geste* and romances of chivalry which have been translated into every language, and which have no parallel in the literature of the Tongue of Oc. (See previous chapter, *Romances.*)

The Tongue of Oil had from its very inception produced two families of poets of utterly different characteristics, and who represented, so to speak, epic poetry and light poetry. The great trouveurs, those who collected the popular songs and the national traditions to convert them into *chansons de geste* and romances of chivalry, were, in many cases, in the domestic service of princes and nobles; they lived all together amongst the warriors for whom they composed the long national poems which they afterwards recited to the sound of the violin at festivals and assemblies. All that relates to romances has been treated of in a previous chapter. But the lesser trouveurs, those who may, perhaps, have been subject to the influence of the troubadours, and many of whom were no better than strolling players, created

Fig. 333.—Trouveur accompanying himself upon the Violin.—Sculptured Work upon the Portico of the Abbey of St. Denis (Twelfth Century).

the gallant and joyous literature of the Tongue of Oil. They had, like the troubadours, their *serventois*, their *descors*, their *rotruenges;* they borrowed their lays from the singers of Brittany, and were the inventors of the *jeux-partis*, the *fabliaux*, and the *contes*, all of which are thoroughly French. The fabliau (metrical tale) is the best, but at the same time the most immoral, of the productions of the trouveurs and jugglers who wrote in the Tongue of Oil. These fabliaux are many of them masterpieces of wit and insinuation, and abound in strokes of humour, while the eight-syllable lines are well adapted to their style. In most of these works it is easy to trace the ancient sources from which the authors borrowed their generally indecent subjects of song. Others, however, were of their own invention, and these latter were not the least immoral, for the trouveurs of the people were, for the most part, men of dissolute life.

Rutebeuf is the most celebrated of these trouveurs-jugglers, and he has left a mass of exquisite and witty compositions, nearly all of which are satires upon the nobles, the monks, and the clergy. He is doubtless depicting his own life of poverty when he describes how he and his companions journeyed from castle to castle, half dead with cold and hunger, begging, often in vain, to be allowed to give their poetry and music. Most of them were not more exemplary in their conduct than Rutebeuf himself; and one of them, Colin Muset, made an attack upon the King, who did not, however, condescend to notice his violent diatribe. But these poetic excesses were not, on the whole, favourable to the trouveurs and jugglers, who soon found themselves repulsed with contempt wherever they went.

There was only one school of trouveurs, most of whom were themselves of noble birth, in favour with royalty and the nobility, and it comprised such men as Quenes or Conon of Bethune (Fig. 334), and Count Thibaud of Champagne, afterwards King of Navarre, who was the most illustrious of them all (Fig. 335). This school, in fact, rivalled that of the troubadours. The songs of Thibaud found their way as far as Italy, and Dante, who had got them by heart, mentioned in his work, "De Vulgari Eloquentiâ," the King of Navarre as "an excellent master in poetry." One of the pupils and rivals of Thibaud of Champagne was his vassal, Gace Brulé. Amongst the princes and lords of whom the gallant spirit of chivalry had made poets at this epoch may be mentioned the Lord of Coucy, Pierre Duke of Brittany, Jean de Brienne, Guillaume de Ferrières, Hugues de Lusignan, and many others who are alluded to by M. Paulin Paris in volume xxiii. of his "Histoire Littéraire."

These trouveurs of the nobility, imitators of the troubadours, would not probably have succeeded in rehabilitating the poetry of the Tongue of Oil, which had been cast into discredit by the trouveurs-jugglers, but for the assistance of true poets, who, declining to emerge from their retreats in order to scour the country, devoted their time to the composition of serious and valuable works. Marie de France, who was one of this number, and who was a Norman by birth, passed part of her youth at the court of Henry III., King

Fig. 334.—"Serventois" of the Trouveur, Quenes of Bethune, upon the Crusade.—Published by Fétis, after Manuscript in the National Library, Paris.

of England, who had asked her to put into rhyme the legends which formed part of the traditions of Brittany. In addition to these sombre and tragic lays, which were well suited to her brilliant imagination, she composed for Count William de Dampierre a collection of fables, imitated after Æsop, called "Ysopet," in which we find something of the naïveté and grace of La Fontaine. These ingenious imitations of Æsop, which were in much favour during the Middle Ages, were preceded by a great romantic and allegorical composition entitled the "Roman de Renard" (the "Romance of the Fox"), the principal incidents in which were also borrowed from the work ascribed to Æsop.

This "Roman de Renard," which comprised thirty-two branches springing from the same trunk, but without forming a connected and homogeneous whole, was undoubtedly composed by different authors, and at different epochs, according to the requirements of the jugglers who recited or sang it in the towns and villages, and who thus acquired for it a very widespreading popularity. The middle and lower classes, more especially, took a lively interest in the amusing and satirical adventures of the *vulpeculus,* personified under the name of Master Renard, and vying in cunning and mischief with

Fig. 335.—Song of Thibaud, Count of Champagne, with the Music.—Published by Fétis, after Manuscript (No. 7,222) in National Library, Paris.

his uncle the Wolf, personified under the name of *Ysengrin.* The only one of the authors whose name has come down to us is Pierre de St. Cloud. Satirical poetry was then in vogue, and the writers, who were no longer the discredited and despised jugglers of a former time, were very severe upon all sorts and conditions of men.

One of these general satires, which had a great success under the title of the "Guyot Bible," was composed by an eeclesiastic, Guyot de Provins, whose work displays much trenchant wit, but of a very truculent kind. He may be called the Juvenal of the Middle Ages. A worthy citizen of Lille, one Jacquemart Gelée, published a work of a similar kind under the title of "Renart Renouvelé." This poet of the end of the thirteenth century rises almost to eloquence in certain passages where he inveighs against the vices which he attributes to the upper classes. Another poet of Champagne, who preferred to remain anonymous, reproduced the original "Roman de Renard" in a very diffuse and prolix poem, entitled "Renart le Contrefait," which,

Fig. 336.—Poetical and Musical Congress at Wartburg, in 1207. The Minnesingers, Walther Vogelweide, Wolfram of Eschenbach, Reinmar of Zweter, Henry called the Virtuous Writer, Henry of Ofterdingen, and Klingsor of Hungary.—Miniature from the Treatise on the Minnesingers.—Manuscript of the Fourteenth Century, in National Library, Paris.

like its original, is a satire upon humanity, represented in the shape of certain animals. The "Roman de Fauvel" is also an allegorical satire upon the luxury and ambition of the great.

The lettered public had taken such a fancy to these satirical poems that the "Roman de la Rose" ("Romance of the Rose"), which Guillaume de Lorris had left unfinished, was resumed and completed by Jean de Meung in a very different shape, and with a meaning diametrically opposite to that which had inspired the author of the first part, who had merely endeavoured to imitate Ovid's "Ars Amandi." The poem of Guillaume de Lorris had caused quite a new sensation at the French court, the ladies more especially being enthusiastic in its favour, and they regretted that the author did not live to finish it. It was not till sixty years afterwards that Jean de Meung, surnamed Clopinel, resumed the work, and though a man of erudition and a philosopher, he did not possess the delicacy and refinement which were the distinguishing features of Guillaume de Lorris's talent. Thus the poem, as continued, was an entirely new piece, except that the personages had the same names as in the first part. It was, in fact, not so much an elegant and picturesque poem as a rhymed encyclopædia, into which Jean de Meung crammed all he knew of philosophy, cosmography, physics, alchemy, and natural history. Jean de Meung was not innately bad, but he was a sceptic and a free-thinker, and very fond of railing at the powers that be. Yet his poem, though ridiculous in form and containing much that was heretical, was greatly admired, and looked upon as the masterpiece of French poetry in the fourteenth century. Jean de Meung, like most of the poets who wrote in the Tongue of Oil, was the reverse of complimentary to the fair sex, in whose favour Guillaume de Lorris had said so much. But he did not express the general ideas of the time, and the "Romance of the Rose" is but the fanciful creation of a man of letters—not the faithful portrayal of the manners of a whole epoch.

Long before this running to seed of French poetry, the national language of France had spread throughout Europe. It was spoken and written in England, Italy, and Germany, and as early as the twelfth century many of the *chansons de geste* and romances of chivalry were translated or imitated in the latter country. In fact, it was beneath the double inspiration of the poetical works of the South and of the North of France that began the golden age of the literature of romance and of chivalry in Germany (Fig. 336). In the latter part of the twelfth century the number of Minnesingers was more than three hundred, most of whom composed their love-songs in the soft and graceful dialect of Swabia. Henry of Waldeck is the oldest of these poets, who imitated the troubadours; while the most prolific and the most sentimental was Wolfram of Eschenbach. To the same epoch belong the great German epodes, in which are embodied the recollections of the heroic age and the historical traditions of Germany. The "Helden-Buch" ("Book of

Heroes ") and the " Nibelungen-Lied " (" Song of the Nibelungen "), which are still popular in Germany, were composed at the beginning of the thirteenth century : the first, it is said, by Wolfram of Eschenbach (Fig. 337), Henry of Ofterdingen, and Walther Vogelweide ; the second by Conrad of Wartzburg,

Fig. 337.—Fragment of a Poem by Wolfram of Eschenbach, with the Notation of the Thirteenth Century.—Published by Fétis, after Manuscript in the Imperial Library, Vienna.

or by Nicholas Klingsor of Hungary ; but this statement is not based upon very trustworthy evidence. The end of this famous school of poetry coincides with the fall of the house of Swabia (1254).

Italy did not as yet possess a national literature or language, for in the thirteenth century there was scarcely such a thing as Italian prose-writing. Several poems had, however, been written in the Sicilian dialect, amongst the first composers being the Emperor Frederick II.; his chancellor, Pierre de la Vigne, to whom has been erroneously attributed the invention of the sonnet; and his sons Enzo, King of Sardinia, and Manfred, King of Naples. It was not till nearly a century later that the poets of the Italian peninsula introduced into their native language the various forms of Romanic versification, and the characteristics of Provençal poetry, in the shape of odes (*canzone*), of poetical dialogues (*tensons*), of ballads, of *sixtines*, of lays, and of tales. These poets imitated not only the rhyme and rhythm of the troubadours, but some of their literary qualities, though they were more successful in copying their defects. It is easy to see that they did not derive their inspiration from the living fountains of antiquity, though the names of Guido Ghisleri and Guido Guinicelli, of Bologna, and of the two Florentines, Guido Cavalcanti and Guitone of Arezzo, have come down to our own day.

Dante, the true creator of Italian poetry, was also a native of Florence, and he was born there of patrician parents in 1265. Nature had intended him for a poet, though at first he devoted himself to the study of various sciences. Love of the highest and most elevated kind inspired him with his first verses. He was not yet ten years of age when he met Beatrix Portinari, who was the same age as himself, and to whom he addressed many tender and pensive pieces, which he afterwards incorporated in his "Vita Nuova." When she died in her twenty-fifth year he dedicated to her memory his immortal "Divine Comedy," a poem at once religious and philosophical, and divided into three parts: Hell, Purgatory, and Paradise. This vast trilogy, the first part of which is in every way the best, is written in tiercets, or rhymed triplets; it embraces every branch of human knowledge, and presents in allegorical shape a striking picture of the history of the age, and especially of the poet's contemporaries. Above all stands the pure and radiant image of Beatrix. It is in this incomparable poem that Dante, by a judicious selection of Italian dialects, and by transforming them into a unique and regular type, succeeded in establishing upon fixed principles the literary language of his country, which, though simple, clear, and powerful, had hitherto been somewhat rough and inchoate. Dante remains, after the lapse of six centuries, the great poet of Italy.

None of the other nations of Europe produced any poet to equal him. In

Fig. 338.—The Mosque of Cordova, founded by Abderam I., King of the Moors, about 692.

England, where the Anglo-Saxon tongue had in the end become merged in the Franco-Norman dialect, an attempt was made to revive the national songs, and all that can be cited in the way of English poetry is a translation of the "Brut," by Wace, an imitation in verse of the Chronicle of Geoffroy of Monmouth by Robert of Gloucester. Spain, where the Romanic language had become naturalised since the eleventh century, at least in the provinces not invaded by the Moors, did not even know the name of the author who wrote that poem of the "Cid" which she pointed to with pride as the first poetical record of her legendary history (Fig. 338). Spanish poets, amongst whom appear Alfonso II., King of Arragon, and Alfonso XI., King of Castile, had already celebrated in a language which, though somewhat rough and coarse, was energetic and noble, the loftiest sentiments of the human heart, especially warlike courage and love of country. The union of these popular ballads and romances formed in part the celebrated collection of "Romancero."

The Minnesingers did not survive the extinction of the house of Swabia, which had always accorded them the highest favours. When the house of Hapsburg succeeded the Hohenstauffens the German nobility ceased to take any interest in arts and poetry, and Germany failed for a time to produce any poets. But towards the end of the reign of Rudolph I. (1291) the middle classes created a demand for singers, and the Meistersingers (masters of song), whose compositions answered the requirements of a public little versed in literature, extended their jurisdiction to poetry which, from sprightly and high-spirited as it was in the time of the Minnesingers, became staid and measured, not to say tame and tedious. The poets of this epoch are not worth mentioning by name, and it was not until the sixteenth century that the Meistersingers emerged from their obscurity.

Dante gave the signal for the literary renaissance in Italy, to which Francis Petrarch, his contemporary, devoted his whole life. The latter was born at Arezzo in 1304, and died at Arquà, near Padua, in 1374. Thanks to the example which he set, classical study began to flourish anew, and Virgil and Horace were read as eagerly as they had been during the reign of Augustus. Petrarch, who had been immersed in study of the ancient poets, attempted at first to imitate them in Latin, but after he had met Laura de Noves at Avignon his thoughts were solely concentrated upon pleasing her, and he wrote his "Rhymes" and his "Canzoni" in honour of her who had inspired him with a passion as delicate and pure as that of Dante for Beatrix.

Petrarch, in the "Canzoni," has given us the most perfect type of the Italian ode, and while he rises at times to the height of Pindar and Horace, his poetical outbursts are tempered by an accent of sorrow and melancholy peculiar to himself. He did not lack imitators, but none of them came up to the original; and his friend Boccaccio, who had perfected Italian prose, wrote

Fig. 339.—The Horse Pegasus. "Behold a Flying Horse, called Pegasus, and several Nobles, some armed and some without arms, of all conditions, kings, princes, and others, which lift up their hands to try and touch the said Horse, but are not able to do so."—Miniature from the "Enseignement de vraye Noblesse."—Manuscript of the Fifteenth Century (No. 11,049).—In the Burgundy Library, Brussels.

but a small number of sonnets, and his first Italian epode, the "Theseide," is far inferior to his "Decamerone."

Almost at the same period, a Scotch poet, Archdeacon of Aberdeen, composed an epic poem in the Scotch dialect upon the achievements of Robert Bruce, the liberator of Scotland. Previously to this the first of the epic poems which appeared in Great Britain, there had been written a few poems concerning the wars of King Edward III. against Philip of Valois and John II. of France. But the writers are not to be compared with John Gower and Geoffroy Chaucer, who had taken as their models the ancient French trouveurs, and who imitated them without citing their authority. Gower, in particular, contributed to purify the language of poetry, and Chaucer, in spite of his imitations, which amount to plagiarism, showed that he was the superior in point of style, if not in invention, to Marie de France, Rutebeuf, William de Lorris, and Jean de Meung.

The literary reputation of Jean de Meung lasted for more than two centuries after his death (1320), though French poetry had taken another shape to suit the taste of the ladies, who, by becoming queens of the tournaments and of other fêtes of chivalry, brought about a sort of poetic revival, not only in France, but in all countries where French was the language of the aristocracy. The satires directed more especially against the fair sex had seen their best day, and though Eustache Deschamps sought to revive them by paraphrasing, in his "Miroir du Mariage," Juvenal's satire upon women, poetry once more acquired the gallant and amorous characteristics which it had inherited from the troubadours. The chronicler, Jean Froissart, who was at one time clerk to Queen Philippa of Hainault, wife of King Edward III. of England, relates that he "narrated to her interesting stories or treatises on love." The poems of Froissart, written in the Rouchi-French dialect of Valenciennes, often have a smack of the troubadour school and of William de Lorris's "Romance of the Rose." These poems, which run smoothly enough, but which are wordy and colourless, are specially interesting from an autobiographical point of view, as the author is continually alluding to himself even in his pastorals and his nuptial songs.

The professional poets who succeeded the trouveurs attempted to revive the literature of *chansons de geste* and romances of chivalry, which they revised and adapted to modern usage; but, as they made no effort to abridge them, these poems only became, under their treatment, heavier and more prosy. They did better with the Chronicle in verse, which they continued to call by the name of romance even when they were treating of contemporary subjects, as, for instance, Cuvelier in the "Chronique de Bertrand du Guesclin." Moreover, the poetical romances of the fourteenth century are remarkable for their immense length and unbroken dulness. The court poetry was more lively and graceful, consisting as it did of songs and ballads, of virelays and roundelays. Eustache Deschamps, who wrote an "Art de Dictier," in which he set forth the rules of these various kinds of fashionable poetry, informs us—but his statement is a poetical license—that formerly no

Fig. 340.—Legend of the "Trois Morts et des Trois Vifs," Poetry of the Fourteenth Century.— From a Miniature of an "Antiphonale."—Manuscript of the Sixteenth Century, No. 5,644.— In the Burgundy Library, Brussels.

one ventured to write poetry of this kind "unless he was noble" (Fig. 339). This same Eustache Deschamps, a warrior, a traveller, and a magistrate, whose writings extend over more than eighty years, has left behind him nearly a hundred thousand lines of poetry, most of which was ballad. He

applied the ballad to all kinds of subjects, and with him it sometimes rises to
the height of the ode. Deschamps was an austere and serious poet, who
showed no mercy to vice and to abuses, and the patriotic spirit of his poetry
comes out in his maledictions against the English, while he shows himself a
man of feeling by his regretful allusions to the sufferings of the people. It
was in this mournful period that was written the popular poem of the
" Danse Macabre " (" Dance of Death "), represented in Fig. 340. Christina de
Pisan, daughter of the astrologer of Charles V., also composed a number of
ballads and roundelays, marked with the impress of melancholy, which are of

Fig. 341.—Alain Chartier comforted by Hope.—Cameo Miniature from the " Triumph of Hope,"
Allegory on the Political Events in the Reign of Charles VII.—Unpublished Manuscript of the
Sixteenth Century.—In the Library of M. Ambroise Firmin-Didot, Paris.

more merit than her long historical and moral poems. Most of them testify
to her love for France, and her sentiments are noble and elevated, though the
style is feeble and confused.

There was a steady increase in the number of French poets, and the poetry
itself, especially the court poetry, continued to improve. Alain Chartier,
whose immense reputation was made at the French court, did much to bring
about this progress. His " Breviary of the Nobles " was a sort of gospel for
the nobility, and Jean le Masle affirms that during the reign of François I.

the pages and young gentlemen of the court were compelled to learn verses from it by heart, and recite them regularly every day, as the clergy do their breviary. In addition to the "Book of the Four Ladies," which contains

Fig. 342.—The Author of the Poem entitled "Le Débat de la Noire et de la Tannée."—Miniature from Manuscript of the Fifteenth Century.—In the Library of M. Ambroise Firmin-Didot, Paris.

some exquisite pages written in a style full of vigour and poesy, Alain Chartier composed a great number of ballads, love-sayings, elegies, and laments (Fig. 341). He was the favourite of kings, queens, princes, and nobles, in spite of his deformity and ugliness. It is told how the Dauphiness Margaret of Scotland, coming upon him one day while asleep, kissed him upon the mouth, from which, says Etienne Pasquier, "issued so many golden words and virtuous discourses." He died in 1458, at the age of seventy-five. One of his pupils, Duke Charles of Orleans, who, taken prisoner at Agincourt, remained a captive in England for the rest of his youth, consoled himself by writing French and English verses, most of them gallant, spiritual, and pensive, into many of which he introduced the metaphysical personages of the "Romance of the Rose." He had around him in London, as well as at his Château de Blois in France, a sort of court of love and poetry, the members of which vied with each other in composing ballads and roundelays. Charles of Orleans often imitated the troubadours and the Italian poets— Petrarch amongst others. His imagination was lively and gay, he indulged in many humorous sallies, and his soul overflowed with true and generous feeling.

The court poetry led, by the natural effect of contradiction and strife, to the birth of a poetry which was of truly popular origin. One of the first essays in this new kind of poetry, which emanated from the genuine emotions of the mind, was, however, made by a man of noble birth, Jean Regnier, Seigneur de Guerchy, who, notwithstanding his birth and his fortune, did not think it beneath him to declare his sentiments with pathetic sincerity. He was at the time in prison at Beauvais, and he was about to be tried for high treason. His painful position made him a poet, and, as a preparation for death, he evoked the muse. After he had bemoaned his "Fortunes et Adversitez" he became resigned to his fate, and he drew up a will in rhyme, half earnest, half jocular, which was doubtless the type taken for his two "Testaments" by Villon, who, though he does not imitate Regnier word for word, undoubtedly had his work before him when he began to write his "Petit Testament" in the Châtelet prison, where he was under confinement for his misdeeds. Villon, a student of the University of Paris, was said to have committed a murder and several robberies, and after being fortunate enough to escape the gibbet, he again was guilty of some misdeed, for which he was imprisoned at Meung. It was there that he composed his best work, the "Grand Testament," owing to which, and to the intervention of Duke Charles of Orleans, he obtained a commutation of his sentence. This work is a singular compound of wild gaiety, of keen satire, of profound sensibility, of calm judgment, and of pensive melancholy. Villon is beyond all doubt a great poet, at once natural and independent; he is distinguished for his lively imagination, his wit, and his good feeling; and though the form of his poetry has become obsolete, the

Fig. 343.—The Castle of Loves.—Miniature taken from the "Champion des Dames."—Manuscript of the Fifteenth Century (No. 12,476).—In the National Library, Paris.

matter itself has lost none of its freshness. It would seem as if scapegraces were poets by nature, for two of Villon's companions, Henri Baude and Jourdain, surnamed the Unfortunate, were his rivals in poetry as in misconduct. The former was the author of the "Débat de la Dame et de l'Écuyer," and of numerous other clever pieces, while the latter composed the "Jardin de Plaisance," which contained several verses written by his friends in addition to those of his own composing.

The example set by Villon, whose popularity was greatest amongst the students of the University of Paris, led to the publication of a host of other satiric poems, mostly by anonymous authors, which were propagated amongst the middle and lower classes by the newly discovered printing-press. This is a striking proof as to the popularity of these fugitive pieces, which M. Anatole de Montaignon and Baron James de Rothschild are endeavouring to incorporate into one vast anthology. Amongst these are the "Complaintes," "Dits," "Débats" (Fig. 342), "Monologues," "Testaments," "Sermons Joyeux," &c., in which the sharpness of French wit shines with great brilliancy. It is certain that many of these trenchant and comic poems were retailed from the stage by strolling players, and respectable people certainly looked upon them as scandalous, and took care not to read them. It was accordingly sought to counteract the bad use to which poetry was put, and in several French towns, at Toulouse, Amiens, and Caen amongst others, there were instituted "Floral Games," "Chambers of Rhetoric," "Puys," and "Palinods," and poets were appealed to to devote their inspiration to the composition of edifying and moral works. These poets set themselves more especially to glorify the blessed Virgin and her Immaculate Conception, composing royal songs, ballads, and cantos, which were awarded, after competition, different prizes. This was the origin of the academies and literary societies in France.

The French poetical school united a great variety of talents in the fifteenth century. Martin Franc, in his "Champion des Dames" (Fig. 343), made an attempt to revive the allegorical style of Guillaume de Lorris and Jean de Meung, but at the same period Olivier Basselin, master fuller of Vire, created the "Vau de Vire," an epicurean, convivial, and libertine song, while drinking his Norman cider. These songs have unfortunately only reached us in a modernised and disfigured shape. Guillaume Coquillart, though a clerk and ecclesiastical doctor at Rheims, gave full play to his caustic wit and free Gallic humour in his farcical "Monologues;" Martial of Auvergne set to rhyme the "Vigils of King Charles VII.," but his verse is rather dull and monotonous; Jean Meschinot, of Nantes, set to poetry the "Lettres des Princes" for the Duke of Brittany, to whose household he was attached as "ducal poet;" and André de la Vigne and Guillaume Cretin did the same for the royal house of France. But the deplorable influence of the poets of the court of Burgundy began to tell with fatal effect upon French poetry.

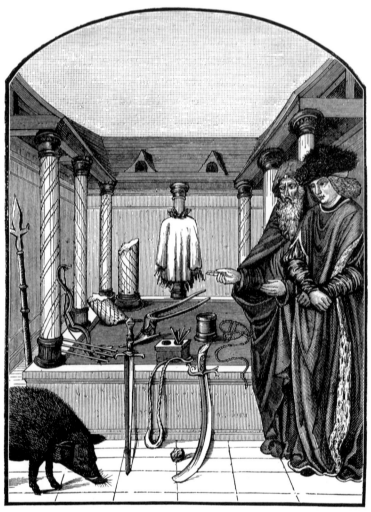

Fig 344.—The Vanity of Human Things.—Miniature from the Allegorical Poem, "Le Chevalier délibéré," upon the Death of Charles the Bold, by Olivier de la Marche.—Manuscript of the Fifteenth Century, No. 173.—In the Arsenal Library, Paris.

Pierre Michault, Olivier de la Marche (Fig. 344), Georges Chastelain, and Jean Molinet conceived the idea of creating difficulties of rhythm, metre, and rhyme, which gave their poetry a mongrel and barbarous physiognomy.

Guillaume Cretin and Jean d'Auton, both of whom were chroniclers of King
Louis XII., went even further in this direction, and Jean Lemaire (born at
Belges, in Hainault), to whom French prosody probably owes some beneficial
reforms, had great difficulty in avoiding these bad examples.

Poetry was not so flourishing in other parts of Europe. In Spain, where
the works of the Provençal troubadours were still imitated, this was the era of
gallant poetry, one of the favourite forms for a poem being the *redondilla*, in
which the writer exhausted every resource of the language to describe his
sentiments. These poems were in especial favour at the court of John II.,
King of Castile, and amongst the most gifted composers of them were the

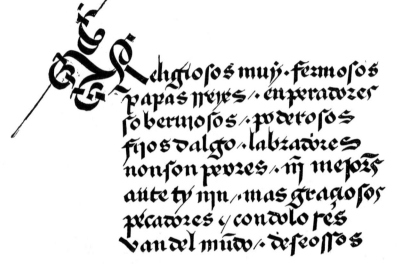

Fig. 345.—Extract from the "Cancionero" of Juan Alfonso de Baena.—Original Manuscript
(Fifteenth Century).—In the National Library, Paris.

Marquis de Villena and Juan de Mena (Fig. 345). Part of these sentimental
and lackadaisical poems, to which no less than a hundred and forty authors
contributed, were collected in 1516 into a book entitled "Cancionero General."
Portugal, like Spain, sought her models from among the troubadours, whom
it was striven to imitate, and even to translate. But these timid efforts ended
in the invention of the pastoral romance, which represented the love-passages
of the shepherds and shepherdesses. This artificial style, which, though
sometimes pleasing, was more often flat and tiresome, was destined to take its
place in the literature of all lands, and—so great is the force of habit—to retain

it for a long time. England, however, was an exception to the rule; and since the death of Chaucer, her poets, or rather her versifiers, had confined themselves to imitating the "Romance of the Rose," and to paraphrasing the histories of mythology.

In Italy, after the death of Petrarch, poetry declined in spite of all the efforts made by Coluccio, Burchiello, and Arispa to revive it. A few poems on chivalry, such as "Buovo d'Antona," "La Spagna," &c., might be passed over without notice, had they not led up to the brilliant writings of Boiardo

Fig. 346.—Portrait of Sannazar.—Fac-simile, on a reduced Scale, of an anonymous Engraving of the Sixteenth Century, published at Rome by Ant. Salamanca.—In the Library of M. Ambroise Firmin-Didot, Paris.

and Ariosto. Laurenzio de' Medici, however, the gonfalonnier of the Florentine Republic, awoke the spirit of Italian poetry in 1469 by his "Canti Carnavaleschi" ("Carnival Songs"), and he was seconded in his efforts by Politien and Pulci, though the former was one of the most fanatical partisans of the ancient classics. Latin poetry had, it may be remarked, many staunch votaries throughout the Middle Ages, and their works, consisting of centos of Virgil, Horace, and Lucan, were in continuous and numerous circulation throughout Europe. The renaissance of ancient literature in Italy during the fifteenth century told much in favour of their efforts to apply the Latin language to modern subjects. Thus Sannazar (Fig. 346), surnamed the Christian Virgil, excited more enthusiasm with his poems, "De Partu Virginis" and "Lamentatio de Morte Christi," than with his beautiful poems written in Italian. In fact, there was throughout the whole of learned Europe, from the fifteenth to the sixteenth century, a Latin poetry consisting of a mass of works of the most varied kind, which were welcomed and praised, especially by the most highly educated.

Next we have the old romances of chivalry, appearing in the shape of poems in *ottava rima;* the romance of "King Arthur of Brittany and the Knights of the Round Table," "Charlemagne and his Twelve Peers." Here we have the Italian epode, a mixture of grave and gay. Pulci writes his "Morgante Maggiore," the hero of which is a great jester; Bello, called the Blind Man of Ferrara, writes his "Mambriano," who pursues Renaud de Montauban amidst a series of the most fanciful and burlesque adventures. Boiardo also seeks for inspiration in the Chronicle of Turpin, and depicts the court of Charlemagne in his "Orlando Innamorato," which would be a masterpiece of the poet's style, were it not so curt and so affected. Ludovico Ariosto, called the Ariosto (Fig. 347), born at Reggio in 1474, would not undertake to rewrite the epic poem of Boiardo, but he continued it with the "Orlando Furioso," one of the most remarkable productions of picturesque poetry, and far before the "Orlando Innamorato." Ariosto's poem combines every charm—variety of imagination, descriptive power, grace and elegance of style, and powerful dramatic incident. Like Homer, Ariosto was surnamed the Divine, and his poem remains the type of the Romanic epode, as the Iliad was the masterpiece of the heroic epode.

Ariosto, in his "Capitoli Amorosi" and his many light pieces of poetry, preserved his superiority over his numerous imitators, none of whom ventured to compete with him in epic poetry. Berni rewrote the "Orlando Innamorato," and he had perfected the burlesque mode of composition, and given his name to what was called *Bernesque* poetry. Yet Petrarch had more than a hundred imitators, none of whom could come up or near to their model. Didactic poetry spent itself in pale imitations of Virgil and of Juvenal, and the poem of the "Bees" is a literal translation of the fourth book of the Georgics, of which Alamanni presented a mere counterfeit in the "Coltivazione." Trissino endeavoured to compose an epic poem upon the deliverance of Italy from the Goths, and he used blank verse, which was not very well received by the fervent admirers of the *ottava rima.* Italian poetry had not, therefore, any influence upon Spanish poetry, which was devoted almost entirely to works touching upon love and gallantry. Boscan Almogaver and Garcilaso de la Vega were very successful in shaping their inspirations into the compass of the sonnet; and while the latter was bringing the pastoral into fashion, Diego Hurtado de Mendoza wrote epistles in imita-

Fig. 347.—Portrait of Ariosto.—Reduced Fac-simile of an anonymous Engraving of the Sixteenth Century, published at Rome by Ant. Salamanca.—In the Library of M. Ambroise Firmin-Didot, Paris.

tion of Horace. The pastoral was always the favourite style of poetry with the Portuguese, and Ribeiro surpassed all his predecessors in this style.

The breath of the Italian renaissance was not felt in France till after the reigns of Charles VIII. and Louis XII. The poetry which was then in greatest favour at the court was still tainted with Flemish influence, and people admired the jingle of such rhymes as *fraternisées, brisées, équivoquées, couronnées, batelées,* which Guillaume Cretin made use of with all the cunning of a juggler. The reminiscences of the "Romance of the Rose" were revived by Gringore's "Château de Labour," by Clement Marot's "Temple de Cupidon," by the "Loups Ravissants," and by the "Espinette du Jeune Prince conquérant le Royaume de Bonne Renommée." Jean Marot and Octavian de St. Gelais put into verse the diary of the expeditions of Charles VIII. and Louis XII. The popular muse inspired only two poets— Roger de Collerie and Pierre Gringore, who in every branch of poetry preserved the stamp of his proverbial and witty style. The epoch of François I. seemed to renew the language, if not the form, of poetry, by imposing upon the writer who aimed at being read a frank, simple, and sprightly style. Clement Marot was the real restorer of this eminently French style. He had not the genius to write great works, and he was too buoyant and too Gallic to think of composing long poems which no one would have read. He composed merely roundelays, epistles, elegies, chants royal, ballads, epigrams, and madrigals, which latter were as yet called epigrams also, as in the Greek anthology. It was in epigram that Clement Marot was so much the superior of all other poets, and for fifteen years his delicate, graceful, and witty style found him numberless admirers and imitators ; but when he placed his services at the disposal of the Reformed Church, and, at the request of Calvin, translated into hymns the Psalms of David, he lost all his merits as a poet. His school, which numbered a few charming versifiers—Bonaventure des Périers, Victor Brodeau, and Charles Fontaine amongst others—remained in favour with the court, thanks to François I., the friend and pupil of Marot. It was that monarch who conceived the idea of translating into French verse all the Greek and Latin poets : Homer, by Hugues Salel ; Ovid, by Clement Marot ; Virgil, by Michael of Tours and Octavian de St. Gelais ; and Horace, by François Habert. The poetry of Mellin de St. Gelais, who was looked upon as the only rival of Marot, already showed signs of being imitated from the Italian, and though the ideas were ingenious and correct, the style was a mixture of pretentious affectation and of Italian concetti.

The Reformation, it must be said, was everywhere fatal to language and literature, and it dealt a specially severe blow at German poetry. Hans Sach, the Nuremberg shoemaker, is perhaps the only poet who, trying his hand at all branches of poetry, ventured to brave the Lutheran intolerance. In England, whither Protestantism had not yet reached, several poets of society were in great favour: William Dunbar, with his allegorical poem of the "Golden Buckler," and David Lindsay and Wyatt, with their satires; while Lord Surrey had introduced blank verse into English poetry, and translated the Æneid. In Italy, too, which the Reformation never reached, the school of Petrarch seemed to spring into renewed life. Bembo was the instigator of this resurrection of amorous poetry; for though his own imitations of Petrarch were but feeble, the Petrarchists—or Bembists, as they ought rather to be called—responded to his appeal to the number of five or six hundred. Other poets, though not despising the sonnets of Petrarch, endeavoured to embody different subjects in new forms. Angelo de Costanzo and Camillo Peregrini returned to lyric poetry, Bernardino Balbi to didactic poetry, and Bentivoglio and Pietro Aretino to satirical poetry. Torquato Tasso, the son of Bernardino Tasso, who obtained great celebrity for his poem of chivalry upon the "Amadis," undertook to write the great epic poem of modern times, "Jerusalem Delivered." This is a true epic poem, based, not like that of Virgil, upon the fabled traditions of the siege of Troy, but upon the positive, though almost miraculous, facts appertaining to the history of the Middle Ages. Tasso is not inferior to Homer: his poem is equal to the Iliad. But his style—noble, poetical, and admirable as it is—is often spoilt by traits of bad taste and by insipid play upon words. Yet we may say that the glory of Tasso lighted up the sixteenth century.

After this every nation was desirous of having its epic poem. Spain, which possessed several good *cancione* writers, such as Herrera, Castillejo, and Lope de Vega, found Alonzo de Ercilla to write an epic poem called "Araucana" upon the conquest of Chili by his fellow-countrymen; but endless digressions and useless episodes marred the brilliant style and descriptions contained in this work. Portugal was more fortunate; for Camoens, who chose for the subject of his national epode the voyage of Vasco de Gama, which he connected with the general history of his country, wrote his poem of "Lusiades" upon the very spots still redolent of his hero. The defects of Camoens in the arrangement of his story and in his choice of the marvellous are only too patent, but the grandeur of his ideas attracts and delights the reader, while his abundant and harmonious style lends itself well to the dramatic character of the scenes and the highly coloured descriptions of a work which in some passages reaches the sublime. Camoens died in obscurity and extreme poverty.

Germany seemed to have become impenetrable to the rays of poetry, but the Northern peoples began to feel their influence. The Danes possessed in Peter Laland a national poet in the first years of the sixteenth century, while, previously to this, the Swedes had had Eric Olaï, who set their chronicles to rhyme. Poland, whose national poetry does not date further back than the fifteenth century, possessed a certain number of poets whose very names were scarcely known to the rest of Europe; amongst others, Nicholas Rey de Naglovice and Jean Kochanowski, called the Prince of Poets, who formed a friendship with Ronsard while staying in Paris. In Holland Dirk Koornhert created national poetry, and, following upon a few translators of the Psalms, Roemer Wisscher and Spiegel laid down the principles of versification. It was in England that the poetical movement was the most brilliant and the most active. Spenser invented a new kind of pastoral, in which the shepherds spoke in the language of shepherds instead of in that of courtiers. His allegorical poem, the "Faery Queen," had an even greater success than the "Shepherd's Calendar." His contemporaries, Sidney, Raleigh, Marlowe, and Green Watson, composed light poetry full of simplicity and grace. Robert Southwell, Samuel Daniel, and John Davies drew their inspirations from religion and philosophy; while, at the close of the century, there appeared two poems, "Venus and Adonis" and the "Rape of Lucretia," the author of which was the immortal Shakspere.

The second half of the sixteenth century witnessed a complete metamorphosis of poetry in France. A few poets had remained true to the school of Clement Marot, who died in poverty abroad. Marguerite de Valois, Queen of Navarre, would have been one of the most charming types of this school, if her attachment to the doctrines of the Reformation had not clouded her ideas and depressed her style (Fig. 348). Two other female poets retarded the decadence of *Marotism*, viz. two women of Lyons—Pernette du Guillet and Louise Labé, the latter of whom was the mysterious muse of Olivier de Magny. Étienne Forcadel composed some neat epigrams and clever epistles; Peletier of Le Mans, who had an unfortunate mania for constructing a new way of spelling, wrote his Poetical Works in plain and excellent French; while Maurice Scève, in his poem "Délie," followed the teaching given him by his friend Clement Marot. There is no need to say anything about such feeble poets as Artus Désiré, Guillaume des Autels, and Barthélemy Aneau, whose compositions are involved and obscure. By this time the Italian influence was everywhere apparent, and it was Joachim du Bellay who gave the signal for the literary revolution, by advising his youthful rivals to imitate the Greeks and the Romans, while declaring himself a devoted partisan of the French language, which was being sacrificed to the Italian. The poets who responded to his appeal overshot the mark without hitting it, and were only inaccurate translators of the ancient classics, instead of imitating it with intelligence and fidelity.

It was in a small Paris college that Joachim du Bellay formed, under the

Fig. 348.—Portrait of Marguerite de Valois, Queen of Navarre, after a Pencil-Drawing of the Time.—In the Museum of the Louvre, Paris.

eyes of his professor of humanities, Jean Daurat, the poetical association, consisting of seven members, which was called the *Pleiad*. These seven poets were Baïf, Du Bellay, Remy Belleau, J. Daurat, Jodelle, Ponthus de Thyard, and Ronsard (Figs. 349 to 355), who was proclaimed unanimously their supreme chief. For half a century Pierre Ronsard remained the master of French poetry. While still a youth he had formed the project of writing a national epic poem, to be called the "Franciade," upon the model of Virgil's Æneid, but he only published four cantos of this epode, which was to have had twenty-four. His Francus, son of Hector, was not, in truth, worthy to figure by the side of Æneas, son of Priam. Ronsard was called the Pindar of France, though he was utterly lacking in lyrical inspiration. His odes, with their accumulation of strophes and antistrophes, were

 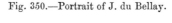

Fig. 349.—Portrait of   Fig. 350.—Portrait of J. du Bellay.   Fig. 351.—Portrait of Remy
Baïf.   Belleau.

Fac-simile of Engravings by Léonard Gaultier, from the Series known as " Chronologie collée."
In the Library of M. Ambroise Firmin-Didot, Paris.

but feeble counterfeits of the odes of Pindar ; his language, overladen with Greek and Latin words, is far too hyperbolic, and is obscured by the array of mythological lore. Yet he possessed in the highest degree nobility of style

Fig. 352.—Portrait of   Fig. 353.—Portrait of Jodelle.   Fig. 354. Portrait of
J. Daurat.   P. Ronsard.

Fac-simile of Engravings by Léonard Gaultier, from the Series known as " Chronologie collée."
In the Library of M. Ambroise Firmin-Didot, Paris.

and harmony of rhythm, and he imitated with success both Horace and Theocritus ; but he distinguished himself the most in his imitations of Anacreon, whose writings had just been exhumed by Henri Estienne.

Ronsard was, beyond all doubt, a poet; but his writings are tedious, though here and there lighted up by some trait of vigour and brilliancy. His reputation was a European one, and Mary Stuart, who beguiled the hours of her captivity by reading his works, sent him a Parnassus in solid silver, with the inscription, "À Ronsard, l'Apollo de la source des Muses."

The most distinguished poet of the Pleiad was unquestionably Joachim du Bellay, who founded it. "His language," remarks the critic Gérusez, "is a perfected imitation of that of Marot, with more attention as to the copying of Latin or Italian." Du Bellay had good taste, which was a point

Fig. 355.—Portrait of Ponthus de Thyard.—Reduced Fac-simile of the Engraving of Thomas de Leu.—In the Library of M. Ambroise Firmin-Didot, Paris.

in which Ronsard and the rest of the Pleiad were lacking; and he also possessed sensibility and elevation of feeling, and deserved the surname of the French Ovid. The remainder were very inferior to him: Baïf was heavy, pretentious, and pedantic; Remy Belleau, surnamed the *gentil Belleau*, had nothing pedantic about him, and did not attempt to write anything but pretty verses; Jodelle, who was one of the founders of the Theatre in France, wrote a mixture of French and Greek; Ponthus de Thyard, who wrote more prose than verse, got a bishopric out of the former; while Daurat composed only a few French verses, all the rest of his works being in Greek and Latin.

But around the Pleiad there were several poets superior to those who composed it: Bérenger de la Tour, the best bucolic poet of the age, author of the "Siècle d'Or" and the "Amie Rustique;" Olivier de Magny, a great lyric poet, as may be gathered from his "Amours," "Odes," "Soupirs," and "Gaietés;" Amadis Jamyn, Ronsard's favourite pupil, and the writer of several charming pieces which have more life in them than those of his master; and Guillaume du Bartas, the creator of descriptive poetry, who, in his poem upon the creation of the world, entitled "La Semaine," reached almost at once the sublime and the ridiculous.

It is most wonderful that France, amidst her civil and religious wars, and the terrible disorder which prevailed during the reigns of Charles IX. and Henri III., should have produced such a number of poets that it is impossible to name them all. Everybody wrote and admired poetry at the court of the Valois—kings, princes, nobles, and ladies alike. Every kind of poetry—ambitious and familiar, amorous and melancholy—was represented by one or more works of merit, and we can only afford space to mention the bare names of a few writers: Marc-Claude de Buttet, a native of Savoy; Flaminio de Birague, an Italian who had been naturalised French; Scévole de St. Marthe, a Loudunois gentleman; Madame des Roches, of Poitiers; Guillaume Belliard, of Blois; Jean Passerat; Etienne Pasquier, &c. A special mention must, however, be made of Philippe Desportes, who excelled in gallant poetry; of Jean Bertaut, distinguished in the same way; of Jean and Jacques de la Taille, better known as dramatic poets; and lastly, of Agrippa d'Aubigné, who may be termed the Petronius and Juvenal of the sixteenth century.

But Malherbe, who had just been born, was destined, in the course of his attacks upon the Ronsard school, to form the new French poetics, of which his odes represent the most perfect model and style.

CHRONICLES, HISTORIES, MEMOIRS.

ONG before the invasions of the Barbarians the countless books of history written by Greek and Latin authors concerning the annals of the ancient peoples had been falling into disfavour. Even the best of them were little read, for the Christians felt but slight interest in these pagan narratives, and this is why works relating to the history of antiquity were already so scarce.

The Church, however, inspired some new historians, who set to write its early annals. Eusebius, Bishop of Cæsarea, during the reign of Constantine, composed in Greek an Ecclesiastical History in ten books, from the birth of Christ to the death of Licinius (324); and Paulus Orosius, a disciple of St. Augustine, composed in Latin, during the early part of the fifth century, seven books of History against the Pagans ("Historiarum adversus Paganos Libri VII."), into which he introduced many interesting popular traditions, narrating the history of the world from the time of Adam to the year 316 A.D. A few Latin writers still strove, as late as the fourth century, to write history after the fashion of Livy, Tacitus, and Suetonius; and Aurelius Victor, surnamed Africanus, wrote at Rome, of which city he was prefect, a History of the Emperors, beginning from Augustus, and a summary treatise of the illustrious men of Rome ("De Viris Illustribus Urbis Romæ"), which has often been attributed to Pliny the younger and Cornelius Nepos. Flavius Eutropius, who was a soldier and a statesman, compiled an Abridgment of Roman History ("Breviarium Rerum Romanarum") in ten books, from the foundation of Rome to the reign of the Emperor Valens; and Ammianus Marcellinus, a native of Antioch, who took part in the wars waged by the Emperor Julian in Gaul and Germany, completed in after life an immense History of the Roman Emperors, from the reign of Nerva to that of Valentinianus, but the first thirteen books of which are lost. This History, though its style is uncouth, forms a brilliant termination to the series of Latin histories of the empire.

But in the fifth century, while the barbarian hordes were pouring in upon the Old World by way of Spain, Gaul, and Italy, where they founded fresh states, the empire of the East became the asylum for a new historic school, which grew remarkable for a number of great works emanating from Christian thought, and intended to celebrate the triumph of the Christian religion. Philostorgius wrote in Greek a general History of the Church, which is only known to us by the abridgment of it made by Photius; Socrates continued the Ecclesiastical History of Eusebius from the year 306 to 439; Sozomen, born in Palestine, compiled an excellent History of the Church, in nine books, from the year 324 to 439; and Theodoret, Bishop of Syria, also edited an Ecclesiastical History, in five books, of the same period. It would appear as if the genius of history was concentrated upon the annals of the Church, when arose quarrels and disputes as keen as those which were formerly provoked by politics alone. This new kind of history seems better adapted to Greek literature, though three or four of the Latin writers appear to have preserved the best traditions of their language. The priest Rufinus, who had been intimate with St. Jerome, and who had lived in retirement in Sicily, where he died (410), translated the History of Eusebius into passable Latin; Sulpicius Severus, his contemporary, a more elegant and correct writer, although born in Aquitaine, and who never left Gaul, where he had followed the apostleship of St. Martin, composed an Abridgment of Sacred History from the creation of the world to the year 410 A.D., and this excellent book earned the surname of the Christian Sallust.

The Greek language, the existence of which was henceforward inseparable from the empire of the East, was perpetuated, with most of its essential qualities, in a mass of historical works written in Greek, down to the capture of Constantinople by Mahomet II. ; but the Latin language, on the contrary, had been subjected to the inevitable mixture of the national idioms of all the barbaric peoples which had collected in different parts of the Roman empire. The Latin language, though more and more corrupted and changed, continued none the less to be the official language of the clergy and of the higher civil administration. Nothing but Latin was spoken at the court of Odoacer, King of the Heruli, and at the court of Theodoric, King of the Goths. Thus books of political rather than of religious history continued to be written in Latin. It was in this semi-barbarous tongue that the Western historians of the sixth and seventh centuries compiled their Chronicles, while the Greek historians were publishing excellent Histories after the style of Polybius and Dion Cassius: Agathias the Scholastic, the History of the Reign of Justinian ; Procopius of Cæsarea, secretary to Belisarius, the History of his Time ; Theophylactus Simocatta, the History of the Emperor Maurice, &c.

The Latin Chronicles, composed during this dreary epoch of the Middle Ages, are none the less valuable and interesting. The most ancient of them relates to France, or rather to the part of Gaul occupied by the Franks : that of Marius of Autun, Bishop of Avenche, in Helvetia. It begins with the reign of Avitus in 455, and terminates in 581 : written in a clear and simple style, it relates more especially to the reign of Gontran, King of Burgundy, and contains some accurate information as to the geography of Gaul. It had been written to serve as a sequel to the Abridgment of the Universal History compiled by Prosper of Aquitaine, and is in consequence dry and concise, like most Chronicles of the time. Cassiodorus, the minister of King Theodoric, gave freer scope to his rhetoric in a voluminous History of the Goths, of which we possess only an excellent abridgment (" De Gothorum Origine et Rebus Gestis ") by Jornandès, Bishop of Ravenna, who also composed a short Universal History. St. Isidore, Bishop of Seville, who died in 636, also wrote a Chronicle from the time of Adam, and a History of the Goths, the Vandals, the Suevi, and the Visigoths, amidst whom he had passed his life.

The most ancient and valuable record of French history is the great work of Gregory of Tours, who in his " Histoire Ecclésiastique des Francs " gave a faithful description of the events in which he took part. Born in Auvergne, of a patrician family which had produced several senators and prelates, he was brought up by his uncle, St. Gall, Bishop of Clermont, and was himself made Bishop of Tours in 573. The esteem in which he was held at the court of Chilpéric and Frédégonde enabled him to play a conspicuous part in the political affairs of the Merovingian monarchy; he had been mixed up in the most secret transactions of Chilpéric's reign, and was conversant with all the details of the deadly struggle between the rival Queens, Frédégonde and Brunehaut. This, no doubt, was the reason which induced him to write his

Fig. 356 —Equestrian Statue of Clovis, King of the Franks (465—511), by Erwin de Steinbach (Thirteenth Century), placed over the Western Portico of Strasburg Cathedral.

History. His book, commencing with the origin of France, embraces a period of 174 years, from the establishment of the Franks in Gaul about the year 429. The first part of this History is written after Sidonius Apollinaris, St. Remy, Bishop of Rheims, the "Acts of the Saints," and, above all, after oral tradition (Fig. 356). With regard to the events of the last fifty years recorded in his History, Gregory of Tours writes what he had himself seen, or what he had ascertained from trustworthy sources. He was not, perhaps, a man of very deep learning, but he was endowed with judgment and intelligence. He possessed, moreover, the qualities which are so often wanting in historians—good faith, candour, and the desire to be impartial. His style, though by no means correct and almost uncouth, is not devoid of colour, though simple and artless, and some of his descriptions are traced with great power. Gregory of Tours, who had read Virgil, Sallust, and Pliny, doubtless sought to imitate them in an age when the study of literature was almost extinct. Nor is he to be blamed for introducing into his work the legends and miracles of which all his contemporaries were full.

Fig. 357.—The Seven Saints of Brittany.—Fac-simile of a Wood Engraving from the "Chroniques de Bretagne," by Alain Bouchard (Paris, Galliot du Pré, 1514, in 4to).—In the Library of M. Ambroise Firmin-Didot, Paris.

This work, priceless and unique of its kind, was more often to be found in the libraries of the monasteries than in the archives of the Merovingian kings, and it must have had a great notoriety upon the death of its author in 593, for the best historian of the seventh century, Frédégaire, surnamed the Scholastic, continuing his history borrowed from Eusebius, Julius Africanus, and other Greek and Latin chroniclers, composed for the third book of this Chronicle an analytical abridgment of Gregory of Tours' book. Frédégaire, who was apparently a Burgundian, brought his story up to his death in 660.

The fifth book of this work contains some very valuable information concerning the reigns of Clotaire II., Dagobert I., and Clovis the younger. The author states in his preface that he relates what he has either seen, or heard from persons in whom he can place reliance, or taken from standard works. It is the only historical record of what took place in France during that obscure period.

It is difficult to give an explanation for the scarcity of contemporary Chronicles in the seventh and eighth centuries, when we remember that the bishops were the true guardians of history, and that monks in all the large monasteries made a point of collecting in chronological order the principal events of civil and religious history. It is true that these Chronicles were diffuse and loosely put together, and in these monastic Chronicles more space is devoted to the internal affairs of the community than to public occurrences, of which only vague rumours often reached them. Some of these Chronicles are nevertheless valuable (Fig. 357), on account of the scarcity of historical documents relating to early ages; and amongst the mass of them which have been published we may cite as the most interesting those of Moissac, Fontenelle, St. Médard de Soissons, Fleury-sur-Loire, St. Gall, and St. Bertin. Nor do we know anything as to the names of the authors who wrote the daily chronicles, the diary as we should say, of the ordinary incidents which occurred in the households of the King and of the nobility, except that two of those who succeeded Frédégaire in his work say that their labours were undertaken, the one by order of Childebrand, uncle of Pépin d'Héristal, mayor of the palace, the other by order of Nibelung, son of Childebrand, who were anxious to possess annals of the First Race. There is reason for believing that many of the Chronicles were lost in the wars and devastations of these barbarous epochs, in the course of which most of the towns and monasteries were burnt and put to sack. This is to be regretted, for, as Lacurne de St. Palaye observes, "No age was so barbarous but what the French felt how useful might be the knowledge of their history, in order to stimulate men, by the example of their forefathers, to lead virtuous and honourable lives." It must not be supposed, however, that the ancient Asiatic and Northern peoples who had successively invaded Europe during the fifth and sixth centuries had no history. Their history, although not committed to writing, consisted of warlike and religious songs, which were transmitted from generation to generation, and which dated from a very remote period. These were the

national songs which Charlemagne had collected from the mouths of their
descendants, who had become merged in the native populations of his empire.
It was from the national songs, also, of the ancient Britons, of the Saxons,
and of the Anglians that the Venerable Bede drew the materials for his
Ecclesiastical History of England, composed by him in the Monastery of
Jarrow, near Durham, where he died in 735.

Charlemagne is credited with the honour of having instituted the monastic
chronicles which were ordered to be preserved in all monastic foundations
formed by the crown.   In each of these it was the monk who was most

Fig. 358.—Coronation of Charlemagne.—Miniature from the " Chroniques de St. Denis."
Manuscript of the Fourteenth Century.—In the National Library, Paris.

distinguished for his learning and uprightness who was intrusted with the
duty of enregistering in chronological order the events of each reign ; and, at
the death of the King, his notes served for the compilation of a Chronicle
which was deposited in the archives of the monastery.   The famous Abbey of
St. Denis doubtless possessed, in preference to all other monasteries, the
privilege of thus composing the posthumous history of the Kings (Fig. 358),
with a degree of religious authority reminding one of the judgment of the
dead in ancient Egypt, and of keeping the depôt of these national archives,
which were so famous throughout the Middle Ages.   One of the oldest of

English historians relates that the kings had in constant attendance at their court certain men of letters who were intrusted with the task of recording their memorable sayings and doings, in order to transmit them, after their death, to posterity. Eginhard, the secretary (*notarius*) of Charlemagne, held this confidential post, and he was also selected by that monarch to supervise the education of the heirs to his throne. It was, no doubt, in order to acquit himself of this task that the learned favourite of the Emperor retired into the Monastery of Selingstadt, where he arranged the materials for his Life of Charlemagne. This work, the best of all those which he has left, was apparently composed in imitation of Suetonius's Lives of the Twelve Cæsars. In reading it one can easily see that the author was a member of the Pauline Academy, and that, in spite of his rugged and faulty style, he endeavoured to imitate the historical writers of ancient Rome.

It is strange that the historical monuments of Charlemagne's epoch should be so few, for that sovereign was fond of literature, and encouraged those who cultivated it, and he must have followed with interest the progress of historical study. He may not, however, have cared to be the subject of works which he could not himself revise, and, as a matter of fact, most of the Chronicles treating of his reign are posterior to his death (814). There is no evidence that any of the distinguished scholars whom he had collected about him were ordered to write his own history. During his meals he had read to him the historical songs of the nations of the North and of Germany (*cantilenæ historicæ*), which he had got together as materials for a history of the past, and he probably listened with not less interest to the songs of the bards who celebrated his warlike achievements in poems which were written in the vulgar tongue, but which were afterwards translated into Latin, and finally paraphrased into *chansons de geste* in the language of the twelfth century. But, excepting Eginhard, there were no scribes or secretaries in the palace intrusted with the duty of writing, under the Emperor's supervision, the official record of his public and private life.

Charlemagne had been long in his grave when the monk of St. Gall, generally believed to be a man named Necker, published in two books, after the evidence of two contemporaries, Priest Werinbert and Chevalier Adalbert, a Chronicle (" De Gestis Caroli Magni ") which he dedicated to Charles the Fat, Emperor of Germany. This Chronicle, composed a hundred and seventy years after the Emperor's death, and the author of which glorified his memory,

is very valuable, in spite of the exaggerations with which it teems. It is
written in an artless and attractive style, and serves at least to counterbalance

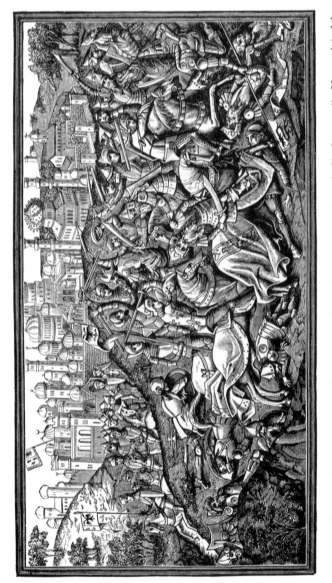

Fig. 359.—Conquest of Jerusalem by Charlemagne.—Miniature from the "Chroniques de Charlemagne."—Manuscript of the
Fifteenth Century (No. 9,066).—In the Burgundy Library, Brussels.

the false Chronicle of Archbishop Turpin, which, though looked upon as
reliable in the Middle Ages, is a tissue of falsehood. This latter Chronicle,
attributed to the Archbishop of Rheims, who holds such a prominent place in

romances of chivalry, relates the fabled expedition of Charlemagne and his paladins into Spain. It is in two distinct parts: the first five chapters were written in the middle of the eleventh, and the others in the beginning of the twelfth century. Here is the place to speak of the beautiful "Chanson de Roland," but there is no need to mention the narrative of the pseudo-Philomène concerning the doings of Charlemagne at Narbonne and at Carcassonne, and his fabled expedition to the Holy Land to restore the Patriarch of Jerusalem, whom the Arabs had driven out (Fig. 359).

Eginhard and Paul Diacre are the only trustworthy historians of the reign of Charlemagne. Paul Warnefride, surnamed Diacre, because he had taken deacon's orders, was secretary to the Lombard king, Didier, and afterwards lived at the court of Charlemagne before he went into the Monastery of Monte Cassini, where he completed his History of the Lombards (" De Gestis Langobardorum ") and his Abridgment of Roman History. It would be a mistake to suppose that barbarism, which appeared to have been arrested in its onward progress during the reign of Charlemagne, resumed its sway in the troubled reigns which followed. There was a rapid addition to the number of historians, who made their voices heard even in this (tenth) century of disorder and social transition. Every reign, every epoch, and every abbey had its chroniclers. In the ninth century, Ermold le Noir, Abbot of Aniane, wrote the Life of Louis the Débonnaire; and Nithard, a soldier and grandson of Charlemagne, who was born in 790 and died in 858, wrote a history of the quarrels and strife which took place amongst the sons of that sovereign.

The tenth century produced many good historians in nearly every country of Europe. In Italy, Luitprand, Bishop of Cremona, and twice ambassador at Constantinople, wrote the History of contemporary Germany (862 to 984); Witikind, monk of an abbey near Paderborn, wrote the Annals of the Imperial House under the Othos; and Dudon, Canon of St. Quintin, undertook the History of the early Dukes of Normandy. There was an abundance of historians, in fact; and while Abbon, Abbot of the old Benedictine monastery of Fleury-sur-Loire (died in 933) described in epic verse the siege of Paris by the Normans ("De Bello Parisiacæ Urbis")—a siege of which he was an eye-witness—Flodoard, Canon of Rheims, who died in 966, wrote some local Chronicles, in which are recorded many events of general interest.

Most of the numerous historians of the eleventh century were prelates and monks, among whom may be mentioned Dithmar, Bishop of Merseburg in 1009, author of a Chronicle of Germany from 876 to 1018; Raoul Glaber, monk of Cluny, whose Chronicle, extending from 900 to 1046, is one of the most interesting produced during the Middle Ages; and Aimoin, of Villefranche in Périgord (died in 1008), who had a well-deserved reputation in the history school of the Benedictines at Fleury-sur-Loire, and who spent part of his life in composing, after documents preserved in that celebrated abbey, a History of the Merovingian kings, which he himself brought down to the reign of Clovis, and which his successors, also Benedictine monks, continued to the

Fig. 360.—Coronation of the Great Khan, First King of Tartary.—Miniature from the "Fleur des Histoires de la Terre d'Orient," compiled by Brother Haycon or Hayton (Hethoum), Lord of Cort, Cousin-German of the King of Armenia.—Manuscript of the Fifteenth Century.—In the Library of M. Ambroise Firmin-Didot, Paris.

year 654. This is a well-arranged history, and one in which the Chronicles have been fused with a view to logical sequence. Thegan, Archbishop of Treves, composed, much upon the same plan, a Life of Louis the Débonnaire; and Helgaud, a monk at Fleury-sur-Loire, an abridged Life of King Robert.

It was not till the close of the twelfth century that the vulgar tongue passed from popular poetry into history, and while it was in its first hesitating utterances, the historians, all of whom were clerks and monks, did not abandon the use of Latin, in which they recorded, without stopping to weigh their probability, the wildest stories and legends (Fig. 360).   But the Crusades, the first of which dates from 1096, gave a fresh impulse to historical writing, and for a century and a half there was a long succession of historians of the Crusades, who described them in various languages, but principally

Fig. 361.—Alfonso X., the Wise, King of Castile (1252—1284), the supposed Author of the famous " Cronica de España." — Votive Statue in the Toledo Cathedral. — After the " Iconografia Española," by Carderera.

in Latin (Fig. 361). These historians relate, for the most part, facts of which they were themselves witnesses, and some of them import into their works the pious enthusiasm which animated those who took part in the Crusades.   Each of these writers has his special characteristics, from Guibert de Nogent, who wrote the History of the first Crusade, down to William of Tyr. Amongst those who wrote in Latin we may mention Bernard the Treasurer, Albert of Aix, Jacques de Vitry, Robert the Monk, Foucher of Chartres, and Odon de Deuil. There are also two French historians of the fourth and last Crusade, both of whose names have become household words—Villehardouin and the Sire de Joinville.

But, before speaking of the French historians who brought about a complete change in the form of historical works, we must refer to the Greek and Latin writers, and also to a few historians in the vulgar tongue, who

Fig. 362.—"How the Duc d'Alançon took the said Town of Alançon."—Miniature from the "Vigiles de Charles VII.," by Martial d'Auvergne.—Manuscript dated 1484 (No. 5054).—In the National Library, Paris.

contributed not a little to the revival of historical science. Cedrenus and Zonoras, like most of the historians of the Middle Ages, commenced with the creation of the world, and brought their Chronicles down to their own day, the one to 1057, the other to 1118. Another Greek historian, Nicetas Choniates, commenced his Annals, of which there were twenty-one books, with the death of Alexis Comnenus, and terminated them with the death of the Emperor Baldwin. The Latin historians were so numerous that a mere list of their names would fill more than ten pages, and the only writers we need allude to are William of Malmesbury, Henry of Huntingdon, and Roger of Hoveden, in England; Otho of Frisingen, Otfrid of Viterbo, and Conrad of Lichtenau, in Germany; Leon, Cardinal of Ostia, in Italy; and Roderick Ximenes, in Spain (Fig. 361). Of the Chronicles in the vulgar tongue the most remarkable is that of Nestor, written in the Slav tongue in a monastery at Kieff about 1116. To the historians who succeeded these in the various countries of Europe we have not space to allude, and it is the less necessary to do so as their names are scarcely remembered.

We must not, however, pass over the universal Chronicle of Matthew Paris, who was a monk and historian in the Benedictine Abbey of St. Albans, in the diocese of Lincoln, and who gave the title of "Historia Major Anglorum" to his history of the English, composed from the various Chronicles of the eleventh and twelfth centuries. Matthew Paris is certainly one of the most remarkable historians of the Middle Ages, and his great work concerns not less France than England, especially with regard to the latter part, in which he described, after what he himself had witnessed, the events occurring between 1235 and his death in 1259. At this time the best historians were to be found in France, and their numbers continued to increase when they had created a school of history, which became of the more importance as Latin was gradually replaced by French in general conversation. As early as the middle of the twelfth century, fifty years before Villehardouin, in his Chronicle of the conquest of Constantinople, had proved that the vulgar idiom was well suited to works of history, Suger, Minister of State under Louis VI. and Louis VII., had, it is said, perceived that this idiom, which had long been in general use at court and among the upper classes, might be employed to advantage in the Royal Chronicles, which had been compiled for the last three centuries at the Abbey of St. Denis, where he died in 1152, and of which he was abbot. This fact is not absolutely certain, but Suger, who had written in Latin, though of a somewhat obscure style, the Life of Louis the Fat and part of the Life of Louis the Young, deserves to be given a prominent place in the list of French historians.

The Latin Chronicles of the royal Abbey of St. Denis had long been famous, and there were deposited the most valuable .manuscripts of French history.

The writers of the romances and *chansons de geste*, with a view of obtaining greater credence for their works of imagination, did not scruple to declare that they had derived their *estoires* (stories) from the archives of St. Denis. (See chapter on *Romances.*) The author of the prose romance, "Beufve d'Antonne," says, "Materials for a narrative of the deeds of King Charles Martel are to be found in the Chronicles of Beufve d'Antonne and elsewhere, as also at St. Denis, where there is nothing but chronicle." The author of the romance in verse, "Doolin de Mayence," says :—

> "Les saiges clers d'adonc, par leur senifiance,
> En firent les Croniques qui sont de grant vaillance,
> Et sont en l'abbaïe de Saint-Denys en France ;
> Puis, ont esté estraites, par moult bele ordonnance,
> De latin en roman." . . .

The first historical romances were originally given as *history in rhyme,* and the jugglers, who visited the châteaux and the plenary courts to recite and chant the adventures of the Knights of the Round Table and other lays already alluded to, taught their credulous and uneducated hearers as much as any of these nobles cared to learn concerning ancient history. The romances of "Rou" and "Brut," of "Godfrey de Bouillon," and a host of others of a kindred sort, composed in verse, were accepted as documents of unimpeachable veracity. The result was that the true historians, in order to prevent the jugglers from having a monopoly of public favour, invented *metrical* histories, which did, in fact, effect that purpose. In this way Guillaume Guiart set to rhyme a Chronicle (from 1165 to 1306) which he entitled the "Branche des Royaulx Lignages ;" Godfrey de Paris composed a Chronicle, of his time, under the reign of Philippe le Bel ; and Philippe Mouskes a Universal History consisting of thirty-two thousand lines, and relating the history of Flanders from the earliest ages to the end of the thirteenth century. These metrical Chronicles had a special class of readers among the lovers of poetry, and two centuries later the lawyer-poet Martial d'Auvergne still further perfected the metrical Chronicle by composing the "Vigiles du Roi Charles VII." (Figs. 362 and 363), one of the best histories of that prince ; while his contemporary, Guillaume Cretin, precentor and canon at the Sainte-Chapelle of Vincennes, set to work at rhyming the Chronicles of France from Charlemagne to François I.

Geoffroy, Sire de Villehardouin, Marshal of Champagne, who had taken

an active part in the fourth Crusade, furnished a model for prose history in
his Chronicle, or rather Memoir, upon the conquest of Constantinople by the
crusaders in 1202.   It is surprising to find in so ancient a work such a
faithful and spirited account of the great events which this nobleman, who
was a warrior and a statesman as well, had seen happen.   His work is, so to
speak, the starting-point for those private memoirs which have always been
highly appreciated in France, and of which there has been a large supply
ever since.   The Chronicle of the Sire de Joinville, written more than seventy
years after that of Villehardouin, also belongs to the category of private
memoirs, though the worthy knight, who composed it in his old age, had

Fig. 363.—" How the Comte de Foix took strong Places in Guienne."—Miniature from the "Vigiles
de Charles VII., by Martial d'Auvergne.—Manuscript dated 1484 (No. 5,054).—In the
National Library, Paris.

intended to write the Life of St. Louis rather than a history of his own.   He
had not assuredly the keen penetration of Villehardouin, but unconsciously
he has written one of the most exquisite works in the ancient literature of
France.   He was not a writer, yet he surpasses all the writers of his day by
the charm, the grace, the sensibility, and the piquant artlessness of his
narrative (Fig. 364).

These excellent Memoirs, written by eye-witnesses of unquestionable
authority, had not, however, at the time they appeared, the amount of
success which their authors may well have expected.   They remained in
the archives of the Sire de Villehardouin in Romania, and in those of the

Château de Joinville, only a few copies being circulated at the French court, and amongst the noblemen who possessed a library. Yet the Sire de Join-ville had written these Memoirs at the request of Queen Jeanne, wife of Philippe le Bel, and when they were printed in the sixteenth century the original manuscript was no longer to be found. Other statesmen and soldiers also compiled their Memoirs, which, remaining buried in the archives of their castles, were destroyed, like so many other manuscripts, during the wars of the fourteenth and fifteenth centuries. The Latin Chronicles in the monasteries and the churches suffered less from the pillage and burning which became the fate of so many castles and fortified towns. Thus there remain a number of these Latin Chronicles, most of which have never been published,

Fig. 364.—The Envoys from the Soudan, having at their head a little old Man walking on Crutches, come to propose Terms of Ransom to the captive Crusaders.—After a Miniature from the "Credo," by Joinville.—Manuscript of the Thirteenth Century, formerly belonging to the National Library, Paris, but at present in England.

but the existence of which proves how the taste for history had spread since the twelfth century. The clerks, monks, priests, savants, and doctors would have considered themselves disgraced if they had written in any other language than Latin; the nobles, the warriors, the politicians, the poets, and the middle classes only used the vulgar tongue to narrate events in which they had taken part, or which they had witnessed. It may, therefore, be considered as certain that from this period there was a very marked distinc-tion between general histories and personal memoirs, the latter being nearly always in French, and the former in Latin.

At the same time an abridged French edition was being prepared, in the Abbey of St. Denis, of the Chronicles of France, and this edition was modified to keep pace with the changes in the language. This is how it came to pass that there were several different versions of these Chronicles. It would appear, according to some verses attributed to Mathieu de Vendôme, Abbot of St. Denis in the thirteenth century, and placed at the head of the oldest manuscripts of these Chronicles, that they were translated into French by his order, about 1274, under the title of "Roman des Rois." These verses are explanatory of the profit to be derived from reading the Chronicles:—

> . . . "L'on ne doit ce livre mespriser ne despire (décrier),
> Qui est fait des bons princes dou regne et de l'empire.
> Qui sovent i voudroit estudier et lire,
> Bien puet sçavoir qu'il doit eschiver et eslire (esquiver et choisir).
> Et dou bien et dou mal puet chascun son prou (profit) faire :
> Par l'exemple des bons se doit-on au bien traire (tirer) ;
> Par les faits des mauvais qui sont tout le contraire,
> Se doit chascun dou mal esloingner et retraire (retirer) ;
> Mains bons enseignements puet-on prendre en ce livre." . . .

M. Paulin Paris, who has published a very excellent edition of this work, says of it with truth, "The Chronicles of St. Denis are probably the most glorious monument of history ever raised in any language or by any people, with the exception of the Bible." These Chronicles, which were not in reality published until the fifteenth century, but which as early as the fourteenth had been shown to kings and great personages, appear to have been regarded with almost religious veneration as the Golden Book of the Church and of the French monarchy. When foreign sovereigns came to the French court they asked to be allowed to see and to handle this venerable book. Upon a manuscript of these Chronicles belonging to the Duc de Berry, brother of Charles V., may be read the following marginal note :—"The which book the said Seigneur de Berry had taken from the Church of St. Denis to show to the Emperor Sigismond (in 1415), and also to copy." King Charles V. had previously had several copies taken, illustrated with miniatures, and he always had a copy open upon his desk, by the side of the Bible.

The monks of St. Denis continued to write in Latin an official account of each reign, according to the privileges of their royal abbey. These accounts took the form of very detailed annals, all the materials for which had been collected with scrupulous care, and which were put together by the best writers in the community. It was in this fashion that Guillaume de Nangis wrote the Life of St. Louis and of Philip the Bold, as Rigord did that of Philip Augustus. The Lives of the latter's successors, down to Charles VI., were also written upon the same plan—that is to say, in great detail—by

Fig. 365.—Betrothal Interview between the Archduke Maximilian and Mary of Burgundy at Ghent, April 18th, 1477.—Miniature from the " Chroniques de Flandre."—Manuscript of the Fifteenth Century (No. 13,073).—In the Burgundy Library, Brussels.

monks who remained anonymous, and whose works are said to have disappeared when the Abbey of St. Denis was three times pillaged between 1410 and 1429 by the Burgundians, the Armagnacs, and the English. There is some reason, however, for thinking that the monks themselves had concealed

or destroyed their original works, in which the history of the deadly wars
between France and England, as well as of the civil wars and political
factions of the fourteenth century, was narrated in too indignant and sorrowful terms.   All that remains to us of these valuable Chronicles of the Kings
of France from Louis VIII. to Charles V. is the general History of the
reign of Charles VI., which gives us a very favourable idea of what the rest
must have been.   Nor do we even know who were the authors of this History,
the last which was written in Latin.

From the time of Charles VII. there was an official chronicler of France
amongst the monks of St. Denis, and the first who held this post was Jean
Chartier, younger brother of the royal poet, Alain Chartier.   We owe to him
an excellent Chronicle of the reign of Charles VII., written in French, but too
much abridged ; and it is supposed that this was the last Chronicle compiled
under the supervision of the Chapter of St. Denis ; for Jean Castel, appointed
chronicler of France after Jean Chartier, was a monk of St. Martin des
Champs, and became Abbot of St. Maur des Fossés.   At his death in 1482,
all his manuscripts were placed in a casket and transferred to St. Denis, but
Louis XI. ordered that the said manuscripts, which doubtless related to the
history of his reign, should be returned to his Seal Office.   Jean d'Auton,
Abbot of Angle, succeeded Jean Castel as Chronicler-Royal in the reign of
Louis XII., while Jean Macé held that office under François I.   The Valois
were not content with having one chronicler, and henceforward there were
three Histriographers of France in place of the chronicler of the King,
and this post, the salary of which was raised from 1,200 to 2,400 livres
(francs) in 1610, was held by Pierre Paschal, Bernard du Haillan, and Pierre
Mathieu.

The "Chroniques de France" or "de Saint Denis," written in French,
stopped at the end of the reign of Charles VII. ; and this great historical
work long retained its renown, notwithstanding the fables which envelop the
cradle of the monarchy, and trace it back to Francus, son of Hector, who is
said to have settled in Gaul after the fall of Troy.   The religious legends, the
lives of the saints, and the miracles which we find interspersed in the history
of the first two races, represent the spirit of the age in which these annals
were put together, and are not documents to be set on one side, though they
have very erroneously been looked upon as discrediting the simple and honest
compilation in which they are embodied.   But it must nevertheless be allowed

that, for the fourteenth and part of the fifteenth century, the "Chroniques de St. Denis," notwithstanding the moderation and precision with which they were compiled, are not equal to the Chronicles of Froissart, or even of Monstrelet.

Jean Froissart (Fig. 368) is certainly one of the most attractive of historians; he is more the chronicler of the chevaliers than the historian of the fourteenth century. Born at Valenciennes about 1337, the son of a painter of armorial bearings, and himself no doubt an heraldic writer, he as a youth attached himself to the Church, and notwithstanding his position as clerk, soon took to travelling about Europe. He was also a poet and a musician, and this gained him admittance to the houses of the nobles, and afterwards to all the courts of Europe. He began by rewriting after his own

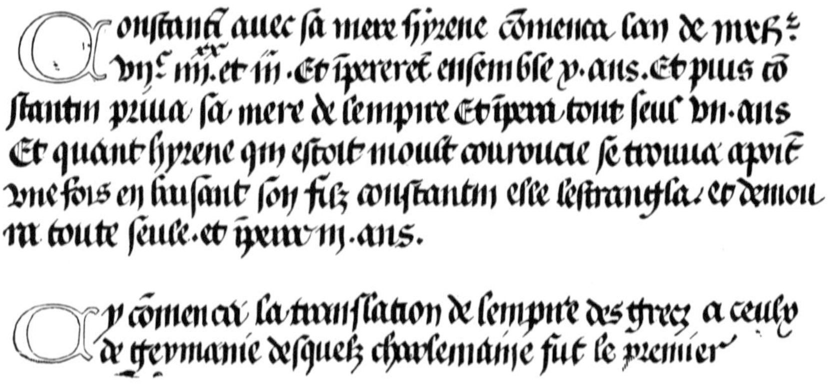

Fig. 366.—Fragment of the "Genealogy of the Kings of France and of England."—Manuscript of the Fifteenth Century.—In the National Library, Paris.

fancy the dull and involved Chronicle of Jean Lebel, Canon of Liége, but, being dissatisfied with his first version, he put it into another shape, and throughout his life perfected it and added to it what he had learned in the course of his travels. As he himself says, "Wherever I went, I questioned the aged chevaliers and esquires who had been engaged in the wars, and who could tell me all about them, and also the ancient heralds, in order to verify and control what I had heard. Thus did I compose the high and noble history." His history is a vivid, animated, and picturesque Chronicle, and the only fault to be found with it is that it contains a few repetitions and mistakes. Froissart is very happy in the variety of tone which he has given to this picture, in which are portrayed festivals of the court, gatherings of the chevaliers, and tournaments, as well as sieges, feats of arms, and battles. His narrative is interlarded with amusing anecdotes and witty dialogue, and his immense Chronicle, of which there are several different texts, extends without a break from 1326 to 1400. He was a very laborious and honest writer, remarkable for his impartiality; and Michel de Montaigne speaks of him as "the worthy Froissart, who has always been frank and artless, who, if he makes a mistake, never hesitates to acknowledge and correct it as soon as it is pointed out to him, and who gives the various rumours which were current, and the different accounts he has heard. It is the raw material for history, and every one can profit by it according to his understanding."

Like Froissart, Enguerrand de Monstrelet and Georges Chastelain, who were simultaneously engaged in continuing his Chronicles by adding thereto the history of their time, both belonged to Flanders and to the court of the Duke of Burgundy, where historians were encouraged as well as poets and artists. Monstrelet (Fig. 369), born in 1390, may, perhaps, have known Froissart, who died subsequently to 1410, and he may even have received his advice when he began to write Chronicles. He was not a poet, but a juris-consult and archivist, and he held the posts of Provost of Cambray and Bailiff of Walincourt. He drew up a Chronicle which began where that of Froissart left off, and he interpolated into it a great number of original pieces to make up for what might be wanting in the way of talent in his own work. Georges Chastelain, while alive, had a much greater reputation than Monstrelet; but his Chronicle, which has only recently been printed, and an important part of which has not as yet been found, was almost unknown, as he had written it exclusively for Philippe le Bon, whose secretary and official chronicler he became after having undertaken several diplomatic missions in France and England. This long Chronicle extended from 1419 to 1474, and is mainly remarkable for the clear and impartial judgment, the discernment, and the elevated style of the writer.

The number of historical works written in French multiplied so rapidly in the course of the fourteenth century that the Royal Library of the Louvre, the inventory of which was taken by the keepers of the library at the death of Charles V., contained more than two hundred manuscript volumes in folio and in quarto, historical works, most of them magnificently bound in wooden boards covered with silk and with silver clasps. Amongst these works were several French translations of Livy, Julius Cæsar, Valerius Maximus, Lucan,

Fig. 367.—Entry of Charles VII. into Rouen in 1450.—Miniature from Manuscript of the
Fifteenth Century, containing the Account of the Hundred Years' War, which terminated in
1450 by the entry of Charles VII. into Rouen. Binding with the Arms of Anne of Brittany,
Wife of Louis XII.—In the Collection of M. L. Double, Paris.

Suetonius, and other Latin writers, undertaken by order of King Charles V.
There were six handsome copies of the "Chroniques de France;" four or five
of Vincent de Beauvais' "Miroir Historial;" eight Lives of St. Louis, comprising, doubtless, that written by Joinville; various Histories and Chronicles
of events beyond the seas ("Chroniques d'Outre Mer," as they were called); five
or six Chronicles of the Popes and the Emperors; a number of Lives of the
Fathers and of the Saints; a few foreign Chronicles translated into French
(Fig. 366); narratives of battles and of war, &c. But in these inventories

Fig. 368.—Portrait of Froissart, after a Red Chalk Drawing preserved in the
Town Library, Arras.

there is not a single work of history written in Latin. Most of the
manuscripts had been acquired at great expense by Charles V., who read
them or had them read to him, and who appended his autograph to each one.
They were seized or purchased in 1425 by the Duke of Bedford, who took
them to England, where they were either destroyed or dispersed, and the
library of the French kings in the Louvre had to be reformed.

The fondness of Charles V. for the study of history did much to aid the

Fig. 369.—King Charles VII., upon quitting Rouen, sets out to besiege the Town of Harfleur.
—Miniature from the "Chroniques de Monstrelet."—Manuscript of the Fifteenth Century
(No. 2,679).—In the National Library, Paris.

progress of that branch of literature. That sovereign, a friend of literature
and of men of letters, like his two brothers, the Duc de Berry and the

Duc d'Anjou, did not confine himself to the composition of sumptuous volumes of history, *bien escripts et historiés*, with rich bindings, for he had in his household several translators—amongst others, Jean de Vignay and Laurent du Premier-Fait—to whom he gave orders what Latin or Italian works he wished to have translated into French; but he had no chronicler holding an official title, and he allowed the monks of St. Denis to continue their task of writing in Latin the history of his reign—a history which has not, unfortunately, been preserved. It is nevertheless from this reign that dates the personal history of each King of France, written in French by the chroniclers of the King's household. Christina de Pisan, who was at once a poetess, a philosopher, and an historian (Figs. 371 and 372), was the daughter of Thomas de Pisan, astrologer to Charles V., and she was therefore enabled, owing to her personal position at court, to collect all the particulars for the "Livre des Faits et Bonnes Mœurs du Roi Charles V.," which she did not terminate until 1404. At this period the poet Eustache Deschamps was royal chronicler, and he was engaged in writing a History of the reign of Charles VI., which, interrupted probably by the wars of that time, never appeared, though some traces of it may, perhaps, be found in the curious History published under the name of "Jouvenel des Ursins." The author of this latter work was not an official chronicler, for he held the dignity of Archbishop of Rheims, and he was concerned in many of the stirring events which he describes. After him we have, as mentioned above, a true French chronicler in Jean Chartier, though his description of the reign of Charles VII. and of the doings of Joan d'Arc has not the fire which it might have possessed.

During each reign the official chronicler of France prepared the materials for a history of the sovereign, but this history was not necessarily written, much less published. Thus Louis XI. appears to have systematically hindered his chronicler from completing the events of his reign, and that which appeared towards the end of the fifteenth century with the inappropriate title of "Chronique Scandaleuse du Roy Louis XI.," and under the name of Jean de Troyes, was merely the outline of the work compiled by Pierre Desrey, of Troyes, chronicler of France under Louis XI., and the only reason for entitling this Chronicle scandalous was that it was published without the royal assent. After Pierre Desrey, André de la Vigne wrote, partly in prose and partly in verse, the "Vergier d'Honneur," with reference to the bold expedition of Charles VIII. for the conquest of Naples. The wars of the

an quatorfe aprez la refurrecti
on nofttref la gloneufe ma g
delaine par fa predication cō

Fig. 370.—Fabled Origin of the Burgundy Cross.—Étienne, a legendary King of Burgundy, makes a Pilgrimage to St. Victor of Marseilles, to whom he has carried the Cross of St. Andrew, out of gratitude to St. Mary Magdalene, who had raised him and his Mother from the Dead. This Cross afterwards figured in the Shield of the House of Burgundy.— Miniature from the "Chroniques de Bourgogne."—Manuscript of the Fifteenth Century.—In the Library of M. Ambroise Firmin-Didot, Paris.

French in Italy during the reign of Louis XII. were recorded by Jean d'Auton, who, in his character of chronicler of France, compiled a very complete Chronicle, the style of which, however, was pedantic and involved. This deplorable style was brought into fashion by the historians of the court of Burgundy, and especially by Canon Jean Molinet, the historiographer of Margaret of Austria, who governed the Low Countries (Fig. 365). François I., Henri II., and their successors, down to Henri IV., also had their chroniclers and historiographers, who received their salaries without ever publishing the result of their labours. One of these historiographers, Pierre Paschal, had made a great stir about a History of France, which, year after year, he was upon the point of publishing, yet when he died in 1565 there were not more than twenty pages of it found among his papers.

History, as it extended its domain, gradually increased in variety of tone and style. Upon the one hand the lives of warriors and statesmen were related by the heralds, the esquires, and the secretaries, who lived in their houses and had witnessed the events which they described; while upon the other hand these warriors, statesmen, and courtiers themselves wrote or dictated to their secretaries and servants the memoirs of their time. These private Chronicles and Memoirs, so varied and so interesting, some of which are anonymous, show that their various authors were animated by the desire of outdoing one another by a description of the stirring events in which they had participated. The ancient Chronicle of the Constable Bertrand Duguesclin was doubtless compiled by one of his companions in arms, and the "Chronique de la Pucelle" must have been written by a clerk attached to the religious service of Joan of Arc, and who had followed her from her entry into Orleans, when besieged by the English, to the coronation of Charles VII. at Rheims. Guillaume Gruel, who wrote the History of Arthur III., Comte de Richemont, Duke of Brittany, was chronicler to the latter prince; Jean d'Oronville, who wrote the life and heroic deeds of Louis II., Duc de Bourbon, great-grandson of St. Louis, was secretary to a prince of the house of Bourbon under Charles VII.; but we do not know who was the author of the History of Jean le Maingre, surnamed Boucicaut, Marshal of France; and it has only recently been discovered that Jean Lefèvre de St. Remy, King-at-arms of the Golden Fleece, composed the Chronicle of the good Chevalier Jean de Lalaing, which had always been attributed to Georges Chastelain. We have never known the name of the "Loyal Servitor" who was secretary to the Chevalier

Bayard; but the "History of the Deeds, Achievements, Triumphs, and Prowess of the good Chevalier, who is without Fear and without Reproach, the gentle Seigneur de Bayard," is rightly regarded as the historical masterpiece of the time of François I.

The best of the Memoirs of which the Sire de Joinville had, so to speak, furnished the model are those rewritten at the end of the fifteenth century by Philippe de Commines (Fig. 373), and published in 1524 and 1528 under

Fig. 371.—Miniature from the "Livre de Faits d'Armes et de Chevalerie," by Christina de Pisan.— Manuscript of the Fifteenth Century.—In the Library of M. Ambroise Firmin-Didot, Paris.

the title of "Chroniques." M. Ludovic Lalanne has pointed out with great truth that he was the first Frenchman to write the history of his time with the profundity, the discernment, and impartiality of a man who had passed his life in public affairs. The style of these Memoirs, though rather tortuous and wordy, is not lacking in vigour and intensity. In addition to the Memoirs of Louis XI.'s favourite, we can do no more than mention the Chronicle-memoirs of Pierre Fenin, Mathieu de Coucy, Olivier de la Marche

(Fig. 374), and Jacques du Clercq, all of whom were attached to the court of Burgundy in the fifteenth century. The sixteenth century possessed a brilliant series of Memoirs, from those of the Sire de Fleurange, of Martin du Bellay, and of the Seigneur de Vieilleville (compiled by his secretary, Carloix), in the reigns of François I. and Henri II., to the Memoirs of Gaspard de Saulx-Tavannes, Montluc, Castelnau, and Marguerite de Valois during the rest of the century. The Memoirs of Brantôme were the last of the Valois dynasty,

Fig. 372.—Miniature from the "Livre de Faits d'Armes et de Chevalerie," by Christina de Pisan.—Manuscript of the Fifteenth Century.—In the Library of M. Ambroise Firmin-Didot, Paris.

and are in striking contrast to the "Économies Royales," or the political Memoirs in which the Duc de Sully described the reign of Henri IV.

But the sixteenth century cared most for long historical works and books of general history. The "Chroniques de St. Denis" had fallen into undeserved discredit since the reign of Louis XII., which king had brought back with him from Verona an Italian historian who wrote in Latin

—Paolo Emilio, or Paulus Æmilius, as he was then called—and commissioned him to rewrite in rhetorical style the History of France, which Robert Gaguin had obscured with the jargon of scholasticism. His work, "De Rebus Gestis Francorum," was highly appreciated by the Humanists, but it had not the success of Gaguin's Chronicle, which was reprinted ten times, and translated into French by the indefatigable Pierre Desrey. The booksellers had ordered from the above, and from several other writers, different historical compilations

Fig. 373.—Portrait of Philippe de Commines, after a Red Chalk Drawing preserved in the Town Library, Arras.

entitled the "Mer des Histoires," the "Rosier Historial," &c. The chroniclers and historiographers of France, who turned out so many bulky volumes that one might imagine they had written with both hands, nearly all composed their universal History of France; and one of the first efforts in this direction was that made by Nicole Gilles, notary and secretary of the King, who had no little success, for the "Annals and Chronicles" of this old historian, who died in 1503, went through numerous editions until the end of the sixteenth century, thanks to the additions and supplements written by Belleforest and Gabriel Chapuis. But this work was soon eclipsed by the more complete Histories published almost simultaneously by the King's historiographers, Bernard Girard, Sieur du Haillan, François de Belleforest, and Jean de

Fig. 374.—Death presiding over Battles.—Miniature from the "Chevalier délibéré," by Olivier de la Marche.—Manuscript of the Fifteenth Century (No. 173).—In the Arsenal Library, Paris.

Serres. The folios succeeded each other with amazing rapidity, yet they did no more than keep pace with the curiosity of the public, who read every line of these ponderous volumes. There was a sort of historical fever, which was only aggravated by interminable incidents of the civil wars recorded by the

Protestant writers, La Popelinière, Jean de Laval, Agrippa d'Aubigné. A great historian, the Polybius and Tacitus of France, President Jacques-Auguste de Thou, wrote an excellent Political History of France, but it has the fault of being too prolix, and of being written in enigmatic Latin instead of in the language of his contemporaries, Michel de Montaigne and Henri IV.

Fig. 375.—The Arms of Henry V. of England, joined to those of Catherine de Valois, his Wife, Daughter of Charles VI.—From a Missal which belonged to Charles VI.—In the Library of M. Ambroise Firmin-Didot, Paris.

THE DRAMA.

CTING on the example of M. Charles Louandre, who has written a very useful treatise upon the origin of the dramatic art, we will divide the history of the Theatre into four distinct periods. As he says, during the first period—that is to say, from the dawn of Christianity to the seventh century—the Greco-Roman traditions reigned supreme. During the second period, from the seventh to the twelfth century, the profane element gave way to Christian inspiration; the theatre, in the modern acceptation of the term, disappeared altogether, and, absorbed in the ceremonial of public worship, preserved nothing but the Latin language as a souvenir of Rome. In the twelfth, and still more during the next two centuries, the sanctuary ceased to have a monopoly of scenic representations; the priests and the monks were gradually driven from the stage by professional actors, and though Christian thought was still the dominating feature in the great dramatic compositions of the time, some of them bore traces of the spirit of raillery which afterwards prevailed. And in the sixteenth century dramatic art underwent its definite transformation, and, by an alliance of Greco-Roman traditions and Christian inspiration, it became at once chivalrous, religious, satirical, national, and classic.

Beyond the comedies of Plautus and of Terence (Figs. 376 to 380) and the tragedies of Seneca, which doubtless continued to be played in some of the towns of the old Roman world where correct Latin was still spoken, we know of nothing except a few feeble attempts at Christian drama, such as *Christ Suffering*, attributed to Gregory Nazianzen; *Susan*, now extinct, which is said to have been written by John Damascenus; a *Dialogue between Adam and Eve in the earthly Paradise*," &c.; and it is quite possible that these dramas were not written for the stage. Christianity had condemned all kinds

Fig. 376.—The Slave and the Lawyer.—Representative Characters of the Ancient Theatre, from the Comedies of Terence.—Manuscript of the Tenth Century.—In the National Library, Paris.

of theatrical representations: tragedies, comedies, pantomimes, and circensian games. The amphitheatres, which, with the pagan temples, constituted the principal ornaments of the Roman cities, were, like the temples, abandoned as the new faith spread. It is true that Chilpéric, King of the Franks, constructed in 577 a circus at Paris, and another at Soissons; but the dramatic art being at that time unknown in Gaul, these buildings were merely arenas, in which appeared buffoons, dancers, and performing dogs and horses, and in which were still given the combats of wild animals. The theatre disappeared in the shipwreck of ancient society.

From the seventh to the tenth century are to be found in contemporary documents two kinds of scenic representations—the one nomad and popular, the other religious and permanent; the former connected more or less with the traditions of paganism, the second betokening vague aspirations of a new and essentially Christian art. The nomad and popular representations were given by *histrions,* who exchanged this name of reproach first for that of *chanteurs,* and afterwards for that of *jugglers* (*jongleurs*), which was given them by the public, and which they retained throughout the Middle Ages.

Fig. 377.—The Old Man and the Maid-servant.—Representative Characters of the Ancient Theatre, from the Comedies of Terence.—Manuscript of the Tenth Century.—In the National Library, Paris.

Mounted upon common trestles, and surrounded by buffoons, mimics, and musicians, who accompanied their utterances with gestures, grimaces, and wind or stringed instruments, they declaimed or sang—it can scarcely be said acted—serious or comic plays. About the ninth century, however, as far as can be ascertained from certain passages in historians of that time, the performances of the jugglers, who mostly took their repertory from the legends of the saints, assumed a certain dramatic character. Plain narrative was succeeded by dialogue, and several singers at once represented, or rather intoned, religious scenes, which were called *urbanæ cantilenæ*, or, as we may translate it, songs intended to be sung in the streets. These may have been theatrical pieces, but it is quite certain that the Church forbade her clergy to take part in, or even to witness them.

Nevertheless there were given in the churches at this period, upon the principal festivals, regular dramatic representations, which appear to have

Fig. 378.—The Parasite and the Soldier.—Representative Characters of the Ancient Theatre, from the Comedies of Terence.—Manuscript of the Tenth Century.—In the National Library, Paris.

formed an integral part of the service, and the clergy in these representations, which they had the sole charge of, acted the principal episodes in the life of Christ. For instance, at Christmas, the manger, the shepherds, the magi, and even the star which led them to Bethlehem were represented at the mass, and it is in the conversational shape of certain parts of the service celebrated at the festivals of Christmas, Easter, and Pentecost that are to be found the origin of the *Mystery-plays* and *Miracle-plays* of the Middle Ages.

Yet, while taking into account these representations, which long held a place in Catholic liturgy, it may be affirmed that from the sixth to the tenth century there was not throughout Europe either a theatre or any theatrical works in the strict acceptation of the word.

To Hrosvitha, a nun in the Convent of Gandersheim, and a native of Saxony, belongs the honour of having composed the first dramatic works worthy of the name; and though these works are crude and barbarous, they are none the less very interesting from an artistic point of view. It is said that she was the authoress of six Latin dramas imitated from Terence, which were represented before the nuns of her abbey, in their chapter-house, about the end of the tenth century. The dominant idea in her dramas is the glorification of chastity, and it must be said that this primitive drama, rude and imperfect as it may appear, contains passages which would be admired in the greatest masters of the ancient and of the modern stage.

From the eleventh to the thirteenth century it was the custom to celebrate in the porches of churches, and even within the sacred building, dramatized services, in which the principal parts were played by the clergy, from the canon to the deacon, and which were used as an introduction to, and adornment of, the holy liturgy. One of these services, entitled *Mystery of the Resurrection of our Lord Jesus Christ*, has come down to us, with the particulars of the way in which it was got up, and the music pricked. Three deacons, arrayed in dalmaticas, and their heads covered with veils "like women," says the text, and representing the three Marys, advanced, with vases in their hands, to the middle of the choir: with their heads bent downwards, they proceeded to the desk, singing the anthem, "Who shall roll away for us the stone from the tomb of the sepulchre?" A chorister-boy, "after the manner of an angel," arrayed in a white alb and holding a palm-branch, addressed them this question: "Whom seek ye here?" to which the three deacons replied, "We seek Jesus of Nazareth." Thus the mystery of the resurrection seemed to be accomplished in the presence of the people, before whose eyes were unfolded the majestic scenes of the gospel.

Henceforward a new kind of scenic dialogue was formed under the name of Mystery, and a new era opened for theatrical art. Written solely in Latin at first, the mystery was gradually put into the vulgar tongue, so as to be understood by the general public, and this led to the creation of certain pieces called *farcitures*, half Latin, half French, upon solemn subjects. It was not until the thirteenth century that Latin disappeared altogether; but the three kinds of play adopted from that time, the Latin mystery, the mystery *farce* (or a combination of Latin and French), and the mystery altogether in French, were represented simultaneously until the migration of the drama from the ceremonies and processions of the Church to the public streets and squares of the city—until, in fact, it exchanged its religious for a secular character.

It is no easy matter, amidst the chaos of theatrical productions in the

Fig. 379.—Bacchis and the Fisherman.—Representative Characters of the Ancient Theatre, from the Comedies of Terence.—Manuscript of the Tenth Century.—In the National Library, Paris.

Middle Ages, to distinguish precisely between them, and to lay down the special principles of each dramatic school. It may, however, be said that the mystery is the representation of a fact taken from the Bible, as the Miracle is the representation of a fact borrowed from the legends of the saints, male or female, especially from the story of their martyrdom. It is worthy of remark, at the same time, that the title of Mystery, originally very limited in its application, was afterwards applied to compositions very different from those to which this name was at first given. It was even applied to dramatic works, the subjects of which were taken from the traditions of chivalry, such as the *Mystère de Berte,* the *Mystère d'Amis et d'Amile,* and the *Mystère de Griselidis,* played in 1395 ; or to the pagan and mythological traditions, such as the *Mystère de la Destruction de Troie,* played in 1459; or even to the events of contemporary history, such as the *Mystère du Siége d'Orléans,* played either during the lifetime of Joan of Arc, or soon after her death.

With a few rare exceptions, the mysteries and the miracles were composed by priests or by monks, which is to be attributed to the fact that the members of the clergy, generally better educated than the laity, considered the representation of sacred pieces as the most practical means of educating their flocks, who welcomed instruction in this attractive form all the more heartily because, during these semi-barbarous periods, their towns were continually laid waste or menaced by the triple scourge of battle, plague, and famine.

There is a rather long list of the authors of miracle-plays and mystery-plays from the twelfth to the fifteenth century. The first of these authors is Hilaire, disciple of Abelard, who composed, under the title of *Ludi* (plays), pieces in dialogue, imitated from the Old and the New Testaments. The last name in the list, at the close of the fifteenth century, is that of the "very eloquent and very scientific" and still more prolific doctor, Jehan Michel, Bishop of Angers, author of the celebrated *Mystery of the Passion,* which another Jehan Michel, his brother or nephew, revised and had represented in his native city. The oldest vestige of dramatic art in France is, beyond doubt, a *Mystery of Adam and Eve,* written in French about the middle of the twelfth century, which we discovered in 1845 in a manuscript at the Tours Library, and which was published for the first time by Victor Luzarche in 1854. This mystery or drama is the most characteristic type of the dramatic representations which were held at the church porticos.

The piece entitled *Representacio Ade* (Representation of Adam) is divided into three acts or parts, which are accompanied by a chorus, and terminate in an epilogue. The first act comprises man's fall ; the second the murder of Abel ; and the third the appearance of the prophets to announce the advent of the Saviour. At intervals the chorus sings Latin verses, and the epilogue consists of a sermon upon the necessity of penitence. The manuscript containing this Bible mystery is all the more curious because it gives the complete stage arrangements for playing it. The whole is preceded by a short summary not only of the theatrical decorations and the dress of all the actors, but also as to their attitude and gestures, and the way in which they are to play their parts. We will give a brief analysis of the first act, in

Fig. 380.—The Cook.—Miniature from the Terence of Charles VI.—Manuscript of the early part of the Fifteenth Century (No. 25, B.L).—In the Arsenal Library, Paris.

which appear four persons: Figura (or God in human form), Adam, Eve, and the Devil. The first scene opens in the Garden of Eden, which is placed upon an eminence, and is bright with sweet-smelling flowers and fruit-trees. God is represented as wearing a dalmatica, Adam a red tunic, and Eve a peplum of white silk. It is to be remarked that whenever God quits the stage, he goes back into the church—a fact which indicates to us precisely the place where the representation was held. The opening part of the scene is as follows, after the original text in old French :—

" FIGURA.

Adam !

ADAM.

Sire !

FIGURA.

Fourmé te ai
De limo terre.

ADAM.

Ben le sai.

FIGURA.

Je t'ai fourmé à mun semblant,
A m'image : ne t'ai fait de terre.
Ne m' devez jamais mover guerre

ADAM.

Nen ferai-je, mais te crerrai :
Mun creatur obeirai.

FIGURA.

Je t'ai duné bon compainun :
Ce est ta femme, Eva a noun ;
Ce est ta femme, e tun pareil.
Tu li deis estre bien fiel (*fidèle*).
Tu aime lui, e ele aime toi :
Si serez ben ambdui (*tous deux*) de moi.
El' seit à tun comandement,
E vus ambedeus à mun talent.
De ta coste je l'ai fourmée :
N'est pas estrange, de toi est née.
Je la plasmai (*créai*) de ton cors.
De toi eissit, non pas de fors.
Tu la gouverne par raison ;
N'ait entre vus jà tençon (*querelle*) ;
Mais grant amor, grand conservage :
Tel soit la lei de mariage."

God, after having thus addressed Adam and Eve, withdraws, leaving them to walk about the garden, playing innocently (*honeste delectantes*). The demons approach them, and show Eve the fruits of the tree of good and evil. The Devil then appears, and counsels Adam to pluck the forbidden fruit. Adam angrily repels him, and the Devil then addresses himself to Eve, who makes but a feeble resistance to his tempting. Adam compels the Devil to go away, but the latter is seen assuming the form of a serpent (a mechanical serpent, *artificiose compositus* as it was called, appeared upon the stage), which crawls close to the tree of good and evil. Eve yields to the crafty advice of Satan, plucks the apple, and offers it to Adam, who, after refusing to take it, eventually eats part of it. He at once sees his fault, and hides in a bush, in order to take off his festal garments (*solemnes vestes*) and assume a costume of leaves. Eve and himself, concealed in a corner of Paradise, are afraid to appear before God, who is seen walking arrayed in pontifical robes. He calls to Adam in Latin, "Adam, ubi es?" At length the two culprits appear, ashamed and repentant, mutually accusing one another. God drives them from Paradise, informing them of all the sorrows which await them on earth. An angel, robed in white and waving a flaming sword, stations himself at the gate of Paradise. In the last scene Adam and Eve are laboriously tilling the ground and sowing corn, but during their sleep the Devil plants thorns and thistles among the wheat. When they awake and behold the Devil's work, they prostrate themselves in the dust, beat their breasts, and abandon themselves to despair. The Devil calls together the demons, who load Adam and Eve with chains, and drive them to the brink of hell, into which the two sinners are precipitated, amidst the laughter and yells which issue from the flaming abyss. This is the analysis of the first act, which forms a complete play of itself, and which embodies the three elements of tragedy, pantomime, and opera.

The dramatic movement which took place in France in the twelfth century was not peculiar to that country. In the year 1110 the Norman poet Geoffroy had played at Dunstable, in Bedfordshire, the *Miracle de St. Catherine*, which was very much admired by the Anglo-Normans. Mention is made in a Chronicle of Frioul of the representation of a Latin mystery in 1218. In Germany the *Passion Play* was given in the Cathedral of Vienna, and the *Sepulchre of Our Lord* in the heart of Bohemia about 1437. Long before this, Armorican Brittany had provided the faithful with a mystery written in the national dialect upon the *Life of St. Nonne,* which certain critics hold to be of earlier date than the twelfth century, and which is still represented in the country districts of Brittany.

These dramas—French, German, English, Italian, and Breton—all composed in the same spirit of fervent piety, were produced at almost the same time in all countries, and in almost the same shape. They were conceived, written, and played by priests or by monks. But the laymen in course of time competed with the clergy for theatrical representations, and it may be said that the whole of Christendom then took part in the performance of the mysteries and the miracles.

In most European countries, notably in France, from the twelfth century, each art or trade was organized as a religious association (*confrérie*) as soon as it had constituted itself into an industrial or trade corporation. Having their origin in local feeling and political emancipation, these associations were in many instances dramatic companies, enjoying the favour of the magistracy and clergy of the town. Moreover, all classes of the population were invited to take parts in the public representations of these great sacred dramas, in which as many as six hundred persons sometimes figured. The Church, so severe at first with regard to the secular theatre, relaxed her regulations in this respect, and encouraged those who took part, as actors or spectators, in these edifying spectacles, which revived the principal facts of Bible history, and popularised the triumph of the Christian religion. The municipalities, for their part, encouraged and remunerated the authors and the actors, and had numerous copies taken of these pious compositions, the official text of which was deposited in the archives of the town.

As long as the mysteries and miracles preserved their exclusively liturgical character, the persons who figured in them as actors were not considered to exercise any special profession, but rather a sort of religious function. Thus, from the fourteenth century, the champions of the dogma of the Immaculate Conception, which had not as yet been proclaimed by the Church, formed dramatic associations for the purpose of propagating this dogma by playing the *Mysteries of Our Lady*, composed in honour of the Virgin Mary, who conceived without sin (Fig. 381). Amongst these confrères, all of whom wore the ecclesiastical dress as a symbol of their clerical origin, there were some who entitled themselves "Brothers of the Passion," and they soon established a permanent theatre in the village of St. Maur-des-Fossés, near Paris, in 1398. This theatre was almost at once closed by order of the

Provost of Paris, doubtless at the request of the clergy of the capital, who complained that their parishioners neglected the Church services to go and see the play of the Brothers of the Passion. But four years afterwards King Charles VI. accorded them letters patent, dated December 4th, 1402, and they were no longer interfered with in the exercise of their vocation. After having obtained, by these letters patent, permission to continue their plays and to show themselves, even in theatrical costume, in the streets of Paris, they obtained from the monks of the Trinity Hospital (in the Rue St. Denis, opposite the Rue Grenetat), a long low room, in which they opened the first permanent and covered theatre which was founded in Paris, and here

Fig. 381.—The Hermit forces Robert le Diable to declare his Identity.—Miniature from the "Miracle de Nostre-Dame et de Robert le Dyable."—Manuscript of the Fourteenth Century. —In the National Library, Paris.

they gave representations every Sunday and fête day from twelve to five in the afternoon.

Long after this the mysteries and miracles continued to be represented in the provinces, the places selected being consecrated ground and graveyards. The Synodic Statutes of Orleans even show that the representation of scenic play stook place in the cathedral, probably in front of the portico, as late as 1525 and 1587. The same was the case all over Europe up to the middle of the sixteenth century. Under the pontificate of Innocent VIII., about 1490, Lorenzo de' Medici, upon the occasion of the marriage of his daughter to a nephew of the Pope, himself composed a *Mystery of St. John and St. Paul,* which he had represented by several members of his family inside one of the Florence churches.

The people of the Middle Ages, from the very fact that their existence was more monotonous than that of the people of the present day, were all the more ready to seize an opportunity for amusement, and the solemn representations of the mysteries were amongst their most cherished enjoyments. The entrance of the King or Queen into a town, the birth of a prince or princess, the court festivals, as well as the ecclesiastical solemnities and the feasts of the Church, were an excuse for these popular spectacles. The representations, prepared a long time beforehand, were announced by the public crier, like the royal and municipal decrees, at the most frequented places of the town. The spectators, who had not to pay anything for witnessing the play, did not seat themselves promiscuously, but each person according to his rank and station. The nobles or dignitaries occupied platforms, upon which, as the representations lasted a long time, they sometimes had their meals served, like the old Romans upon the balconies of the amphitheatre or circus. The plain bourgeois and the lower classes occupied places, either seated or standing, upon the bare earth or the pavement, as the case might be, the men being to the right, and the women to the left, the same as in church. The local clergy, in order to let their congregations have an opportunity of witnessing the whole spectacle, advanced or put back the hour of divine service. In fact, the fondness of the public for these spectacles was so great that the houses were left almost deserted, and armed watchmen paced the silent streets to protect the property of the inhabitants while the representation was taking place.

There were not as yet any permanent theatres in the towns, but the dimensions of the temporary theatres erected were regulated according to the number of actors who had to appear upon the stage. As a matter of course, when, as in the thirteenth and fourteenth centuries, the only pieces represented were episodical dramas, such as the *Miracles de Notre-Dame,* these theatres were not nearly so large or so complicated as when there came to be represented the great poems or mystery-plays of the *Old Testament,* the *Passion,* and the *Acts of the Apostles.* The theatre and the platforms used for these public representations, which often lasted several days, must have been of immense dimensions, and have entailed considerable expense.

M. Charles Magnin, in his work upon theatrical archæology, says, "The

Miracles de Notre-Dame did not require more than two stories or stalls, the one raised above the other. The upper story represented Paradise, in which were seated upon a throne God and the Virgin, surrounded by their celestial court. The lower story was reserved for the human scenes, and divided by partitions and tapestry into as many chambers or compartments as there were different places to represent. The upper story (Heaven) communicated with the lower (Earth) by means of two spiral staircases placed at each side of the stage. It was by these that descended and reascended in procession God, the Virgin, and the Angels, when they manifested themselves to the inhabitants of Earth. The floor of the theatre, the area, or, as it would now be called, the pit, was formed of the turf of a meadow or graveyard;" unless, that is to say, the town in which the representation was to take place possessed the remains of some ancient theatre, in which case it was utilised for the occasion. This indirect use of the pagan theatres for the religious plays of the Middle Ages took place all over Europe before the Brothers of the Passion and other similar associations had acquired permanent and covered buildings. In about the middle of the fifteenth century the permanent and provisional theatres increased in size in proportion as the framework of the mystery-plays represented in them became enlarged. To the two primitive stories were superadded a number of compartments intended to represent in perspective, upon different planes and at different elevations, Heaven, Hell, the World, Jerusalem, Egypt, Rome, the house of St. Joseph, &c. The actors, while they were upon the stage, moved into one of these compartments, designated by placards or inscriptions, every time that the place in which the scene was laid changed, and, after having "done their play," they leisurely resumed their place upon the raised seats of the theatre.

As far as can be judged by the few documents relating to this subject, there were two kinds of scenery; the one kind painted as in the present day, the other constructed of wood, or even stone, which had a regularly embossed surface. Moreover, as the spectators would often have experienced much difficulty in following the plot amidst the host of persons who appeared upon the stage, and the frequent change from one place to another, the author always offered in an explanatory prologue some general notices which enabled them to understand what was going on. He would say, for instance, " We are about to narrate the blessed Resurrection. Let us first arrange the stage accordingly. Here the Cross, and there the Tomb. . . . Hell will be on this side; the house upon the other; then Heaven. . . . Caiaphas will take his place here, and with him the Jewish people; next, Joseph of Arimathea. . . . In the fourth compartment will be seen Nicodemus. . . . We shall also represent the town of Emmaus, in which Jesus Christ was entertained."

In addition to these prologues addressed to the public by the author or by the "director of the play," we meet in some of the mysteries with short sermons in prose delivered by priests, who appeared upon the stage in their stoles to excite the devotion of the actors and audience. Sometimes even a high mass would be held just before the representation, as a preparation for witnessing a piece in which was to be given an episode in the life of our Lord (Fig. 382) or the martyrdom of some saint. When these religious dramas were still played in the churches they generally terminated with a Te Deum or a Magnificat, sung by the principal actor when he reached the end of his part. As a rule, the play was not begun until all the actors who were to appear in it had " done the show," as it was called, either on foot, or on horseback, or in a carriage; that is to say, had exhibited in the streets not only the costumes to be worn, but the engines or mechanical contrivances to be used on the stage. The representation once begun, the actors who were not required on the stage were compelled, in the intervals, to remain in view of the audience, seated upon benches placed at each side of the theatre, for the "slips" were not then invented to increase the optical illusion by favouring the entry or egress of the players. The unity of time was altogether disregarded, as well as the unity of place. Thus, for instance, in representing the history of Notre-Dame, a child of four or five years old would take the part of Mary in the beginning of the piece, and would be succeeded, as the play progressed, by another girl fifteen or sixteen years old, who would in her turn be succeeded by a third person to represent Mary when married to Joseph, and the mother of Jesus. The result of this triple change was that the spectators had before them upon the benches three incarnations of one and the same person, each of a different age, appearance, and dress.

It may be guessed that there was no great accuracy with regard to dress in these representations. The playwrights and actors, or dramatic poets, who represented the funeral of Julius Cæsar with choristers bearing the crucifix and holy water, did not trouble themselves about historical and archæological truth. But, excepting these primitive errors, it may safely be said that the theatre of the fifteenth century was little inferior, in point of splendour and

Fig. 382.—Scenes at the Birth and in the Childhood of Jesus, as they were represented in the "Mystère de la Conception," by Jehan Michel.—Large Chest of the Fourteenth Century, of Carved Wood, in which were kept the Ecclesiastical Vestments and the Church Ornaments.

magnificence, to the modern stage. There were some very quaint costumes assigned by tradition to certain parts. Thus the devils were always in black, and the angels in white, blue, and red; while, as the priestly garment was looked upon as the most worthy of respect, God was always represented with cope and stole, and a bishop's mitre or a pope's tiara. The actors who had to represent the dead dressed "as souls;" that is to say, they covered themselves with a veil—white for the saved, red or black for the lost. In the *Mistère du Vieux Testament*, in which it was desired to represent the blood of Abel shed by Cain, the actor who had to represent this blood was wrapped in a large red cloak, and writhed at the feet of the murderer, crying, "Vengeance!"

The mysteries, some of which contained seventy or eighty thousand lines, would have taken several consecutive weeks to play through, so that, in order to give players and the public breathing-time, an interval of several days was given after each representation, and when the play was resumed the attendance was as numerous as at the beginning. As M. Louandre justly observes, "Could it be otherwise? The public beheld in a living and animated form the world of the past and of the future, the Paradise of their first parents, and the Paradise in which they would one day contemplate their God. They looked at all this with the eyes of faith, and the influence of this sacred drama was not a triumph of art, but a miracle of belief. Of art, in fact, there were but a few flashes in these compositions, at once barbarous and artless, and in which were reflected the real and the fantastic world, sacred history and profane."

The miracles, which contained, like the mysteries, so many touching and graceful passages, are filled with singular details, which the careful historian should on no account overlook. This simple-minded and confused accumulation of dissonant ideas did not exclude the shrewd humour which we find in all the French poems of the fifteenth century. It is a mistake, therefore, to say that the miracles contained neither satires on manners nor allusions to contemporary events, and numerous instances might be cited in contradiction. Thus, in the miracles composed and played in the reign of Charles VI., Queen Isabeau of Bavaria, and her brother-in-law, the Duke of Orleans, are severely assailed; the court, too, is very roughly handled; the military party is inveighed against; and even the clergy do not always escape. In many parts of these popular pieces the noble inspiration of the poet bursts forth beneath the coarse envelope of an as yet imperfect language. It will be sufficient to cite, as a model of sombre and tragic force, the following dialogue between Judas and the Demon :—

" LE DÉMON.

Meschant, que veulx-tu qu'on te fasse ?
A quel port veulx-tu aborder ?

JUDAS.

Je ne sais. Je n'ai œil en face
Qui ose les Cieulx regarder.

LE DÉMON.

Si de mon nom veulx demander,
Briefvement en auras demonstrance.

JUDAS.

D'où viens-tu ?

LE DÉMON.

Du parfond d'enfer.

JUDAS.

Quel est ton nom ?

LE DÉMON.

Désespérance.

JUDAS.

Terribilité de vengeance !
Horribilité de dangier !
Approche et me donne allégeance,
Se mort peut mon deuil allégier.

LE DÉMON.

Oui, très-bien." . . .

In striking contrast with this grand scene between Judas and the Demon, we will quote a model of gracefulness and artlessness—the Shepherd's scene in the great *Mystery of the Passion*, by the brothers Arnold Greban, a mystery far superior to that which Jehan Michel composed on the same subject :—

" UN BERGER.

Est-il liesse plus serie (*joie plus sereine*)
Que de regarder ces beaux champs
Et ces doulx aignelets paissans,
Saultans à la belle praerie ?

SECOND BERGER.

On parle de grand seignourie,
D'avoir donjons, palais puissans ;
Est-il liesse plus serie
Que de regarder ces beaux champs,
Et ces doulx aignelets paissans,
Saultans à la belle praerie ?

TROISIÈME BERGER.

En gardant leurs brebiettes,
    Pasteurs ont bon temps :
Ils jouent de leurs musettes,
    Liez (*joyeux*) et esbatans ;
Là dient leurs chansonnettes,
Là sont les doulces bergerettes
    Qui vont bien chantans,
    Et belles fleurettes . . .
Pasteurs ont bon temps ! "

Nothing can be more touching than the scene from the *Mystère de
St. Louis,* in which Enguerrand de Couchy, the savage hunter, having
surprised three youths shooting at his rabbits, hands them over without
remorse to the executioner. The latter, with his assistant's help, at once
hangs them to the gibbet, not, however, without manifesting a feeling of pity
which forms the most striking contrast with the unflinching severity of his
sinister profession :—

" DEUXIÈME ENFANT.

(*Après que le premier a été pendu.*)

. . . Hélas ! que diront
Nos nobles parens, quand sauront
Nostre mort très-dure et amère ?

TROISIÈME ENFANT.

Je plains mon père.

DEUXIÈME ENFANT.

Et moi, ma mère.

ENGUERRAND, *au bourreau.*

Meshui (*à présent*) depesche-le, paillart !
        (*Le bourreau le jette,* c'est-à-dire le pend.)

LE BOURREAU.

Le voilà depesché soudain.
L'autre ?

LE VALET.

        Je le tiens par la main.
Il est tendre comme rosée,
Le jeune enfant.

LE BOURREAU, *à son valet.*

        Tay-toi ! Tay-toi !
A l'enfant :
Mon amy, muntez après moi,
Et pens :z à Dieu !''

Thus all styles are to be found mixed up the one with the other in the great dramas of the Middle Ages, which are at once mystic and grotesque, sombre and joyous, trivial and solemn. Men, angels, earthly kings, and the King of kings pass in turn before the audience, and for several centuries all the theatrical compositions which appear by the side of the sacred are only, so to speak, detached chapters—*branches,* to employ the term then in use.

Tragedy did not exist in the Middle Ages, and it is a mistake to imagine that the Provençal poets or troubadours, Arnaut Daniel, Anselme Faidit, and Bérenger de Parasol were the principal *factors* of tragedy in the twelfth and thirteenth centuries. This form of dramatic composition did not assume definite shape until the middle of the sixteenth century, when Baïf and Thomas Sibilet produced a few imitations of the Greek tragedies, and when Jodelle represented, in 1552, *Cleopatra,* which must be considered as the first French tragedy in verse.

Comedy had already been in existence for a considerable period, for it may be said that the vein of comedy is essentially Gallic, and the nearer we come to the Renaissance, the faster does this vein expand itself upon our stage, which has continued to be without a rival in the way of tragedy as of comedy. In the thirteenth century, Adam de la Hale, nicknamed the Hunchback of Arras, produced the first French comedy, called the *Jeu de Mariage d'Adam,* or the *Jeu de la Feuillée,* and the first comic opera, a sort of pastoral, entitled *Le Jeu de Robin et de Marion,* of which he composed the words and music. These two ancient pieces, as well as the famous *Farce de Pathelin* (Figs. 383 and 384), which dates from the second half of the fifteenth century, and which long enjoyed a universal reputation, are in all respects very remarkable productions. If the author of the *Farce de Pathelin* were known, his name would rank beside that of Molière.

The comic pieces of the Middle Ages, which were called *jeux*, *soties*, or *farces*, are for the most part notable for their fund of humour and gaiety.

Fig. 383.—Pathelin taking the Piece of Cloth which he steals from the Draper.

Fig. 384.—Pathelin pleading for the Shepherd before the Judge.

Fac-similes of Wood Engravings of the "Farce de Pathelin" (Gothic Edition, Paris, Germain Beneaut, 1490, in 4to).

They may be considered, according to the taste of the present day, rather too broad, but we must make allowance for the time, as these crude expressions did not offend the taste of the age, and passed muster with the most polished court in Europe. The Moralités stand midway between the farces, of which they possess the satirical spirit, and the mysteries, of which they imitate to a certain extent the moral and religious tendencies. They were not more than a portrayal, sometimes even a criticism, upon the Church in its human and temporal aspects; canons, bishops, cardinals, and even popes are not spared, and the actor—that is to say, the author—shows no mercy in his condemnation of the vices and faults which he can discern in them. The moralité also

Fig. 385.—The Actor (Author) listening to the Personification of his Thought.—Miniature from the " Chevalier délibéré," by Olivier de la Marche.—Manuscript of the Fifteenth Century (No. 173, B.L.).—In the Arsenal Library, Paris.

deals with the kings and temporal nobility, and, often assuming a political character, calls them to account for their public or private conduct. Sometimes, again, a fact taken from the sacred books, or some idea occurring to the poet, furnishes the theme for a sort of moralité which may be described as legendary. For instance, the *Histoire de l'Enfant Prodigue*, the *Luz d'Amour Divin*, the *Histoire de Ste. Suzanne, exemplaire de toutes femmes sages et de tous les bons juges*, are moralités in which religious mysticism is allied to the teachings of practical wisdom, and the characters in which—Envy Reason, and Good Renown—are introduced into the plot, like the Chorus of ancient tragedy, to control, judge, and appreciate the respective position of the personages in the drama, into which the author then introduces a sort of dialogue, or moral and allegorical poem, similar to the *Chevalier délibéré* of Olivier de la Marche (Fig. 385).

The soties, farces, and moralités were never put upon the stage with the splendour of the mysteries, and save with a few exceptions, the number

Fig. 386.—Portrait of Clement Marot.—Fac-simile of an Engraving by Léonard Gaultier, from the Series known as "Chronologie collée."—In the Library of M. Ambroise Firmin-Didot, Paris.

of the personages introduced was always very small. Moreover, a capital difference is to be established between these two kinds of spectacle, viz. that the mysteries were represented, so to speak, by everybody and for everybody, under the patronage of the Church, whereas the farces, soties, and moralités were played for a special public by private companies of laymen, who were, no doubt, regular comedians.

The jugglers and tale-tellers, who were many of them authors of satirical and amusing poems, which they went about reciting from place to place, to the accompaniment of the violin, might be regarded as the first actors of secular pieces; for not only did they sojourn in the castles of the nobles to recite their poems, but they performed plays in character, which were in reality scenic romances and dialogues, such as the metrical tale, "Aucassin and

Nicolette." After the jugglers came various literary and dramatic associations, some of them stationary in Paris or some large city, whilst others travelled through the provinces, who are only known to us by their theatrical names, such as the Enfants sans Souci, the Bazochiens, the Enfants de la Mère Sotte, the Mère Folle de Dijon, &c. It has been said, but without sufficient authority, that the Chambers of Rhetoric, which also represented comic pieces, existed in Belgium and Flanders as early as the thirteenth century. Whatever may be the truth as to this assertion, it is certain that Antwerp possessed two Chambers of Rhetoric, and Ghent four; and the theatrical taste of the Flemish and the Belgians was carried so far that their communal companies

Fig. 387.—Token of Pierre le Dru, Printer of Gringore's Poetry at the Sign of the "Mère Sotte," near "the End of Nostre-Dame Bridge" (Paris, 1505).

of archers and crossbow-men sought relaxation from their military exercises in dramatic entertainments, and eventually became regular comedians.

The festivals of Christmas and Epiphany, the Carnival, and a few local solemnities were annually celebrated in Paris and in the principal French towns by burlesque representations, often degenerating into scandal, given by the Bazoche, which consisted of the law licentiates and all the young men belonging to the courts of justice. The Enfants de la Mère Sotte and the Enfants sans Souci did not long form two separate and distinct troupes, and several of the best poets of the time—amongst others, François Villon and Clement Marot (Fig. 386)—were actors in both of these troupes. Another excellent poet, Pierre Gringore, herald-at-arms to the Duke of Lorraine, was the principal author and the manager of the troupe named Enfants sans Souci, the members of which, recruited amongst the wealthy bourgeois families, had set up in opposition to the Brothers of the Passion. Gringore's theatre, established close to what are now the Paris markets, was in great vogue during the reign of Louis XII., and his representations generally took place during the Carnival. The pieces in his repertory, though interlarded with sharp hits at the higher clergy and the court of Rome, were for the most part somewhat severe upon the score of morality, for he had taken as his motto, " Raison partout, rien que raison " (Reason everywhere, nothing but reason).

The people had a keen liking for spectacles of every kind during the Middle Ages, and always turned out in crowds to witness the cavalcades, *pomps*, and processions which accompanied the tournaments, plenary courts, and feudal ceremonies. In a history of the theatre it is necessary, there-fore, to mention the plays in dumb-show, the allegories, and the pantomimes, which were principally represented upon the occasion of a royal visit, or of public rejoicings in celebration of some great local or political event. (See, in the volume on " Manners, Customs, and Dress," chapter on *Ceremonial.*) Then, again, there was the *Dance of Death*, known as the *Danse Macabre*, which in the fifteenth century was one of the spectacles which produced the greatest effect upon the common people (Fig. 388). It is almost certain that at first this *Danse Macabre* was a sort of pantomime, a compound of music and singing; and in 1424, the English, then masters of Paris, had it publicly performed in the Cemetery of the Innocents, to celebrate their victory at Verneuil.

Another pantomime, but of a less lugubrious kind, was offered to the people of Paris in 1313, by order of Philippe le Bel, in honour of the recep-tion of his two sons into the Order of Chivalry. Godefroy de Paris, a rhyming chronicler of the time, describes it as follows:—

> " Vit-on Dieu, sa Mère rire . . .
> Nostre Seigneur manger des pommes, . . .
> Et les Anges au paradis . . .
> Et les Ames dedans chanter . . .
> Enfer y fut noir et puant,
> Diables y ot plus de cent." . . .

In 1437, when Charles VII. entered Paris, a representation was given of the *Combat of the Seven Capital Sins against the Three Theological Virtues and the Four Cardinal Virtues.* When Charles the Bold entered a town in the Netherlands a sort of *tableau vivant* called the *Judgment of Paris* was given in his honour. In the famous entertainments at Rouen in 1550, in honour of

Fig. 388.—The Actor (Author), conducted by Fresh-Memory, is shown the Burial-places of the Chevaliers, Kings, and Emperors.—Miniature from the " Chevalier délibéré."—Manuscript of the Fifteenth Century (No. 173, B. L.).—In the Arsenal Library.

the entry of King Henry II., there were represented at the same time Faith and Virtue, Olympus and the Parliament of Normandy, the Muses, and all Kings of France from Pharamond's time. Thus all epochs and all kinds of belief were put under contribution by the inventors of pantomimes, so as to give more attraction and splendour to these spectacles, which were solely intended to gratify the eye.

Up to the middle of the sixteenth century, the farces, soties, and moralités continued to attract the public, and the scenic tradition of the Middle Ages was still much the same as it had been two centuries previously. But in 1541 the Paris Parliament forbade the actors who represented the *Mystery of the Acts of the Apostles* to open their theatre upon saints' days and Sundays, and even upon certain week-days. This was the origin of a hot dispute, in which the Provost of Paris and the King himself intervened, and which terminated, after many delays and difficulties, by a definite authorisation granted to the actors, who took up their quarters at the Hôtel de Bourgogne, in the Rue Françoise. The ancient privileges of the Brothers of the Passion were confirmed by a decree of the Parliament dated November 19th, 1548, upon the express condition that "for the future they shall play only secular, lawful, and decent subjects, and no longer introduce into their plays anything touching the mysteries or religion." The miracles, the mysteries, and the moralités were accordingly eliminated from their repertory. The Brothers of the Passion, who had the right to represent *grandes histoires par personnages* (narratives with the characters in them personated), such as the *Destruction of Troy the Great*, by Jacques Millet (Fig. 389), abandoned their dramatic undertaking, and ceded their play-room and privileges to a troupe of regular actors who gave there representations of tragedy and comedy. The Hôtel de Bourgogne, over the principal entrance to which was still retained a sculptured bas-relief with the instruments of Christ's Passion, became the cradle of the Théâtre Français.

Thus exiled from the capital, the mysteries took refuge in the provinces, where they held possession of the stage, in some few towns, for the whole of the sixteenth century, competing for public favour with the buffoons and mountebanks who attended the fairs (Fig. 390). The farces and soties had also been proscribed. In 1516 the Bazochiens were forbidden by parliamentary decree, and by order of the Provost of Paris, to make any allusion to the royal family in the pieces which they represented. In 1536 they were forbidden to "exhibit spectacles or writings taxing or noting (blaming or criticizing) any person whatsoever." Two years later they were compelled to submit their pieces to the censorship of Parliament before putting them

upon the stage; and, as the satirical boldness of these pieces continued to
increase, the clerks of the Bazoche who did not conform to this order were
threatened with the gibbet. Such severities were necessarily fatal to the
soties, and at about the end of the sixteenth century they disappeared
altogether.

These restrictions upon the liberty of the stage—the establishment of
dramatic censure, and the prohibition of pieces representing sacred subjects—
accelerated the disappearance of the ancient drama, and there then dawned a

Fig. 389.—The Abduction of Helen.—Fac-simile of a Wood Engraving from the "Istoire de la
    Destruction de Troye la Grant, mise par Personnaiges," by Master Jacques Millet (Paris,
    Jehan Driart, 1498, in folio, Goth.).—In the Library of M. Firmin-Didot, Paris.

new period in dramatic art all over Europe. By the side of the mysteries,
which were still represented in Spain under the names of *autos sacramentales*,
appeared the brilliant dramas of Calderon and Lope de Vega. Shakspeare
at the same time appeared upon the English stage, and in Italy Machiavelli's
Mandragora revealed a modern Aristophanes. At the court of Leo X.
classic tragedy revived in Trissino's *Sophonisba*. In France, too, where there
was a reawakening of the souvenirs of ancient Greece and Rome, Sibilet,

Guillaume Bouchet, and Lazare de Baïf translated Sophocles and Euripides; Octavian de St. Gelais, Bonaventure des Périers, and Charles Estienne translated Terence into prose and verse; and Ronsard had scarcely terminated his university studies when he translated into verse the *Plutus* of Aristophanes, and he and several of his fellow-students played at the Boncourt College, where he had been a student. This is a favourable opportunity for pointing out that with this new kind of dramatic pieces there appeared a new class of actors; for the university students, under the direction of their teachers, played in the improvised theatres of their colleges, and were even admitted occasionally to play before the court. The same thing occurred in England, as is shown by a passage in *Hamlet;* and there were university theatres in Germany, upon which were represented the Latin comedies of Reuchlin and Conrad Celtès, imitations of the *Farce de Pathelin* and other French soties.

Tradition and imitation successively held the upper hand, and tragedy was at first, and for a considerable time, preferred far above comedy. The authors of the first classic tragedies—Etienne, Jodelle, Jacques de la Taille, Charles Toustain, and Jacques Grevin—minutely observed the traditions of the Greek drama, conforming themselves to the rules as to unity of time and place, interspersing the dialogues with lyric choruses, and resisting, so to speak, every kind of innovation, as from Robert Garnier (Fig. 391), who produced the first piece in 1573, down to Rotrou, who definitely marked the starting-point of modern tragedy, the ideas of the tragic poets are framed after the same pattern, just as their Alexandrines are cast in the same mould. For two centuries the French were all for tragedy, though the tragic writers, when inventing a subject of their own, did not limit themselves to Greece and to Rome. Pierre Mathieu's *Esther and Vashti*, and P. Bardou's *St. Jacques*, remind one, so far as the subject is concerned, of the mysteries; but the composition and form of these pieces did not outstep the rules of rhetoric, and French tragedy not unfrequently introduced upon the stage, within the limit of these well-defined rules, French subjects and personages even while living, as, for instance, Joan of Arc, Coligny, the Guises, the League, &c.

The old comic plays, which were cultivated with more or less success at the Hôtel de Bourgogne by Pierre Leloyer, Remy Belleau, Honoré d'Urfé, Pierre Larivey, and others, developed into comedies, tragi-comedies, pastorals, *fables bocagères* (fables of the gross), and *plaisants devis* (waggish sayings). Some of

Fig. 390.—The Stage of a Mountebank Seller of Drugs.—After a Coloured Drawing in Manuscript of the Fifteenth Century, preserved in the Town Library, Cambrai.

the poets, too, who had succeeded at tragedies, also tried their hand at the less serious style. First of all they imitated Menander and Plautus, and in many cases produced works full of amusing situations and witty sayings, and with dialogues in verse remarkable for their ease, not less than for their animation and brilliancy. It must be allowed that the comedies of the sixteenth century are not less broad in their language than the Greek and Roman comedies; but, as one of the best writers of the time, Pierre de Larivey of Champagne, remarks in one of his prologues, "If any man should be of opinion that there is an occasional departure from propriety, I beg him to remember that, in order to express correctly the fashions and tendencies of the present day, the acts and the words must be of corresponding wantonness." The authors of that period composed their comedies after the models which they had before their eyes, and in representing the corrupt morals of

Fig. 391.—Portrait of Robert Garnier.—Fac-simile of an Engraving by Léonard Gaultier, from the Series called "Chronologie collée," in the Library of M. Firmin-Didot, Paris.

their time they did not offend either the eyes or the ears of their audience. Besides, these pieces did not go nearly so far as the Italian comedies, such as the *Abusés* of the Sienna Academy, translated into French, and Ariosto's *Supposés*, also translated into French, and represented all over the country. The Italian comedy had also come into favour since the performance at Lyons of Bibiena's *Calandra*, which was represented there in 1548, before the court, by some Italian actors, whom Catherine de' Medicis had sent for. But the first Italian troupe which settled in Paris had been brought from Venice, in 1577, by order of King Henry III., who allowed them to give their representations in the Hôtel du Petit-Bourbon. This troupe became sedentary, and Italian comedy, the repertory of which surpassed in licentiousness and extravagance the farces of the old French drama, remained in existence in Paris, almost without interruption, to the close of the seventeenth century.

CIVIL AND RELIGIOUS ORATORY.

The Oratorical Genius of the Gauls.—The Origin of the French Bar.—Christian Oratory in the
First Centuries.—Gallo-Roman Oratory. — Preachers and Missionaries. — Orators of the
Crusades.—St. Bernard and St. Dominic.—Pleadings at the Bar under Louis XI.—Political
Oratory under Charles VI.—Popular Preachers.—Orators of the Reformation.—Orators of the
League.—Parliamentary Harangues.—Oratory in the States-General.—Military Oratory.

 HE veneration in which all the great men of
antiquity have held the gift of eloquence,"
says M. Louandre, of whose treatise, as in
the previous chapter, we avail ourselves with
reference to this subject, "the historical
prestige attaching to the names of pagan
orators, the victories gained by the generals
who were able to address their soldiers, and
the influence acquired by the demagogues
who knew how to captivate the attention
of the crowd, show that in the ancient
world it was not merely literary renown,
but a share in the direction of state affairs which resulted from the *art de bien
dire*" (the art of speaking).   But, at the close of the first century of the
Christian era, this marvellous art, which had reached so high a pitch of
perfection in the flourishing periods of Athens and Rome, fell into complete
decadence, and the three following centuries possessed nothing but turgid and
insipid spouters.   Rhetoric took the place of inspiration, and if oratory was
still professed in the Greek and Roman schools, the pedantic mode of teaching
produced only rhetoricians.   Thus all that remains of that period is panegyrics
and congratulatory harangues; for the sole aim of these rhetoricians was to
flatter the emperors and the great, obtain favour, and guard themselves
against disgrace.   Amongst them may be mentioned Claudius Mamertinus

Major and Mamertinus Minor, Nazarius, Drepanius, and several Gauls from Aquitaine.

Eloquence had from the earliest period been held in great honour amongst the Gauls. The ancient Gauls paid worship to Hercules, of whom they had made the god of speech, and whom they represented in allegory as attacking men with golden chains issuing from his mouth. Thus the art of oratory was in their esteem the highest of all, and they were very fond of hearing good speeches. This will explain why the Emperor Claudius instituted at Lyons oratorical jousts, the defeated in which were compelled to efface with the tongue their unsuccessful speeches, under penalty of being cast into the Rhône. Juvenal and St. Jerome (Fig. 392) are agreed in recognising the natural talent of the Gallic race for speaking. In the principal towns of Gaul—at Toulouse, Bordeaux, Marseilles, Treves, Besançon, and Autun—there existed public schools of oratory, which produced thousands of orators, or rather of rhetoricians, but which left no permanent record of civil or purely literary eloquence. The reason was that a new stamp of eloquence, such as paganism had never been able to inspire, was suddenly called into being with the Christian religion. The pagan rhetoricians were awed into silence, like the oracles of the false gods, at its first accents, and the pulpit of sacred oratory henceforward stood alone in the midst of the ancient Forum.

For centuries the art of oratory had no annals in political life, and speaking, which held such a large place in the records of ancient history, does not occupy more than a few pages in the histories of the early ages of the French monarchy. Gregory of Tours, in his "History of the Francs," makes it sufficiently clear that the warriors of these barbarian times set more store by deeds than by words. King Clovis, when urging his warriors to undertake fresh conquests, merely said to them, "It pains me to see the Arians in possession of a part of Gaul. Let us march against them, with the aid of God, and after we have vanquished them let us reduce the country into our power." And the Franks forthwith prepared to undertake the campaign. Mummolus, Count of Auxerre, and patrician of the troops of King Gontran, said to the Saxons, who, after having devastated all the land which they had overrun, were about to cross the Rhône to invade the kingdom of Sigebert, "You have depopulated the land of the King my master, carried off the crops and the cattle, delivered the houses to the flames, cut down the olive-trees, and rooted up the vines. You shall not set foot upon the other side of the stream until you have made compensation to those whom you have reduced to misery. If you refuse, the weight of my sword shall be felt by you, by your wives, and by your children, to avenge the wrong done to the King my master." This proud utterance is full of simplicity, but it no way resembles the allocutions addressed by the generals of Greece and of Rome to their soldiers—allocutions of real eloquence, in which was united to beauty of diction the power of moving and carrying away popular feeling.

In certain circumstances, however, the Gauls must have employed the

Fig. 392.—St. Jerome and two Cardinals.—Miniature from the "Petit Traité de la Vanité des Choses Mondaines."—Manuscript of the Fifteenth Century (No. 30, Sc. and A.).—In the Arsenal Library, Paris.

gift of speaking with success, but we possess no written record of their civil oratory. This oratory they undoubtedly employed in judicial pleadings, even at the time when the Germans and the Franks were established in Gaul. The Franks, who did not hesitate to assume the language, and even to imitate the customs, of the peoples whom they had subjected, found the Gallo-Roman bar in regular practice in the sixth century, and far from fettering an institution which, as has been ingeniously suggested by a modern historian, appeared to them like a mimic battle-field, they were the first to declare that the profession of barrister was a noble one, and they soon sought to obtain admission to it, by asking to be given the title of advocate, or *avoué*, to the churches and monasteries—offices which compelled them not only to defend by force ecclesiastical territory and privileges, but also to protect them, when necessary, by word of mouth, at the pleas wherein were publicly debated questions at issue, in presence of the *leudes*, or of the richest and most influential freemen of the district.   This is all we know on the subject, and even when we come down to Charlemagne's reign there is nothing extant except a few capitularies which regulate the administration of justice, but which make no allusion to the speeches of the barristers.   In fact, the doings of the French bar (to use a modern term) are involved in complete obscurity until the reign of St. Louis, though we are told that the advocates of the Church were enjoined to be conversant with the law, to be gentle and peaceable, to fear God, and to love their country.

This decadence was the natural consequence of the promulgation of the barbarian laws which took the place of the Roman Code.   The accused had no need of an advocate when, in order to prove their innocence, they had to submit to the ordeal of fire, red-hot iron, or boiling oil.   Speech was of no use in quarrels and disputes which were decided by duel.   The best advocate was the man who could wield the sword with the greatest skill, and it was not until after the abolition of the duel and of the ordeals by fire that the bar resumed its normal existence.   We must, therefore, look back through many centuries of barbarism, in order to behold the triumph of Christian eloquence in Europe (Fig. 393).

It would be interesting to read the speeches and sermons of the first apostles of Christianity in the West, but they were not preserved until the end of the fourth century, when the edicts of Constantine enabled the Christian Church to raise its voice against the then expiring paganism.   It is in this fourth century that is to be found the cradle of Christian eloquence, delivered in Greek by St. Athanasius, St. Gregory Nazianzeñ, St. Gregory of Nyssa, St. Epiphanius, St. Dionysius, St. John Chrysostom ; in Syriac by St. Ephrem ; and in Latin by St. Ambrose, St. Augustine, and St. Jerome.   "The sublime proportions of Christian oratory," says Villemain, "seem to increase as the other kinds fade away."   And after citing the orators named above, he adds, "Their genius alone remains erect amidst the decay of the empire.

They look like founders surrounded by ruins." Nothing could damp the zeal of these apostolic spirits, and Chrysostom has revealed to us the secret of their undaunted consistency and courage when he exclaims, in

Fig. 393.—Allegorical Composition, representing the different Degrees of University Teaching.— Fac-simile of a Wood Engraving of the "Margarita Philosophica" (Bâle Edition, in 4to, 1508).

presence of the great whose vices he condemned, and of the princes whose power he braved, "All earthly terrors are contemptible in my sight. I disdain all worldly goods, and do not fear poverty; I do not desire riches, and I do not dread death; I only wish to live in order to save your souls."

From its birth the Gallic Church was associated in this great work of oratorical proselytism. In the fourth century the preachers were already numerous, and their inspired word had an immense influence upon the faithful (Fig. 394). We can estimate the authority which the Catholic pulpit must have possessed when we read the Greek sermons ascribed to Eusebius, of Emesa in Syria—sermons which are now said to have been delivered in Gaul. His oratory is of a very simple kind, and yet these primitive preachers, whose very names are unknown, had vividly in their minds the recollections of pagan literature when they related the spiritual combats of a saint, or the blood-stained struggles of a martyr. In one of these sermons upon the resurrection of Christ, God made man is compared to Antæus, son of the Earth, and like that giant, whom mythology represents as struggling with Hercules, the Saviour is represented as only touching the ground, the better to triumph over Sin, the father of Death. In another sermon the preacher depicts Tartarus as in a state of consternation, and the black wardens of the obscure prisons as struck with dismay at the arrival of the Son of God, "who comes there to command, and not to suffer."

These ancient sermons form, together with the legends of the saints, the most important part of the literature of the barbarous ages. From the fourth to the seventh century, in Roman Gaul, the Church had no lack of brilliant orators (Fig. 395). In the first rank stood St. Hilary of Poitiers, whom St. Jerome surnamed the "Rhône of eloquence," so rapid and majestic was his speech, and St. Martin of Tours, who was the most perfect model of Christian charity; he who said to his congregation, which consisted of herdsmen and shepherds, "See this sheep which has come back from the shearing. She has fulfilled the commands of the gospel; she has given part of her garments to clothe the naked. Go ye and do likewise." And he set them an example by dividing his cloak, and giving half to a poor man who was shivering with cold. In the fifth century appeared St. Eucher, whose learning was as great as his eloquence; St. Paulinus, who has left us a magnificent sermon upon almsgiving; St. Hilary, St. Mamertus, and St. Valerian, whose speeches are filled with the purest sentiments of Christianity, ardent love for his neighbour, and boundless charity. In the sixth century we have the famous St. Cæsarius of Arles, who, while preaching the purest and most

Fig. 394.—Preaching of an Apostle of Christianity.—After a Picture painted upon Wood, attributed
to Fra Angelico.—In the late Collection of M. Quedeville, Paris.

everything to the Divine inspirations of faith, to the noble impulses of the human conscience, and, above all, to the ardour of Christian feeling.

The invasions, which were continually letting loose a fresh torrent of barbarians into Gaul, the intestine struggles of conquerors and invaders, and the laborious transformation of pagan society had in nowise checked the impulse of Christian proselytism. It was then that Ireland, which had not long since received the Gospel revelation conveyed to that country by St. Patrick, in her turn supplied a noble band of missionaries who preached the Christian religion. Amongst them shone in the first rank (540—615), St. Columba, the founder of the Monastery of Luxeuil, whose utterances, bearing the impress of the most burning zeal, were marked by a vehemence of ideas which anticipated, so to speak, his words. In one of his sermons he exclaims, "Oh, fragile life! Thou art the way, and not the life. Thou startest from sin to arrive at death. An arid road, long for some, short for others; sometimes dreary, and sometimes pleasant, but alike rapid for all; many follow thee, without asking whither thou leadest. Human life is a thing to dread, and it is beset by dangers; it passes like a bird, like a shadow, like an image, like nothing." One might imagine that Dante had this passage in his mind when he began to write his "Divine Comedy." These Irish missionaries made, especially in Northern Gaul, numerous disciples, who also devoted themselves to preaching the Gospel. They were to be met with everywhere, in the towns and the country districts, travelling from place to place on donkeys, preaching as they went, and stopping at the houses on the road. The people humbly saluted them as they passed, the rich and the great esteemed it an honour to accord them hospitality, and even kings were proud to give a seat at table to these holy men, who, as a hagiographer has said, "placed beside the master of the house, and amidst the pleasures of the festive board, served also to the guests the wholesome food of the Divine word."

Germany, like Gaul, was visited by these Catholic missionaries from Ireland. The most celebrated of them was St. Boniface (675—755), whom Michelet described as "a hero who crossed the Rhine, the Alps, and the sea so often that he was, as it were, the connecting link between nations. It was through him that the Franks came to an understanding with Rome and the other Germanic tribes. He it was who attached these nomad tribes to the soil by means of religion and civilisation, and unwittingly prepared the way for the armies of Charlemagne, as the missionaries of the sixteenth century opened America to the armies of Spain."

Preaching was not the sole arena in which religious oratory had to do battle. The Councils, which were, so to speak, the guardians of the sacred deposit of orthodox faith, and to which the Middle Ages owe, even in the

Fig. 396.—Preaching of the first Missionary Apostles.—After a Tapestry in Tournay Cathedral, made at Arras in 1402.

civil order, the wisest of their laws—these Councils, which have been so happily termed the Champs de Mai of the Church, offered to ecclesiastical speakers a vast field for the display of what ability they might possess. Whatever subject was laid before these illustrious assemblies was carefully studied, and often gave rise to eloquent debates. Unfortunately nothing is extant of these discussions except the text of the decrees which they had prepared. It seems that spoken utterances were less easily preserved in these periods of social renovation, for we possess but few records of religious oratory dating from Charlemagne's reign, though we know that such celebrated preachers as Alcuin, St. Anscaire, St. Agobard, Radbert, Hincmar, Raban Maurus, &c., must have delivered many sermons worth recording. But scholasticism was already in course of formation, and the spontaneous outbursts of the heart were kept under by the subtleties of the mind. The priest was lost in the rhetorician, and it needed the imperious force of circumstances to revive the ardour and enthusiasm of early times; as, for instance, at the period of the Norman invasions, when the bishops preached a holy war against the Northern forces with a patriotic eloquence which has not been forgotten.

This irresistible power of speech was all the more strange because, during the tenth century, which was justly called the "iron age of the Church," more than one clerk frankly admitted, when a holy book was shown to him, that he did not know how to read (*nescio literas*). The year 1000, which was expected to bring with it the day of judgment, was drawing near, and all public and private contracts were dated from "the time near to the end of the world." The Christian preachers mourned, amidst the lamentations and sobs of the people, the coming death of the human race. In all the churches homilies were pronounced upon the Antichrist and the resurrection of the dead. When the dreaded epoch had passed by, religious fervour was again displayed, and out of gratitude to God new churches were built, in which the preachers announced the holy enterprise of the Crusades.

It may be said that the Crusades created a new kind of religious eloquence, which filled the whole world during the eleventh, twelfth, and thirteenth centuries. This eloquence was represented by two different kinds of orators, both working to the same end, but by different means. There were the true apostles, full of faith and enthusiasm, who travelled all over Europe preaching the holy war against the infidels and the oppressors of Christianity in the East; and there were the priests, and more especially the monks, who proclaimed, in the churches and in the cloisters, that the time had come for the clergy and the religious orders to abandon a life of contemplation, in order to form the great army of Christ, and go to Palestine to deliver his tomb by dispossessing the Saracens of Jerusalem. Religious eloquence never wielded a wider influence than then. The whole West answered to the appeal with one voice, " Dieu le volt ! "

The two great orators of the first Crusade were Peter the Hermit and Pope Urban II. The former was the people's orator, for he traversed the land upon his mule, cross in hand, preaching, weeping, and beating his breast. It was Pope Urban II. who, at the Council of Clermont, brought to a climax the resolution in favour of the Crusade by the warmth of his utterances. As contemporary Chronicles have it, "Those who heard him preach believed that they heard the heavenly trumpet." His speech was answered with the unanimous shout, " Dieu le veut ! " Thus thousands of pilgrims started for the East with no other hope or thought save of obtaining remission for their sins and an eternal recompense. It was Christian eloquence, too, which, during the hardships of this distant expedition, sustained the courage of Godfrey de Bouillon and his companions. (See, in volume on " Military and Religious Life," the chapter on *Crusades*.)

The second Crusade was resolved upon in 1146 at the assembly of Vezelay, which St. Bernard, Abbot of Clairvaux, had convoked by order of Louis VII. Suger, the King's minister, had endeavoured to get the new Crusade adjourned in the interests of the State, but St. Bernard protested, in the name of the Church and of the national honour, that it was necessary to avenge the recent disasters of Christians. The eloquence of the Abbot of Clairvaux prevailed over that of St. Denis, and Suger was compelled to abandon his opposition to the popular movement. St. Bernard, inflamed by a holy zeal, at once set out to raise armies by the mere power of his word. Wherever he went the churches and the public places of assembly were not large enough to contain the excited crowds which pressed around him, and he then preached from rude platforms erected for the purpose in the middle of the fields. When he was addressing the clerks and doctors he spoke in Latin, only employing the vulgar or Romanic tongue to address the people ; and so great was the respect felt for him that when he preached at Mayence, Cologne, and Spires, his hearers, though they could not understand a word of what he said, were inflamed by the enthusiasm of his gestures, and flew to arms as eagerly as the French crusaders.

The same enthusiasm was reproduced a century later, when Foulques de Neuilly was authorised by Pope Innocent III. to preach the Crusade of 1198. " When Foulques opened his mouth to preach," relates the chronicler

Jacques de Vitry, who was himself an eminent preacher, "it was God who conferred upon him his persuasive accents. Those who had heard him struggled to get a piece from his garments, and he was compelled to have a new frock every day. He was obliged to provide himself with a stout stick, with which he kept off the crowd which would otherwise have suffocated him. They did not murmur at the wounds inflicted by the blows which he dealt them, and, in the ardour of their faith, they licked their own blood, as if

Fig. 397.—Portrait of Pope Honorius III. (1216—1227), who exhorted Louis VIII. to undertake the Crusade against the Albigenses, and instituted in 1216 the Order of Dominican Friars.— Fresco Painting upon Gold Ground in Mosaic, in the ancient Basilica of St. Paul-without-the-Walls, Rome.

it had been sanctified because made to flow by this man of God." Foulques had all the outspoken boldness of the popular preachers of the end of the fifteenth century, sparing no man in his criticisms and anathemas. One day, when preaching before Richard, King of England, he exclaimed, "I advise you, in the name of God, to marry as quickly as possible your three daughters, lest some evil befall you." "You are mistaken," rejoined the King; "I have no daughters." "I tell you that you have three," said the preacher; "they are Pride, Avarice, and Luxury." Whereupon, the King, addressing himself to the barons, said, "I give Pride to the Templars, Avarice to the Cistercian monks, and Luxury to my grand feudatories." We need merely mention, after Foulques de Neuilly, of other doctors who preached the Crusade with no less success, Geoffroy of Bordeaux, Hildebert of Le Mans, Jean de Bellesme, Amédée of Lausanne, Eudes of Châteauroux, Geboin of Troyes, Jean de Nivelle, and Robert of Arbrissel.

Fig. 398.—Portrait of Gregory IX. (1227—1241), the eloquent Defender of the Rights and Privileges of the Holy See.—Fresco Painting upon Gold Ground in Mosaic, in the ancient Basilica of St. Paul-without-the-Walls, Rome.

Sacred oratory, which in the twelfth and thirteenth centuries did wonders in the way of raising armies, almost instantaneously, for the Crusade, had to combat in those days the profane oratory of the heretics. These heretics seemed to derive encouragement from the brilliant triumphs of the orators of the Church. All rebellions and religious insurrections had their beginning in mischievous addresses, which had but too great influence upon weak and fanatical minds. Thus Pierre de Bruys ventured to deny the Real Presence, and condemned the custom of praying for the dead; and Eon issued from the heart of Armorica, declaring that he had come to judge the quick and the dead. In other places we had the *publicains* of Flanders and Burgundy, who endeavoured to revive the monstrous doctrines of Manicheism, the Valdenses, and the Albigenses, dissenters half religious, half political, who, after having preached humility and renunciation of worldly goods, found more response among the lower classes by preaching the cessation of manual labour, the overthrow of ecclesiastical authority, and the community of goods. As each schismatic orator arose, he was at once opposed by an orthodox orator, who became the eloquent champion of the Church (Figs. 399 and 400). St. Bernard fought in the first rank, taking for his motto the maxim of Christian charity, "Let us persuade, but not constrain." He was supported by Pierre de Castelnau; Cardinal d'Albano; Jacques de Vitry; Arnauld, Abbot of Clair-vaux; and William, Archdeacon of Paris. But the most eloquent of the Catholic orators was the Spaniard St. Dominic, founder of the order of Dominican Friars (Fig. 399). Dominic, who preached for ten years in the southern provinces of France, and who never showed any mercy to heresy, was one of the most heroic soldiers of the Church militant. His irresistible eloquence produced such a prodigious effect upon his contemporaries that the people believed that he was the direct exponent of the heavenly will. According to some, flames issued from his mouth when he spoke; according to others, the church bells rang of themselves when he was about to preach; and it was also affirmed that during one of his sermons a statue of the Virgin had been seen to lift out its arm, as if to threaten the hearers who did not hearken to his words.

Nothing remains to us of these celebrated denunciations of heresy, nor of the sermons preached in favour of the Crusades; they were all delivered extempore, and were never committed to writing. But we have a somewhat large number of those belonging to the theological and mystical school, and which were, therefore, carefully prepared beforehand. Here, again, we have St. Bernard, surrounded this time by Hugues and Richard de St. Victor, Abelard, and Maurice de Sully, Bishop of Paris (Fig. 400). With Abelard, notably in his Latin discourses to the "Virgins of the Paraclete," we have the dialectician always ready to call in the authority of philosophy in support of the authority of the Church. With St. Bernard, upon the other hand, we can always hear muttering, behind the long-drawn sighs of asceticism, the internal convulsions of the human soul. Metaphysics, psychology, a profound sentiment of the realities of earthly life, fiery denunciations of the indolence

Fig. 399.—The Glories of the Order of St. Dominic.—Fac-simile of a Wood Engraving of the Fifteenth Century, from the " Meditationes," by Turrecremata (Rome, M. Gallus, 1478, in folio).—In the Library of M. Firmin-Didot, Paris.

of the monks, and theological arguments, all are to be found in the magnificent sermons of St. Bernard. The sermons of Hugues and Richard de St. Victor, like those of Isaac, Abbot of St. Étoile, reflect in a more chaste style the warm aspirations of the piety of the cloister and the purest ecstasies of a contemplative life.

Sacred oratory had attained its apogee in the sermons of the twelfth century (Fig. 401), from which time it began to suffer from the intrusion of scholasticism, of the formula, and of vague subtleties. We may say that it already had begun its downward progress towards the decay into which it fell before the end of the thirteenth century. Numerous abuses, too, crept into the ecclesiastical system. Not only did certain simoniacal clerks make money of their sermons, but mere laymen vied with them in making a trade of preaching, and offered to take the place of the priests upon payment of a certain sum. Associations of preachers, having no religious character, were formed for the purpose of farming, so to speak, a parish, or even a diocese, undertaking to supply as many preachers as might be wanted. The Church would not countenance so scandalous a proceeding, but her most strenuous efforts were not always sufficient to prevent these acts of simony. Many priests and curates excused themselves for having allowed them upon the ground of their incapacity to preach themselves. Some talented preachers who had remained true to their mission, then conceived the idea of composing manuals, or grades, in which the priests could obtain the materials for composing their sermons. The most esteemed of these preachers' manuals were those of Humbert de Romans and Alain of Lille.

While this decadence of pulpit oratory was taking place, the art of speaking, with regard to politics, jurisprudence, and scholastic teaching, had come under the favourable influences of the intellectual progress which, from the twelfth century, was universal in all spheres of civil society. History has not, unfortunately, preserved any written record of the efforts of eloquence which accompanied the establishment of communes, the drawing up of charters of franchise, or the reunion of local and general assemblies, at which were present the elected representatives of the nobility, clergy, and bourgeoisie; in a word, all the struggles of an incipient liberty against the trammels of the feudal system. The oratory of the bar was doubtless still enveloped in the fetters of scholasticism, and the advocates of the first Parliaments are only known to us through the severe satires of which they were made the subjects. An eminent theologian, Pierre Le Chantre, reproaches them with having extorted money from both sides, with having betrayed the cause of the widow and the orphan, with having employed their talents in prolonging and multiplying suits, and inventing all manner of cavils to obscure the truth and prevent the triumph of right. Another theologian denounces their unbounded avarice, and indignantly declares that by their venality they have discredited a profession once so glorious.

St. Louis endeavoured to reform the abuses of the bar; the Jews, heretics, and excommunicated persons were all excluded; and afterwards men of evil lives, and those who had been sentenced to punishments entailing the stamp of infamy, were expelled. The King himself arranged the rules as to pleadings, enjoining the advocates to expose their case with the utmost

Fig. 400.—Sacred Oratory, represented by a Bishop, a Doctor of Theology, and a Clerk.—The Supplicant goes upon her Knees before them.—After a Miniature from the " Petite Traicté de la Vanité des Choses Mondaines," composed in 1466.—Manuscript of the period (No. 30, Sc. and A).—In the Arsenal Library, Paris.

possible clearness and concision; only to take honourable causes; to be moderate and courteous towards their opponents, using no insulting language, not distorting the text of the decrees and customs, or making use of any false allegations, the whole under pain of being deprived of the title of advocate and the right of following their profession. This severe discipline, the tradition of which has been in part perpetuated to the present day, restored a portion of its lustre to the French bar, amongst the members of which, at this epoch, may be cited Pierre de Fontaines; Gui Foulques, or Fouquet, who afterwards entered holy orders and became Pope Clement IV.; and Yves of Brittany, whose Christian virtues caused him to be placed amongst the number of saints, and whom the advocates adopted as their patron. The study of jurisprudence had certainly revived, but there was not the same revival in the art of oratory; and the advocates, upon leaving the schools in which were taught dialectics, logic, and philosophy, lost themselves in endless discussions bristling with Latin quotations, and utterly devoid of method, simplicity, and true eloquence.

The profession had nevertheless acquired great importance, owing to the reforms introduced by St. Louis into the judicial institutions. The bar of the fourteenth century can boast of having produced Pierre de Cugnières, Arnaud de Corbie, Regnault d'Acy, and others who exercised an influence upon public affairs due in part to their oratorical talent. Jean de Meheyé, for instance, distinguished himself by the way in which he discharged the functions of advocate-general in the trial of Philippe le Bel's unhappy minister, Enguerrand de Marigny (1315); and François Bertrand, selected in 1329 to defend the ecclesiastical jurisdictions against the encroachments of the nobility, acquitted himself of this task with so much zeal and discretion that the court of Rome rewarded him with the cardinal's hat. These great political trials awoke a general sentiment of curiosity. The imposing spectacle presented by a sitting of Parliament under such circumstances always attracted a numerous attendance. The nobles quitted their hunting parties at home to assist at the pleadings; but the ladies, even those of the highest rank, scrupulously abstained from appearing in the Parliament. The talent of the advocates had much to do with the popularity of these judicial tournaments, and a well-known formulary of the courts, entitled the "Style of the Parliament," enumerates the professional qualities of a good advocate, which were as follows :—" He need possess a noble carriage, have an open and good-humoured physiognomy, not affect a presumptuous assurance, demean himself soberly before the tribunal, speak in a loud and clear voice," and so forth. In spite of this good advice, many advocates justified by their conduct the bad opinion of the public conveyed in the popular proverb, "Much eloquence, little conscience."

But with the fifteenth century the field was opened to every species of exaggeration born out of the political dissensions which occurred during the reign of Charles VI. The preachers became the principal agents of the two parties in presence (Fig. 403), known as the *Armagnacs* and the *Burgundians.* In 1402, one of these preachers named Courtecuisse, in the pay of the Duke

Fig. 401.—Flemish Doctor haranguing the People in the open Street (Fifteenth Century).— Miniature of Manuscript from the " Chroniques de Hainaut."—In the Burgundy Library, Brussels.

of Burgundy, solemnly declared from the pulpit that the King's brother, the Duke of Orleans, was the partisan and supporter of the schismatics. In

1405, Jacques Legrand, an Augustine monk, preaching before Queen Isabeau of Bavaria, exhorted her to exchange her sumptuous attire for a plain dress, and walk through the streets of Paris to hear what the people said of her. In another sermon, preached before the court at the Hôtel St. Pol, the same preacher boldly reproached Charles VI. with having caused the tears and the groans of the people. But in 1408, Jean Sans-Peur, Duke of Burgundy, had his enemy, the Duke of Orleans, assassinated, and he convoked at the residence of the King, who was insane, a numerous congregation, in whose presence the Grey Friar, Jean Petit, pronounced a solemn justification of the murder and of the murderer. In this set discourse, which was indirectly addressed to the whole of France, Jean Petit, after a pompous eulogy of the Duke of Burgundy, had the audacity to set forth his reasons for taking up the Duke of Burgundy's defence. He said, "The first of these reasons is that I am compelled by the oath which I took three years ago to serve him. The second is that he, seeing how poorly I was paid, has given me a large pension each year, to assist me in keeping up my schools, from which pension I have been able to defray a large part of my expenses, and shall continue to do so, if it still please his grace." After this fulsome exordium the orator set forth the division of his speech, comprising a *major*, in four parts, to prove: 1st, that covetousness is the mother of all evils; 2nd, that it leads to apostasy; 3rd, that it makes subjects disloyal and untrue to their sovereign; 4th, that it is lawful to kill apostates, traitors, and disloyal subjects. This fourth point, composed of eight principal truths, eight corollaries, and twelve syllogisms, formed the capital object of the discourse. Jean Petit had recourse to all the quibbles of dialectics to justify the murderer and glorify the murder. He invoked the examples of Lucifer, Absalom, and Athaliah in support of his detestable doctrines; he showed, finally, that the Duke of Orleans had fallen into the sin of covetousness by trying to usurp the crown; that he was, therefore, an apostate, a traitor, a disloyal subject, guilty of high treason; and that the man who had killed him had done what was praiseworthy in the sight of God and of man.

This disgraceful discourse so excited public curiosity that Jean Petit had to pronounce it over again upon the following day from a platform erected upon the square in front of Notre-Dame, in presence of an enormous crowd. Nevertheless, the widow of the murdered man, Valentine of Milan, had obtained permission from King Charles VI. to have herself and her children represented by an advocate of the courts named Jean Cousinot, who replied with dignity to the apologist of assassination, and who created a profound impression upon the audience when he appealed upon behalf of the blood which had been shed to the justice of the King of France. This great criminal trial was destined to remain pending before the tribunal of public opinion until the unpunished murderer was in his turn assassinated, fifteen years later, under the eyes of the heir to the throne. This catastrophe did not give rise to any oratorical debate, and Jean Petit had no imitator. But a

Fig. 402.—Portrait of Jerome Savonarola.—Reduced Fac-simile of the Engraving of Leonardo da Vinci in Vienna Museum (Albertine Collection).

few years later, in another political trial, more memorable and more worthy of notice, a new kind of eloquence was suddenly revealed in an unlettered young girl, who drew her inspiration solely from her conscience and her heart. In this trial, during which every rule of justice was disregarded or violated, Joan of Arc, taken prisoner by the English, had no advocate to assist her, and all her defence was confined to her replies to the interrogatories of her accusers. The judges, or rather the torturers, the most hardened of the doctors of the school, were more than once touched and confounded as they listened to the proud and simple utterances of their prisoner; and Joan of Arc, cruelly accused of imaginary crimes, returned with a smile upon her face to her prison, saying to her gaolers, who looked upon her as a sorceress, "Do not be afraid; I shall not fly away; I am not an angel." Her replies, so simple, and yet so telling, often sublime, and always true, are not the least striking evidence of her Divine mission.

In the meanwhile the art of oratory seemed to authorise the most extreme license of speech. The same speaker could venture, without fear of discredit, to support in turn the most diametrically opposed doctrines. So willed it that sphinx of the schools called Dialectics, and these contradictory statements did not strike any one as being blamable. Thus all speakers, whether of the bar or of the pulpit, were considered to be inviolable, and no one ever thought of calling any of them to account for what they had said. Even Louis XI., despot as he was, did not dare to interfere with the utterances of the preachers. The latter had not the same immunity in Italy which they enjoyed in France, for they were kept under control not only by the ecclesiastical, but by the civil authorities. Thus Jerome Savonarola (Fig. 402), whose original, abundant, and indomitable eloquence had led him to attack the greatest and most powerful of human institutions, was more than once compelled to quit the pulpit, and after having been interdicted, and even excommunicated, he was imprisoned by order of the Seigniory of Florence, and condemned to be burnt alive as a heretic (May 23rd, 1498).

The oratory of the bar was more restrained and dignified. In truth, the involved and sententious prolixity of the lawyers did not deserve the name of oratory, and their pedantic language, bristling with subtleties borrowed from scholasticism, was not calculated to move or to carry away their hearers. We must, however, cite a few pleaders who, like Jacques Maréchal, La Vacquerie, and Antoine Duprat, combined with the science of the jurisconsult force, and in some cases elegance, of diction. But most of the preachers, who affected a sort of rough and uncouth eloquence appealing to popular intelligence, belonged to the trivialist school which Gabriele Barletta had created at Naples, where his burlesque sermons had an extraordinary success. It was after this jack-pudding type that the art of preaching was everywhere reduced to this one axiom: "Nescit predicare qui nescit barlettare" ("No one knows how to preach if he cannot imitate Barletta"). Barletta's example was,

therefore, followed, and even outdone, by his imitators, amongst whom were
Geyler in Germany, and Robert Messier, Guillaume Pepin, Michel Menot,
and Olivier Maillard in France. These preachers, who were none the less
pious and sincere, went to the greatest lengths in their sermons, the Latin
context of which was interspersed with words and phrases in the vulgar
tongue, into which they foisted pell-mell proverbs, songs, jokes, apologues,
and ill-timed pleasantries. But their audiences were not, as a rule, particular
in this respect, and when Olivier Maillard was going to preach at his parish

Fig. 403.—Sermon upon the Vanity of Human Things.—The Actor (or Author) instructs the
Supplicant opposite the Shop of a Goldsmith and Money-changer.—Fac-simile of a Miniature
from the "Petite Traicté de la Vanité des Choses Mondaines," composed in 1466.—
Manuscript of the Period.—In the Arsenal Library, Paris.

of St. Jean-en-Grève the church was crowded by daybreak. No preacher
ever produced so potent an effect. At first his hearers laughed at his satirical
allusions, but they were in the end subdued and stirred by his eloquence,
which had its root in the most ardent faith.

Olivier Maillard, whose sermons preached in Paris re-echoed throughout
France, afterwards travelled through the provinces, and preached in the

different patois. At Toulouse he repeated in the local dialect his " General Confession," which he had first delivered in Poitevin at Poitiers; and at Bruges, in 1502, he repeated a Savoy *bergeronette* which he had delivered from the Toulouse pulpit at Whitsuntide. Michel Menot was not so poetic as Maillard, but he denounced the vices and follies of all classes of society. At Tours, preaching in a medley of Latin and French, he exclaimed, " Oh, city of Tours, pride dishonours thy daughters! The wife of a shoemaker wears a tunic like that of a duchess. People who have twenty pounds a year keep horses and dogs; those who have fifty are friends with the nobles, and keep their town and country house." Then, addressing himself to the ladies who always came in late to church, " It is now nine o'clock (A.M.), and you are

Fig. 404.—Portrait of Claude Despence.   Fig. 405.—Portrait of the Cardinal de Lorraine.

Fac simile of Line Engravings by Léonard Gaultier, in the Series called "Chronologie collée." In the Library of M. Firmin-Didot, Paris.

still in bed. Forty horses might have been bedded up while all your pins were being put in their places. When you are at your toilette you resemble the cobbler who requires a lot of pieces to put his work together. And if, while the priest is elevating the Host above the altar, some young dandy presents himself at her seat, Madame, in compliance with the customs of the nobility, must rise and offer him her hand! Let such privileges be put down without form or ceremony " (Fig. 403).

The fiery Luther, for all his double merits as a theologian and a man of letters, belonged, as an eloquent preacher, to the popular school, and he himself said, " I preach as simply as possible, so as to be understood by the common people, by the children, and by the servants. I do not preach for the learned; they have their books." The most powerful agency of the Reformation was, in fact, preached and brought within the comprehension of the people. Calvin, Théodore de Bèze, and the leaders of Protestantism at Geneva were also indefatigable preachers, but they did not do more than

Fig. 406.—Portrait of Sixtus Quintus (1521—1590).—Reduced Fac-simile of a contemporary Etching, by an unknown Italian Artist.

paraphrase, and that rather drily, the text of the Gospel; and, taking as a principle that the Word of God had no need of profane ornamentation, they did not seek to move men's hearts, or appeal to their imaginations. The

Catholic preachers who rose in all directions to defend the Church against the efforts of the Protestants were, for the most part, unequal to their mission, for a few only, such as Claude Despence and the Cardinal de Lorraine (Figs. 404 and 405), distinguished themselves by real oratorical talent. Many others, such as Vigor and Seneschal, were only remarkable for the violence and hastiness of their rejoinders. It may be said that by the end of the sixteenth century true religious eloquence had disappeared, and then were renewed in France the pulpit scandals of the epoch of the Burgundians and the Armagnacs. The preachers of the League, who claimed to be inspired and authorised by Pope Sixtus Quintus (Fig. 406), went to excesses which not even the disorders of that time could excuse.

But we may turn from this unedifying spectacle to consider what was the

Fig. 407.—Portrait of　　　　Fig. 408.—Portrait of Pibrac.　　　　Fig. 409.—Portrait of
B. Dumesnil.　　　　　　　　　　　　　　　　　　　　　　　　　J. Faye.

Fac-simile of Line Engravings by Léonard Gaultier, from the Series known as " Chronologie collée."—In the L brary of M. Firmin-Didot, Paris.

condition of civil oratory during this troubled period. The bar, as it shook off the yoke of scholasticism, had gradually undergone a complete literary transformation. The classic renaissance of the sixteenth century naturally made its influence first felt in the courts, but unfortunately the advocates were addicted to prolix discourses, and to an unstinting use of the flowers of rhetoric. From the year 1550 the reopening of the sessions of the Parliament, after its annual vacations, was made the occasion for harangues carefully prepared. In 1557 Baptiste Dumesnil delivered an oration upon Asconius Pedianus, while in the following year Guy du Faur de Pibrac spoke, being succeeded by Jacques Faye (Figs. 407 to 409), and the illustrious Jacques-Auguste

de Thou. In 1585 Jacques Mangot spoke " for three consecutive hours, and
was as fresh at the finish as at the beginning of his discourse," says Estienne
Pasquier. These harangues were printed, and they were considered "more
agreeable to read" than to listen to. Advocates and magistrates alike
distinguished themselves, and the names of Seguier, Dumoulin, the first of
the Lamoignons, Lemaître, Cujas, Chopin, Brisson, and Pithou (Figs. 410 to
414), shed a lustre upon the history both of the Parliament and the bar. If
their discourses are not literary and oratorical masterpieces, they are at all
events, as regards logical argument, sentiment, and sincerity, worthy of all
praise. There is instinct in them, at all times, a consistent tradition of honour
and virtue, from Jean de la Vacquerie, First President of the Paris Parliament,
boldly replying to the threats of Louis XI., "Sire, we come to remit our

Fig. 410.—Portrait of   Fig. 411.—Portrait of C. Dumoulin.   Fig. 412.— Portrait of
P. Seguier.   G. Lemaître.

Fac-simile of Line Engravings by Léonard Gaultier, from the Series called " Chronologie
collée."—In the Library of **M. Firmin-Didot**, Paris.

functions into your hands, and to suffer what it may be your good pleasure to
inflict upon us, rather than offend our consciences," to the Chancellor Olivier
enjoining the members of the Normandy Parliament (Oct. 8th, 1550), as he
showed them the crucifix, to "remember, as you fulfil your charges, that He
to whom all hearts are open is in your midst; He to whom you will have to
render an account of your judgments, and whose sentence is inevitable, even
if you escape the hand of the King and of justice."

Parliamentary eloquence became in a degree political when the great
magisterial bodies addressed themselves to the sovereign, who generally
listened to them with deference. But political eloquence had freer course in

the grave circumstances which led to the convocation of the States-General, when the deputies of the orders which represented the nation deliberated with closed doors as to the wording of the *Cahiers*, in which they expressed the resolutions which were afterwards submitted to the King in the shape of *plaints, doléances*, and remonstrances. These deliberations often gave rise to harangues in Latin or French, which enabled the speaker to indulge in very high-flown eloquence. It was thus that, at the States-General of Tours in 1484, one of the representatives of the Burgundy nobility, Philippe Pot, Seigneur of La Roche, pronounced a Latin speech, in which he enunciated with great boldness and logic political doctrines which were not understood until two centuries afterwards. "Royalty," he said, "is a duty, and not an hereditary privilege, and it should not always pass, like property, to the nearest relatives.

Fig. 413.—Portrait of   Fig. 414.—Portrait of P. Pithou.   Fig. 415.-—Portrait of
J. Cujas.   M. de l'Hospital.

Fac-simile of Line Engravings by Léonard Gaultier, from the Series called " Chronologie collée."—In the Library of M. Firmin-Didot, Paris.

The State, deprived of a chief, will, it may be objected, remain exposed to accident and disorder. Not at all, for its safety may be left in the hands of the Assembly of the three orders, not to govern it themselves, but to select persons capable of governing. Originally the suffrage of the people, who were the masters, created kings, and the people selected the most virtuous and the most able. Each nation, in selecting a king, acted in its own interest and for its own advantage; for princes are made princes not to prey upon the people, but to make them richer and improve their condition. The kings who fail to do so are tyrants and bad shepherds, because they devour their sheep; thus they are wolves, and not shepherds."

At the Orleans States-General, in 1560, the Chancellor of France, Michel de l'Hospital (Fig. 415) opened the first sitting with a very powerful speech, in which he declared, as Philippe Pot had done, that institutions such as the States-General were very useful to the monarchy, and that the Kings of France could not do better, in certain circumstances, than consult their subjects. After enumerating all the ills which desolated the kingdom, torn as it was by civil and religious wars, he advised the Crown to combat this social anarchy by wise tolerance and well-conceived reforms. "We have," he declared, "been like the captains who assailed their enemies with all

Fig. 416.—Portrait of Henri III.—Reduced Fac-simile of an Engraving by Gaultier.—In the Library of M. Firmin-Didot, Paris.

their forces, leaving thus our homes unprotected. It is for us, fortified with virtue and morality, to assail the enemy with the arms of charity, prayer, persuasion, and God's Word." These words were uttered nine years before the massacre of St. Bartholomew. Later the kings presided in person at the opening of the States-General, and delivered a speech. These speeches have been preserved, and, amongst others, those of Henri III. (Fig. 416) to the States-General of Blois in 1576 and 1588. Mézeray relates that Henri III., who spoke well, was very fond of delivering these speeches, and also that his unpremeditated replies to the ambassadors and deputies whom he received were much better than their set speeches.

Henri IV. did not convoke the States-General during his reign, but he found other opportunities for showing that he could speak as readily and with greater sincerity than his predecessor in public assemblies. He possessed the true kind of political eloquence, inasmuch as he was able to persuade and stir his hearers in a few words. Take, for instance, his brief unstudied speech at a meeting of the Notables of Rouen (1596): "I have not called you together, as my predecessors did, for you to ratify my will,

Fig. 417.—"How Gergeau was taken."—Miniature from the "Vigiles du Roi Charles VII." French Manuscript of 1484 (No. 5,054).—In the National Library, Paris.

but to receive your advice, to put confidence in it and to follow it, and to place myself in your hands—a thing which is not often done by kings, grey-headed men, or victorious soldiers."

Henri IV. also excelled in military eloquence. In the early ages of the monarchy it was not the generals who stimulated the enthusiasm of their soldiers, but the soldiers who stimulated their own enthusiasm by warlike songs or cries, in which were embodied the names of their respective chiefs. History, however, has enregistered the speech delivered to his army by Philip Augustus, before the battle of Bovines (August 27th, 1214), and there is reason for believing that this speech, as recorded by the chroniclers, is quite authentic. It forms a singular mixture of energy, simplicity, and confidence, which is much to be admired when we remember what a coalition of foreign princes had been formed to overthrow the French King. Philip Augustus said, " Behold Otho the excommunicated and his adherents. The money with which they have equipped themselves was stolen from the poor and from the churches. We fight for our God, our liberty, and our honour. Sinners as we are, let us have confidence in the Lord, and we shall vanquish our enemies." And when some of the soldiers murmured against having to fight on a Sunday, the King added, " The Maccabæus family, dear to the Lord, did not hesitate to affront the enemy, and the Lord blessed their arms." The captains and generals, carried away by their enthusiasm, exclaimed, " And you, the elect of God, bless our arms ! " The army, falling upon its knees, repeated the cry.

Two centuries later, the example of military eloquence was set, not by a King of France, but by a plain peasant girl, and Joan of Arc's simple language exercised even greater influence over those who heard her. When Charles VII. ordered the Duc d'Alençon to accompany Joan of Arc to the siege of Jargeau, which was held by the English, the latter, addressing the Duke, exclaimed, " Forward, gentle duke, to the assault ! The hour is at hand when God wills. He bids us press forward, and He will aid us. . . . . Art thou afraid, gentle duke ? You know that I promised your wife to bring you back safe and sound." The assault once begun, she mounted upon a ladder, from which she was thrown to the ground by a large stone, and the French thought she had been killed. But she rose to her feet, and, waving her banner, cried, " Forward, friends ! Our Lord has condemned the English ; we have them in our power." And the town was taken by assault (Fig. 417).

It was not for another century and a half that such eloquent accents were heard from the mouth of a sovereign. Henri IV. had accepted the challenge of battle offered him by the Duc de Mayenne in the plains of Ivry, upon the banks of the Eure (August 14th, 1590). When about to have the charge sounded, he addressed his soldiers as follows :—" My companions, you are Frenchmen. If you lose your colours, do not lose sight of my plumes ; you will find that they are always in the path of honour." During this memorable combat it was rumoured that the King had been wounded, and the army began to give way. Henri galloped up to them, and shouted in loud tones,

"Look at me; I am full of life; be you full of honour!" And, when victory had declared itself in his favour, he passed along the ranks of his troops, who were massacring the fugitives, and said to them in beseeching tones, "My children, spare the French!" This generous utterance shows that military oratory needs but a few words to make its influence felt. Henri IV. was at once the most eloquent of warriors and of statesmen.

Fig 418.—Fragment of a Binding of G. Durand's "Rationale."—Manuscript of the Fourteenth Century.—In the Library of M. Firmin-Didot, Paris.

THE END.